The New Guide to Study Abroad

~~~~~~

by John A. Garraty and Walter Adams

From Main Street to the Left Bank
Michigan State University Press (1959)

Is the World Our Campus?
Michigan State University Press (1960)

The New Guide to Study Abroad

Summer and full-year programs for high-school students, college and university students, and teachers

by John A. Garraty, Walter Adams
and Cyril J. H. Taylor

Woodcuts by Gail Garraty

HARPER & ROW, PUBLISHERS

New York, Evanston, and London

We would very much appreciate hearing from participants in any of these programs about their experiences, especially if they note any inaccuracies in our program descriptions. Please write The New Guide to Study Abroad, *49 East 33rd Street, Sixth Floor, New York, N. Y. 10016.*

LIBRARY OF CONGRESS CATALOG CARD NUMBER: 68-28197

6970717273 87654321

Contents

PART IV   The Teacher Abroad

PART V Foreign Study Outside the Classroom

Preface

As interest in study abroad grows steadily, the need for a comprehensive guide to the subject increases proportionately. What was once a privilege reserved for a handful of advanced scholars and the very rich has, since World War II, become almost a mass movement that attracts tens of thousands of students of every age and size of purse. And as the opportunities have expanded, the institutional arrangements designed to make them available have proliferated both in number and in type. This book attempts to provide general guidance to students, teachers, and educational administrators interested in study abroad and also to describe and categorize the kinds of programs that exist all over the world. It also contains the essential facts about the specific programs: what is taught, how much it costs, when sessions begin and end, entrance requirements, and so on. In short, it is both an analysis of this ancient yet dynamic and expanding form of education and a reference work describing the institutions that are engaged in the field on five continents.

This book has had a complex and, we believe, interesting history; its evolution reflects directly the enormous expansion of interest in study abroad in recent decades. In 1957–1958 our first researches, which led to the volume *From Main Street to the Left Bank* (East Lansing, Michigan, 1959), were devoted almost exclusively to junior-year-abroad programs, most of which were run by small private American colleges in western European countries. But in the late 1950's the number and variety of these programs were rising in spectacular fashion, while at the same time foreign universities were expanding and greatly improving the special courses for foreigners that many of them were offering. Therefore, after further field studies and extensive work with the catalogues of hundreds of institutions, we published *A Guide to Study Abroad*

(New York, 1962), which analyzed and described most of the college-level programs then available. Since that time, however, there has been a still further expansion of the field, and (perhaps even more important) a whole new branch of study abroad—the program for high-school students—has leaped into prominence. We have thus added to our "team" Cyril J. H. Taylor, president of one of the largest organizations engaged in sending high-school students overseas, and have produced this new volume covering the whole field. We believe that anyone considering studying or teaching in a foreign country, and even persons planning to work or travel abroad with an educational purpose, will find this volume useful. The high-school student interested in spending a summer improving his French or German, the collegian who wants to join a junior-year program, the graduate scholar planning to immerse himself in foreign archives, the teacher or professor with a sabbatical at hand who wishes to study or teach in a foreign setting— all these and more will find in this book the essential data needed in formulating plans and the means of locating further information about every country and every institution in which they may be interested.

We have tried to cover all aspects of study abroad in the following pages, but a few words about the recent outbursts of student discontent in foreign universities is perhaps in order here. It is too soon to know whether these troubles are over or merely beginning, but it is our view that they should not discourage persons interested in foreign study, the values of which outweigh any ephemeral problem or inconvenience. Moreover, these conflicts are in a sense unavoidable: similar outbursts have occurred among students all over the United States. American students abroad should of course exercise discretion and avoid getting mixed up in matters which are not their particular affair. It is important to recognize that while the student protest movement is international in scope, the particular causes of discontent are in most instances local and in many cases unrelated to educational problems. As such they are not the direct concern of outsiders. The difficulties that have convulsed the universities of Berlin, Paris, and Mexico City, for example, even to the extent that they have involved educational policy, have been related to the professional and academic dissatisfactions of students pursuing the regular degree programs of these universities, and not with the interests of foreign students engaged in work related to their own education, and thus independent of German or French or Mexican systems. And there is value, even at the cost of some interruption in the routine of classes and formal study, in having a front-row seat when dramas such as these unfold. The ferment associated with student protests is part of the modern world and thus part of any intelligent student's education.

A book such as this could not have been written without the assistance of many persons. Our thanks go out to the hundreds of students and teachers, American and foreign, who have shared with us their impressions and experiences and also to the many government officials, university administrators, and program directors who have aided our work. Members of the staff of the Institute of International Education have repeatedly allowed us to use their files of catalogues and other data in checking details. Gail Garraty, in addition to creating the woodcuts that illustrate our book, has assisted extensively in interviewing students and teachers in France, Germany, Spain, Austria, England, and Mexico. John Rousmaniere and Maria Jacobson have prepared program descriptions and checked facts. Helen Rodnite, Julius Kirshner, and Gary Osteraas, graduate students at Columbia University doing research in Europe, have visited programs for foreign students in France, Germany, and Italy and given us their impressions, based on interviews with students and administrators. Ernest Colowrat and other members of the staff of the American Institute for Foreign Study have also provided much valuable assistance. None of these persons, however, should be held responsible for whatever errors of fact or opinion may remain in our book.

New York, N.Y.
August 12, 1968

John A. Garraty
Walter Adams
Cyril J. H. Taylor

Introduction

When *A Guide to Study Abroad* appeared in 1962,
its authors, John A. Garraty and Walter Adams, were credited with
having produced a comprehensive and dependable reference work
and praised for having attempted, insofar as was feasible, a much-
needed qualitative and evaluative analysis of interntional educational programs. Sarah Blanding, then President of Vassar College,
reviewing the book for the Institute of International Education's
publication *Overseas*, commented: "This book belongs in the library
of every college and high school in the United States; it should be
on the desk of every dean or counselor whose advice is sought by
the hundreds of students who for innumerable reasons yearn to
study or travel abroad. Parents whose children beg to go to far-away
places will profit . . . and young people themselves will find invaluable information within its pages." Having read *The New
Guide to Study Abroad*, I want to make the same recommendations.

Surely comprehensive and evaluative information on study opportunities in other countries is needed more than ever before by both
students and their counselors. In the time since this book first
appeared there has been unprecedented change in the educational
systems of nearly every country in the world.

During these years there has also been a proliferation of organized study-abroad programs. There are programs for the academic year, for the semester, for the summer; for professors,
secondary-school teachers, graduate students, undergraduates, and
high-school students. It is, it would appear, in the high-school category that the largest expansion has occurred and it is for this
reason that the authors have asked Cyril Taylor, a specialist in
that area, to join them in the preparation of this edition. The
chapters dealing with opportunities for teen-age students should
be read *in toto* by those interested in joining any kind of organized
program, and the advice given by the authors should be followed

faithfully. There are excellent programs for high-school students, but also poor ones and many shades in between. (The State Department has even published a pamphlet, *A Word of Caution*, aimed at helping to separate the sheep from the goats!) Since so many of the programs are not what they purport to be, this book will provide invaluable aid to school advisers, parents, and students.

The chapters which deal with the various educational systems and the organized study programs are the heart of this book, but the general advice in Part I is an equally important component of *The New Guide to Study Abroad*. Under the heading "Planning for Study Abroad" the authors offer a mass of information, rich in example and detail, which, particularly if read well in advance, will enable prospective students to equip themselves generally and academically for the great adventure. One of the major recurring criticisms of exchange-of-persons programs is that students—and teachers—who go to a foreign country for educational purposes are often inadequately prepared for the experience and that their orientation, in whatever shape or form it occurs, is none too meaningful and rarely very effective. "Had I only known that foreign universities suspend their regular teaching activities during the summer months!" "No one told me that a *Hochschule* is an institution of higher learning and not a high school."

In his introduction to *A Guide to Study Abroad* Lyndon B. Johnson, then Vice President of the United States, wrote: "Our young people must know more about other languages, other lands and other ways of thinking and doing. They must know more about their own country, its value systems, its traditions and its aspirations. They must have more information on which to base a meaningful plan of study, so that their overseas experience will be of maximum benefit to them as individuals and to us as their fellow countrymen." The information referred to by President Johnson is indeed essential, and it is available in this book in a more complete and up-to-date form than in any other book I know of. *The New Guide* also refers the reader to other works dealing with international education which are readily accessible in college, university, and public libraries, and it contains an appendix that lists and describes organizations in the United States and in other countries that provide aid and guidance to students.

There is no question but that international exchange of persons continues to be of major importance for the maintenance of contact between nations, particularly in times of discord and strife. Study abroad by Americans will always be an essential part of this exchange. The number of Americans studying and teaching abroad has increased with each passing year and there is little doubt that it will continue to do so. However, 1969 is a very critical year. Federal support for international education has been severely cut by Congress. No one knows exactly how this will eventually affect this vital dimension of education. Obviously, it will not end the tendency of students to go abroad, but there is real cause for concern. Ironically, the number of American government grantees abroad will probably decline in 1970, the year that has been declared by the Economic Committee of the General Assembly of the United Nations as International Education Year. Is it not, therefore, all the more important that those who are able to go abroad to study be well prepared to make maximum use of the experience?

"Each traveler is on his own journey and on more than one journey at the same time: to discover his own identity, to learn the meaning of life." So writes Professor Irwin Abrams in a delightful essay, "The Educated Traveler," published in *Antioch Notes* (March, 1965). "Let us equip him for this journey," Abrams adds, "with a full complement of skills, skills of communication in a foreign tongue, in personal relationships, of observation and of social analysis and description; but above all let us nourish in him certain qualities of mind and heart: sensitivity to others, honesty toward himself, a zest for learning, and a spirit of adventure. For if we educators are up to our tasks, he may be venturing forth on the most significant voyage of intellectual spiritual discovery of his young life." I think it can be said that the authors of this book are, in Abrams' phrase, "up to their task." But in the last analysis, it is really up to the student himself. In this connection I can do no better than conclude with a quotation from Boswell's *Life of Samuel Johnson:* "As the Spanish proverb says: 'he who would bring home the wealth of the Indies, must carry the wealth of the Indies with him.' So it is in travelling, a man must carry knowledge with him if he would bring home knowledge."

January 3, 1969

Lily von Klemperer
Consultant in International Education
Formerly Head, Counseling Division,
Institute of International Education

PART I

Planning for Study Abroad

CHAPTER 1

The Benefits of Foreign Study

Students comment on their experiences studying abroad . . . Americans have been traveling to study since colonial times . . . choosing where you will go . . . some fringe benefits . . . a first look at important differences in foreign educational systems . . . some difficult adjustments for American students

Her name was Mary W——. We met her in the Luxembourg Gardens, and she was hesitant and strained at first because we *were* trying to strike up an acquaintanceship without an introduction. But she looked us over briefly, saw that we were decent sorts, and then she smiled and said yes, she was an American and a student. How had we known, and what did we want?

We had known because we had heard her chatting in French with a couple of other young people in the park. Her accent revealed her origin; yet her French was so good that we knew her to be no tourist. Now we wanted to talk with her about study abroad. Mary smiled broadly. "Come on," she said. "Let's sit down on this bench. I've been in Paris since September [it was now June], spending my junior year of college here. I've never had such a terrific time. And I've learned so much: French, of course, but other things, too—art and history and . . . well, mostly about people and how they live. This has been the greatest year of my life."

George R—— is a sixteen-year-old high-school student from a large eastern city, but we encountered him at Oxford, in England, where he was attending a four-week summer course. "Europe has opened the minds of many American students like me to the fact

3

that people are the same all over. On the trip I've met students from all over the world. I've come in contact with ideas from all over the world. I've discovered that the world is a wonderful place full of people with emotions, likes and dislikes, personalities and beliefs—just like me."

The place was a large public room in a Madrid hotel. We were with four American schoolteachers, and we asked them why they were studying in Europe. They all tried to answer at once; then Robert J——, a hefty, balding fellow of about forty, a language teacher from a large New Jersey high school, quieted his comrades with a gruff, good-humored shout, and said: "Why, we're here for a dozen different reasons. I'm trying to remember how to *talk* Spanish, instead of just reading it out of a book. All of us are stocking up on impressions and insights to pass on to the kids in our classes next fall. Mike and Bill are here to earn credits toward advanced degrees. And, frankly, we're all having a good time, too. We've worked hard and saved for years for this trip, and we're out to enjoy it." One of his companions interrupted: "I'm an art teacher from Kansas," he said, "and I don't see how I've managed to teach art history all these years without ever having studied here. When I get back, I'm going straight to the principal and I . . ."

A third member of the group chimed in. For two hours we jotted down our impressions. The consensus: Overseas study is a wonderful thing. All language teachers should spend at least every third or fourth summer abroad. *Any* teacher will profit from visiting foreign lands. The government ought to provide more grants to help get our teachers overseas. And—"We've never enjoyed ourselves as much as we have this summer."

We found Carol B—— at a work camp, helping build homes for refugees from East Germany. The road that led us to her was tortuous, both literally and figuratively. It took us first to the Centre Quaker International in Paris, and then to Bückeburg, a town in north Germany. There a young man directed us on to the headquarters of the Internationaler Zivildienst in a Hamburg office building, where two young volunteers found Carol's name on one of their lists. Then back across Germany to Sechtem, a village near

Bonn. And thence, finally, up a winding, rutted road to the building site.

Carol was wearing blue jeans and a gray sweat shirt. After we explained who we were, and after she had recovered from the surprise of having been tracked down so relentlessly, she explained why she was spending her summer as a day laborer, nailing up concrete forms and trundling loads of brick. "Work draws people together," she said. "Being a tourist is okay if you want to see the famous sights and the fashion showings—but in a camp like this you get to know people. And they're people from all over the world. Of course, it's in a good cause, too. I've seen the gratitude in the eyes of men and women now living in houses built here last year. Honestly, I've gotten so much out of the whole experience, it's hard to know where to begin. My German is still pretty sketchy, but I've learned to communicate just the same. And I've made real friends—not the 'Hi, there!' type, but *real* ones. Yes, I've learned more in three weeks here than in any other period of my life."

Edgar I—— is almost a professional "overseasman." We met him at an Italian summer school, but he had been studying and living abroad for over three years—in Austria, France, Holland, and Germany. His plans included a stay at the University of Belgrade next, and he hoped eventually to earn his Ph.D. in education at the University of Vienna. Why, we asked, this extended period of study abroad?

Edgar was used to being interviewed; he seemed to answer with editorials. He began with a few remarks about his general interest in international relations. "Many of the world's difficulties rise from ignorance of other people and other countries," he said. "I want to soak up as much information and get to know as many people as I possibly can before returning home and beginning my career."

Edgar is a Negro, and we interrupted to ask him a sharp question: Was he staying overseas so long in order to avoid the prejudice that members of his race are sometimes subjected to in the United States? "No," he replied quickly. "It's not that at all, though I can understand why you might think so. As a matter of fact, one visit to East Berlin showed me that the American way of life is far more important than the problem of prejudice. What I'm really over here for is this—perspective, stimulation, the excitement of new things, new ideas, new people. I've been around, I tell you, and I know. Study abroad is the greatest experience a student can have."

Americans, Peripatetic People

These samples of the opinions of Americans studying in foreign countries could be matched a dozen times by anyone who has met and spoken with our students and teachers abroad. Naturally enough, such comments, gathered in dormitories, corridors, and cafés, tend to stress human values. But much is also said about academic benefits, world affairs, and the wonders of Old World monuments and museums. Americans abroad frequently voice complaints and discuss problems, too, because studying in a foreign land presents difficulties, demands great effort to achieve adjustment, requires much tolerance and willingness to work hard, and demands an independence of body and spirit not always present in today's young Americans. Nevertheless, Americans abroad almost unanimously insist that the benefits far outweigh the disadvantages and inconveniences.

The proof that they think so may be seen in the statistics. In 1965 the State Department issued passports to nearly 32,000 persons who were going abroad for educational purposes. The Institute of International Education reports that in the same year nearly 25,000 Americans were actually registered in institutions of higher learning outside the United States.

Some of these "students" are, of course, themselves teachers. Recognizing the great value of bringing teachers of one country in touch with their colleagues and with students of other lands, the State Department operates a vast exchange program which in the academic year 1964–1965 involved more than 8,600 persons from some 130 countries.*

Countless other teachers go abroad each year on their own.

---

* The Department of Health, Education, and Welfare publishes a booklet entitled *Teacher Exchange Opportunities* which may be obtained from the Government Printing Office, Division of Public Documents, Washington, D.C. 20025.

Many American educators spend their summers in advanced language programs in foreign countries under the sponsorship of either the American government or the host nation. For instance, several hundred educators spend the summer studying in Germany. All in all, study abroad is growing even more lustily than study at home. During the regular academic year 1960–1961, 1,575 Americans were formally enrolled in German universities. By the academic year 1965–1966, this figure had soared to 2,392.

Mass migration by students is generally considered an air-age phenomenon. Yet even when travel was dangerous, expensive, inconvenient, and immensely time-consuming, Americans recognized the special values of study abroad, and for the favored few this was an established feature of one's training. In colonial times, for example, the sons of wealthy southern planters were frequently sent to England or France to be educated. William Byrd, II, ancestor of the polar explorer and of Senator Harry Byrd of Virginia, studied in London's famed Middle Temple in the Inns of Court. Charles Carroll, of Maryland, a signer of the Declaration of Independence, was educated at the Collège de St. Omer in Flanders and studied law in Paris and London. Robert "King" Carter, of Virginia, master of a thousand slaves and 300,000 acres, sent five children to be schooled in England. And so many wealthy South Carolinians studied in England in the eighteenth century that Charleston became a sort of cultural replica of London.

New England colonists were somewhat less likely to seek a general education in Europe because of the early development of Harvard College (founded in 1636). But since there were no medical or law schools in America in colonial times, fledgling doctors and lawyers simply had to cross the Atlantic if they wanted more academic knowledge than could be obtained through apprenticeship to established practitioners. For much the same reason, such colonial artists as Benjamin West, who studied in Italy as early as 1760, and John Singleton Copley and Gilbert Stuart, who began working in England in 1774 and 1775, found it necessary to go abroad for first-rate instruction.

Although the number of American colleges expanded rapidly after the Revolution, many intelligent young men continued to study abroad. At that time Germany, because of her high standards of scholarship and the complete academic freedom that prevailed, was the magnet that attracted the finest scholars. Edward Everett, of Massachusetts, became the first American to win a Ph.D. abroad, when Göttingen awarded him the doctorate in 1817. Historians George Bancroft and George Ticknor also learned their trade at German universities around that time. And by the 1830's and 1840's, it was fashionable for bright young men to spend at least a year studying in Germany before settling down to their careers. Henry Adams did this; and so, later, did Theodore Roosevelt.

Nevertheless, until recently only a relative handful of very wealthy Americans studied abroad, and even for these, in the words of one historian, it was nearly always the "event of a lifetime" to do so. Nowadays, as we have seen, a small army leaves the United States each year in search of education. Most are college students in their late teens and early twenties, while others are scholars doing advanced research or working for higher degrees. More and more secondary- and elementary-school teachers, men and women who used to go abroad during the summer or on sabbaticals as mere tourists, are now enrolling in formal programs of study and are thus returning home with new skills and with credits earned toward advanced degrees instead of just the traditional photographs and souvenirs.

Nor do these students confine their academic *wanderjahre* to Europe. A 1966 survey by the Institute of International Education showed nearly 3,500 Americans enrolled in Mexican universities during the regular academic year and more than 3,000 in Canadian institutions of higher learning. Europe may still attract the largest percentage of our students, but in smaller numbers they are also scattered from Ghana to Guatemala, from Israel to Argentina, from Japan to the Republic of South Africa. According to the same IIE report, for example, there were 295 Americans attending classes at the Hebrew University in Jerusalem, 603 at the University of the Philippines, and 114 at Yonsei University in Seoul, Korea.

Putting the situation in a slightly different perspective: in 1964, 14 per cent of all the foreign students in Italy were American, as were 34 per cent of the students from abroad in Canada. Americans made up 9 per cent of the foreign students in Great Britain, 5 per cent of those in Switzerland, 7 per cent of those in France, 9 per cent of those in Belgium, and so on.

Why do so many American students flock to foreign educational centers? What are the advantages to be gained from foreign study? The answers to these questions are complicated, but extremely interesting. In part the trend is a reflection of the times in which we live. People are far more conscious of the rest of the world than they used to be; when newspaper headlines make them aware of the vital importance of Southeast Asia, Africa, Latin America, and the Middle East, simple curiosity fosters the desire to see such places. Furthermore, our national interest demands that specialists be trained who know these lands, their people, and their problems firsthand. Then there is the fact that every year travel becomes faster and more comfortable. In the colonial era, a landlubber who crossed the ocean committed himself, body and soul, to six or eight weeks of torture: cramped quarters, filth, dampness, wormy and inadequate food, seasickness, and a very real danger of drowning. Nowadays, ocean liners are floating palaces, while jets span the Atlantic almost as fast as the sun. We have become a nation of travelers, very likely the most peripatetic people on earth. More than 76,000 American citizens granted passports in 1965 were traveling for business reasons and another 7,000 for religious reasons, the State Department reports. Students are caught up in this movement along with businessmen, government officials, members of the armed forces, and ordinary tourists.

The Best Place to Study Norwegian Is Norway

From an academic point of view, some students go abroad because certain specialized knowledge is more readily available in other countries. This was the principal reason why eighteenth- and nineteenth-century students went to Europe. In our own day, of course, there is no need to leave the United States to get a first-rate education. As a matter of fact, there are far more foreign scholars here than American scholars abroad.

But many countries have developed *particular* fields to a high degree; the Dutch, to cite a single example, are, with their long experience in dike and canal construction, world leaders in hydraulic engineering and land reclamation. Or consider the question of foreign languages. No matter how fine the language instruction in our colleges—and unfortunately, despite all the new audiovisual techniques, it is not always outstanding—it cannot compete with on-the-spot training. The best place in which to learn Norwegian, for example, is Norway, where the student is surrounded by his subject. He sees Norwegian every time he looks at a sign. He hears it nearly every waking moment of each day.

Professors and their students are almost unanimous on this point. Here are typical comments:

Professor: "Instruction really continues after classes end. Every experience the student has is a form of language education."

Student: "While you're living here there is a tremendous incentive to keep on studying. You want to talk to people—actually, you must—and to do this you need the language."

If the student's early efforts produce some practical results—when his stumbling request for directions leads him to the address he is seeking, for example—he is stimulated to work harder. Even Thomas Jefferson, that intense nationalist in educational matters who numbered among his many accomplishments the founding of the University of Virginia, admitted that "the habit of speaking the foreign languages cannot be so well acquired in America."*

It is almost equally important for the student of history to have some firsthand experience in the area of his special interest, and the same applies to literature, art, music, and many other disciplines. "How can you understand *Faust* unless you have seen it performed in German?" asks Professor Frederick Strothmann, of Stanford University. "And where can you see a performance in German except in Germany or Austria?" Books—even pictures—are no substitute for actual observation, whether the subject be Goethe's *Faust*, Renaissance architecture, contemporary political thought, the economics of underdeveloped areas, or Oriental philosophy. Furthermore, the intuitive understanding of a people and their culture—an awareness that develops with personal contact—is very important. In studying any subject, one profits from familiarity with the environment in which the subject developed.

Getting New Viewpoints

Studying in a foreign country also brings rewards far beyond those coming from formal classroom work. Everyone concedes that

---

* Jefferson objected to American youths' studying in Europe, however. He was afraid they would develop a taste for "luxury and dissipation" and "a passion" for women of easy virtue.

it is "educational" merely to see how other people live, to attend their theaters, to wander about in their cities and villages, sip strange drinks in their sidewalk cafés, chat with their taxi drivers and shopkeepers. Travel is broadening, whether you are Marco Polo, Peter the Great, the President of the United States, or a sophomore from Wichita or Milwaukee. Jack Egle, Paris Director of the Council on International Educational Exchange, emphasizes that "the first objective of sending students abroad should be to open them up, get them out of their limited environment and into a situation where they can meet new stimuli and new people."

Interviews with many government officials and with hundreds of professors and students who have worked in foreign countries show that almost without exception this wider understanding of the world and its people is one of the most cherished results of study abroad. "Young men and women who study in foreign lands widen their horizons immeasurably," says General J. B. de Jongh, Secretary-General of the Academy of International Law at The Hague. "They learn not merely from their teachers but from each other. The implications of this for international peace are quite apparent."

Howard H. Russell, United States Cultural Exchange Officer at the Embassy in Bonn, believes that "there is a great deal of value in introducing American undergraduates to foreign academic life. If they already have a firm foundation in the language, living within a foreign community does, no doubt, enrich their knowledge of the language and understanding of the culture—which, in turn, contributes to the over-all objective of bringing about greater mutual understanding."

Professor Robert Davril, a member of the French Fulbright Commission and an important official in the French Ministry of Education, provides a practical illustration of this principle drawn from everyday life. "To take a simple thing," he says, "consider food. Americans tend to have the idea that the grand cuisine of France is a universal thing, and that every Frenchman eats as though he were having dinner at Maxim's every day. Coming over here and living in France, they soon learn that this is not true." A matter of no great moment, but one that adds its bit to the student's general tolerance and understanding. To study abroad is to experience hundreds of small but important insights.

Then there is the more general impact of any alien culture on the mind and heart of a visiting student. Plunged into a strange environment, he is impelled to try to adjust, to attempt new things, to strive for independence, to speak a new tongue. As one student expressed it: "The situation requires responsibility, self-sufficiency, and broad-mindedness." An American teacher was more specific: "Every student must learn what to do with his freedom."

Younger students in particular often look upon a period of study in a foreign country as a time for self-examination. An art student at Fontainebleau, her ideas uncrystallized but in a process of growth, says: "I came here to find something, I wasn't sure what. And although I still don't know *exactly* what it was, I'm sure I've found it." Similar comments crop up over and over again when students talk about their aims and aspirations while abroad.

The Student Ambassador

In these critical times many American students go abroad to try to develop good will for their country and to further their own understanding of other nations. Here is a stirring expression of this motive by a girl from Smith College:

> I consider it the DUTY of a citizen of the United States and of the world to take any opportunity he can to increase his knowledge and understanding of other peoples. It is my ardent belief that this understanding lies at the root of any possible world peace. I feel a strong necessity for the younger generation to become aware of the responsibility which awaits us in a world which cannot afford a third World War.

Another student makes the same point in a quieter manner: "I am abroad," he says, "to seek . . . those factors which unite mankind."

Most students are aware of the importance of serving as representatives of their country. "You have to *explain* your country," one American says in speaking of criticisms by foreigners. A German boy in Paris expressed the same feeling this way: "Many people are prejudiced against me because of what my people did in the last war. I can't blame them. But I want to show them how Germans really are."

Generally speaking, students make excellent "ambassadors." They are intelligent, eager, curious, purposeful, energetic, and (being young) attractive. Furthermore, it is flattering to have students come to one's country, since the act obviously implies a respect for the nation's accomplishments. It is human for the natives of any country to resent the mere tourist who is idling away his time, often frivolously, while they work. But serious students tend to attract sympathy and respect, especially if they are not overprosperous.

It does not always happen that American students make a good impression or that the foreign country makes a good impression on them, and some of the reasons for this will be discussed in a later chapter. But foreign study leads at least to better *understanding*. A Frenchman with a negative attitude toward the United States because of his observations of uncouth American students in certain cafés is to be preferred to one whose opinions are based on an axe-grinding propaganda campaign.

Satisfying an Urge for Travel and Adventure

Students have many other reasons for wanting to study abroad. By far the most common of these—nearly every student mentions it—is the thirst for travel and adventure. One need not be a student to find adventure in a foreign land, but by settling down for a time and becoming part of the local community, the student does usually experience life abroad at a far deeper and more meaningful level than does the tourist who whisks from sight to sight at a hectic pace guided by a bored and empty-headed tour leader parroting clichés and misinformation. Those who have traveled as tourists but also have lived for some time in one place abroad agree almost unanimously that the tourist looks at more but *sees* far less.* The high-school teacher, for example, who spends his summer studying the French language and literature at the Institut d'Etudes Françaises pour Etrangers at Pau in the Pyrenees will probably come home in September with knowledge not only of France but of all Europe and with more "adventures" to describe to his friends and students than will those of his colleagues who wore out several

---

* Of course there are many advantages to organized tours. An American teacher studying in a small German village comments almost plaintively, "Some of us don't know much, and have to be led about by the nose if we are going to see what we ought to see."

pairs of shoes clambering through cathedrals and ruins from London and Paris to Rome and Athens. He will also be less exhausted
—in purse as well as in body and spirit. "Just being in Oslo for a
long period enables you to learn so much about it," one student
reports. This is a typical reaction.

American students, when asked why they are studying in a foreign country, offer many reasons having nothing to do with formal
schooling. Some have relatives abroad. Others express a vaguely
defined interest in a particular land. A boy studying in Denmark,
for example, explains that there are few opportunities to pursue
Scandinavian studies in the United States, but then quickly adds
that he really went because of his admiration for the way the Danes
protected their Jewish fellow citizens during the Nazi occupation.
Others hope to escape surroundings at home: one student wished
"to get away from parental control"; another wanted to "forget" a
broken engagement; a third was bored with his American college;
another sought "the prestige" which she assumed automatically
accrues to those studying abroad. One young man admitted, "My
parents wanted to separate me from my girl friend." Some students
actually confessed that the opportunity to buy a sports car at cut-
rate prices was a factor in their trip. Others wish to try their luck
with the local females in order to collect conquests to boast about
at home. Some go simply because they win scholarships; others,
sheeplike, because several friends have decided to do so.

None of these objectives is necessarily wrong in itself; the difficulties arise when students go abroad *primarily* for such reasons. If
one goes as a student, he should not lose sight of the main object.
"International good will is important, but academic aims come first;
it's *study* abroad." So says H. G. Quik, Director of the Netherlands
Universities Foundation for International Cooperation, and we
heartily agree.

Adjusting to New Educational Systems

But just as it provides him with many rich rewards, foreign study
involves many difficult adjustments for the American student, and
getting used to a different system and philosophy of education is
the most important of these adjustments. The number of study programs open to Americans all over the world is very large, as we

shall presently see, but nearly all of them have one element in common: they operate within the context of the "European" system of higher education—a system quite unlike our own. It would require many volumes to explain all the national variants,* but a sort of "composite" picture of the system can be drawn that will highlight the ways in which it differs from the American.

First of all, in comparison with the United States, a much smaller percentage of the population in other countries of the world goes to college. The United States (population 200,000,000) has more than 6,000,000 students in some 2,200 institutions of higher education. Spain has only a little over 100,000 such students, in a population of about 35,000,000; France, 380,000 in a population of about 50,000,000. Even the Soviet Union, which has emphasized mass education of late, has 1,400,000 fewer college-level students than we do, despite a population considerably larger than that of the United States. This situation means that competition for a place in any foreign university is tougher by far than it is in most American colleges.

In most countries, the weeding-out process begins early. Although the opportunities for higher education are everywhere improving and "late-bloomers" are often allowed back on the path to the universities, only those who pass stiff examinations taken at about age fourteen are eligible for entrance to the *lycées* and *gymnasia* which prepare students for the universities. Furthermore, these secondary schools waste little time on educational frills. They drive their students relentlessly in comparison with American high schools. Secondary education also continues for one year longer than it does in the United States. As a result, it is generally agreed that graduates (that is, students entering the universities) are equivalent to American *juniors*. This usually makes it impossible for an American freshman or sophomore to enroll in a university abroad except in a special program of some kind. The Sorbonne, for example, requires any American seeking admission to present proof of junior standing in a recognized college. Actually, most foreign universities more closely resemble our graduate schools than our colleges. Their students are working in narrow fields, preparing for specific professions. The kind of program that Americans

* Brief descriptions of higher education in the principal nations where Americans study appear in Chapter 6.

think of as a "liberal arts curriculum" is associated by the foreigner with his secondary schools.

The next significant difference between foreign and American schools concerns the course of study. The "European" pattern does not call for quizzes or mid-term examinations nor does it require the writing of term papers or the accumulation of a specified number of credits. Instead, the student remains in residence until he feels that he can pass the general examinations in his field of study —law, say, or philosophy. He chooses his own classes and attends them when he feels like doing so. Chiefly he studies on his own; professors and their lectures are meant to provide only inspiration, bibliographical guidance, and a close analysis of whatever narrow field the professor himself is interested in at the moment. The final examinations are generally exceptionally difficult, and consequently the rate of failure is extremely high. And despite the lofty standards of the secondary schools, attrition at foreign universities is frightful. Not long ago, a law class at the University of Aix-Marseilles in France was trimmed, in a single academic year, from 665 students to 165. Estimates of the over-all rate of failure in France range as high as 60 per cent. From the practical point of view, this system makes it difficult for an American undergraduate, who seldom intends to study abroad for more than a year, to obtain "academic credit" for the work he does. He may attend a series of courses faithfully, read widely, learn a great deal; but unless he can make special arrangements, there is generally no official way of testing his achievement and no record that can be transmitted to his own college.

Furthermore, it is often impossible for the American abroad to find university courses that meet his needs. Obviously the foreign universities do not offer regular courses in the native language or its literature at a level that most American students can handle. Nor do they generally provide what we call "survey" courses. Titles like "A History of Spanish Literature," or "The Novel in the Nineteenth Century," or "History of Europe Since 1870" do not appear very often in their catalogues. And if they do, the titles are misleading; professors almost invariably confine their actual lectures to some quite narrow topic; when they cover a broad field, they do so in cycles of up to several years. The *Bulletin* of the Sweet Briar College Junior Year in France makes this point plainly:

The schedule of lectures given by the professors at the Sorbonne is established primarily for French students who are preparing for the *license* or the *agrégation*. . . . Although the titles suggest that an entire period or century may be treated, this is not the case, since survey courses as such do not exist. The professor often chooses to study minutely one author or one aspect of an author. The student is expected to have a good background knowledge of the entire period, and to do independent reading in preparation for the examination. This is his responsibility, not that of the professor giving the course.

Conditions in other countries are usually very similar to those in France.

In foreign universities there is little of what is known in this country as campus life. Usually the university buildings are in the heart of a city, but scattered over a considerable area and separated one from another by residences, stores, and factories. Students generally live with their parents or in furnished rooms. Dormitories are in short supply, although more are being built every year. Inevitably there is much less "student life" than in America.

"The U.S. university is very much a social unit, often a little society in itself," a Fulbrighter points out after a year in Spain. "One eats, drinks, dances, studies, loves, and hates, all within the walls. . . . In Spain, however, student life goes on outside university precincts. One comes for classes and for coffee in the bar. One chats awhile. . . . Then one takes the streetcar home."

There are fewer clubs, fewer social affairs for students, and no organized sports in foreign universities. As one French professor who tried to develop some extracurricular activities abroad told a *New York Times* reporter: "The university [of Aix-Marseilles] provides me with nothing except its blessing. Some of us have tried to encourage sports as a normal, healthy outlet, but it doesn't seem to take." This poses problems for strangers, whether they be native or foreign, but, as we shall see, the problems are not insurmountable.

Foreign universities are public institutions; tuition is nominal by American standards. With very few exceptions, however, they are not as well off as either the privately or publicly supported colleges in America, which means that foreign universities are forced to operate with much higher student-teacher ratios. In France this ratio in the Arts Faculty is in the neighborhood of 150 to 1. The Free University of Berlin has more than ten thousand students but only 327 teachers, including assistant lecturers. In contrast, the University of Buffalo in the United States, which also has more than ten thousand students, has a teaching staff of about 1,400 full-time and part-time faculty members, while a great university like Harvard, also enrolling between ten and eleven thousand students, has more than 3,400 teachers.

Because of the shortage of teachers, classes in most foreign universities are very large. Except at the most advanced levels (and at a few institutions like Oxford and Cambridge) the lecture method is used almost exclusively. It is common for Americans to feel lost and even frightened by the size and impersonality of these classes, at least in the beginning.

The Professor on a Pedestal

Another result of the scarcity of teachers is the great prestige of the professor. Although not always accompanied by high pay, this prestige is universal in foreign lands. "The professor," a well-known Frenchman writes, "is not a salaried official, but a *free* man . . . who is *fed at the expense of the State* as being a particularly useful citizen."

In America, while professors are usually respected, they are certainly not deferred to or placed on a pedestal. Informality and an easy give and take between teacher and pupil are aspects of the accepted pattern, as seen in this amusing story told us by an American professor of political science when we were preparing our book *From Main Street to the Left Bank.* * Shortly after the war he traveled through France, Germany, and Italy. Everywhere he was struck by the honor shown him by all kinds of people. Luxuriating in a new-found sense of his own importance and the dignity of his profession, he bought some calling cards and grew a neat Van Dyke to add to his distinction. However, shortly before returning home he was sharply brought down to earth when he went to visit an American friend stationed at a huge army camp in Germany. He walked to the gate of the compound, produced his passport and one of his new calling cards, and asked for his friend.

* Michigan State University Press, East Lansing (1959).

The sergeant of the guard examined his credentials briefly. "A professor, eh? Hmmm." Then, abruptly, he pointed to a bench inside the guardhouse. "O.K., Mac," he said. "Go park yourself over there. I'll see what I can do for ya in a minute."

His "home" reception was a jolting experience for this professor, but for American students the shock usually comes when they go abroad. They are seldom properly prepared to understand the attitude of the average professor toward his students. Here are some typical comments made by American students in Europe:

Two law students studying at the Sorbonne: "The student troubled by a point of law certainly does not air his perplexity with his professor, who, besides being unavailable, is a non-approachable, awe-inspiring deity."

A scholar in Madrid: "The Spanish student . . . is simply not pampered and guided by the faculty. The blinding light of the great man's eloquence shines into the student's life for a few hours each week; after this, he is left to grope his own way in the lonely darkness which the brightness has caused."

A student in Munich: "There is an informality between American students and professors that you'd never find here. I brought a German student I know to visit a professor from my college back home who is living here this year. She couldn't believe her eyes and ears. She said that no German student would ever just drop in on a professor. And the friendly informality of our conversation simply appalled her."

A student in Italy: "There is very little personal relationship between professor and student here. Professors are much more academic; they make no allowances at all for personal differences between students."

A graduate student at the Free University of Berlin: "The professors just didn't give a damn about the students. One of the courses I took, for example, met every Thursday. The first meeting lasted only fifteen minutes. The professor told us what he was going to do and then left. For the second meeting he didn't show up. The following Thursday was *Pfingsten,* and the next another holiday. The fifth class meeting was a failure because the professor had just had a tooth extracted and couldn't speak. The next Thursday he said it was so late in the term and we had missed so much that it wasn't worth starting."

Actually, the attitude of most foreign professors is perfectly understandable. Most, of course, are not as irresponsible as the Berliner just described; many are conscientious and brilliant lecturers whose classes are frequently interrupted by spontaneous bursts of applause. The respect they demand is really respect for *learning*, surely not a bad thing. And their attitude is not based on contempt for students, but on the idea that it is better to learn for oneself than to be spoon-fed by a teacher. "It is . . . undesirable for students to ask their professors to solve their problems for them," a German professor remarks. "When a student wants the answer to a question, he should read. He may read a thousand, or even two thousand pages without obtaining the answer, but on page 2,001, there the truth will lie! It is better for a student to *search* than for the student to be *taught*." Although most foreign professors recognize that the lecture system is far from perfect as a means of instruction, they generally consider the spirit of independence it fosters desirable. They also criticize the American "discussion" method, which, as Professor Louis Landré, of the Sorbonne, once said, "puts too much stress on having something to say for the sake of talking." And many consider the American student terribly immature. "He remains too long a Boy Scout," said one foreign educator, with a smile.

Students—The Intellectual Elite

Americans who study overseas must also adjust to the attitudes of foreign students. As we have seen, these scholars are older, often brighter (because they are more rigorously selected), and of course better prepared for the work at their own universities than the average student from the United States. Most are very serious about their studies, for there is a direct relationship, often absent in America, between academic success and obtaining a good start in one's chosen career. In France, for example, graduates of the universities can count on earning 50 per cent more than those who fail; therefore most students pursue their work assiduously and systematically. Many learn shorthand in order to be more proficient at taking lecture notes. An American visitor passing through a foreign university hall is bound to be impressed by the fact that there is almost no horseplay and very little aimless conversation. At most, he might observe a couple of young men bent intently over a chess-board. Foreign students "are more serious," "are more ambitious in a farsighted way," "read more, think more than an American," and "lack the 'trade-school mentality.'" These are typical observations of foreign university students in France, Norway, Germany, and Spain, made by Americans who have studied abroad.

The medieval concept of the student as a member of a special class in society is still alive in many places. Society views him with a degree of respect only somewhat less than that accorded the pro-fessor,* and the student sees himself as participating in a special way of life—a temporary phase, to be sure, but no less dignified and important. He tends to act, even among his fellows, with great formality and reserve. It is not at all unusual to sit next to another student in a class for a whole year without exchanging more than a polite nod at the start of each session. Can you visualize this happening at State Tech?

In short, students have an attitude of independence and indi-vidual responsibility based on the assumption that each is mature enough to pursue his work in his own way. They are intensely proud of their freedom and resist all efforts to tie them down to the kind of prescribed routine that is common in American colleges. Such concepts as compulsory attendance at classes, weekly quizzes, and "assigned" readings are unknown to them. When several law professors at the University of Frankfurt attempted to introduce the American case method of legal education, their students balked at having to prepare specific cases for particular class sessions. Their "academic freedom" was being violated, they contended. Naturally this whole attitude poses problems for the American student. He is eager to meet new people; his previous experience leaves him unprepared for the reserve and isolation of his local counterparts. His way of adjusting to the life of the foreign uni-versity will have a very large influence on his whole educational experience abroad.

At this point, the student considering foreign study might well be expected to ask: "Why bother?" If the European system poses such difficulties, if the problems of adjustment are so great, can the ad-vantages possibly counterbalance them? Of course they do. Indeed,

---

* "A sure-fire way of obtaining a ride when hitchhiking," one American reports, "is to carry a sign identifying yourself as a student."

much of the profit in foreign study rises from the fact that there *are* differences between the systems. If Heidelberg were exactly like Harvard, there would be little point in going from one to the other to study. The satisfactions gained by dealing with new problems, the perspectives achieved through observing a foreign educational system firsthand, easily outweigh all the difficulties. Generations of students have testified to this.

CHAPTER 2

Before You Leave: Basic Considerations

Your intellectual preparation should start as early as possible . . . choosing your style of living and study . . . urban or provincial universities? . . . arranging your accommodations . . . language preparation . . . becoming an expert on two countries—your own and the one in which you'll study

"A spell of study abroad can be a decisive and unforgettable experience in a student's career," Sir Eric Ashby, Master of Clare College, Cambridge, and Vice-Chairman of the Association of Universities of the British Commonwealth, has written. "But," Sir Eric adds at once, "if it is to be profitable it calls for careful planning: a deliberate and hard-headed choice of the scholar under whom to work or the course of study to follow." Everyone with any experience in international education will agree with this advice.

It is never too early to begin making plans for study abroad. Ideally, parents who value the breadth and understanding that come from being educated in a foreign country should start their children in the right direction by seeing to it that they begin language training early—in grade school, if possible. It does not matter too much *which* language, for tests have shown that children who have been exposed to *any* language learn other languages more easily than those who have not. Parents can also encourage their children by showing interest themselves in foreign lands and foreign peoples.

The prospective student himself should begin by thinking about where to go—and under what auspices—as soon as possible in his career. Now that so many high schools are encouraging students to participate in study-abroad programs, both for summers and in some cases during the regular academic year (see Chapters 10 and 11), many young people are being exposed to the advantages of early preparation in the schools themselves. However, for those who, for one reason or another, prefer to wait until they are college students before studying abroad, it is still important to plan ahead. The student should begin by collecting catalogues and brochures of programs that interest him. He should also write to some of the many organizations that provide guidance for students interested in study abroad.

Once the high-school student has decided on the country in which to study, he should plan a school program that will allow an abundance of training in the appropriate language and courses that will add to his knowledge of the history and culture of that land. And he should read as widely as he can about the country, its people, their literature, their arts.

His plans for study abroad may even influence his choice of an American college. Some colleges operate overseas programs exclusively for their own students, and anyone interested in such a program had better make sure that he has the grades and other requirements demanded for admission to that college. (It is true, by the way, that the student who can show in his application that he has planned for some time to enter the college because of its overseas offering will probably improve his chances of being accepted.) Needless to say, students who first begin to think of studying abroad after they have entered college are under greater pressure to acquire the necessary fundamentals of language and knowledge of the country.

Much Depends on Your Major Field of Interest

At the college stage, the next item for the student to consider is the particular subject or subjects in which he wants to specialize while overseas. As we have said, most special overseas programs tend to concentrate on the language, literature, art, history, politics, or economic development of the locality. If this coincides with the student's interests, well and good; his choice will be relatively free. But if his heart is set on anthropology, say, or music, he will find fewer opportunities. He ought, therefore, to discover as early as possible where he can find special programs devoted to such subjects. Since most special courses in anthropology, for instance, are to be found in Latin America, a future candidate would naturally be wise were he to make Spanish his foreign language in high school. Oberlin, for example, has a large program for music majors in Austria; and it should be obvious that a young student with ambitions in this direction ought to study as much German and European history as possible in high school.

If, from a perusal of the descriptive literature of a particular program, the student cannot tell whether he will be allowed to pursue the subjects of his special interest, he ought to consult his adviser. If the answer is "no," and he wants to study abroad anyway, he may have to arrange his whole college program with special care so that he can fulfill the requirements for his major on the home campus. However, there *are* programs that offer courses in the sciences and social sciences, and the student capable of handling work in a foreign university on his own can study any subject he chooses—in dozens of excellent institutions.

Sources of Information

Information about studying in almost any country in the world can be obtained by writing to the embassy or nearest consulate of that country in the United States. In most cases, however, it is better to write to the more specialized agencies, public and private, that have been established to aid foreign students. In the United States, the Institute of International Education is the best source of information about studying abroad, but there are many others, such as the National Education Association, particularly important for teachers who are interested in foreign programs.

In France the National Office of French Universities can be most helpful; in Germany, the Academic Exchange Service (Akademischer Austauschdienst) is important. Probably the most complete listing of organizations of this type can be found in *Study Abroad,* published annually by UNESCO. The student is warned, however, that this volume is so exhaustive that it is difficult for inexperienced persons to decide exactly which organization in a given country is most likely to provide the information desired. In the Appendix we have listed the names and addresses and chief functions of the most important organizations in all the nations to which any considerable number of Americans are likely to want to go to study.

Metropolis or Province?

Another question any student should ask himself in an early stage of planning is whether it is better to study in a great metropolitan center or in a provincial town. Is the University of London to be preferred to the University of Nottingham? Is Graz superior to Vienna? The advantages and disadvantages of city and town are fairly obvious. The big cities are centers of culture. They have the best museums, libraries, and theaters; generally their universities are larger and have more varied offerings. Big cities give students the freedom that comes with anonymity. One encounters less prejudice and more tolerance as a rule than in a small community and a wider choice of people and ideas.

But the city is also more impersonal. Its citizens are busier and less friendly toward strangers. Life is more expensive and more complicated. Housing is hard to find and when available is often located far from the universities. There are also, of course, many distractions in the cities and sometimes a degree of cynicism that visitors from abroad may find distressing. One more fact is that many of the great cities of the world, particularly those in Europe, have acquired a patina of international culture, especially American, that may be all too familiar to a student who has come abroad to benefit from a dose of a new and different style of life. In short, the cities offer more cultural advantages, but the small centers often provide a friendlier, more intimate way of life.*

Ideally, the visiting student will want to live in an environment where he can sample many different aspects of the foreign culture and society and at the same time develop reasonably close personal ties with local people. In this connection, let us consider Paris, one of the world's most popular centers for foreign students. Paris provides every imaginable facility for intellectual and social

---

* As with most generalizations, there are exceptions. For example, a Dutch official remarked, "In Holland, small-town people tend to reject foreigners. We have our best results in getting students into homes in large cities like Amsterdam."

stimulation. But it is actually a poor choice for the student who hopes to get to know France or her people. In the first place, the institutions of higher education in Paris are, as the official French agency in charge of student housing reports, *surpeuplée* (overcrowded). This applies to both classrooms and housing. "In spite of the continuing effort in the field of student center and dormitory construction," the Service Parisien d'Acceuil des Etudiants Etrangers goes on to say, "each new academic year sees a multiplication of the applications of students for housing." Paris is also expensive and impersonal; Parisians, though charming, sophisticated, interesting, and gay, do not generally discommode themselves to entertain uninvited visitors. Blasé and intensely occupied with their own affairs, they allow foreigners the freedom of their city, but do not offer to assist in their enjoyment of it. The director of the Office National des Universités et Ecoles Françaises advises that foreign students in France who study for only a year should try to go to the provinces. This is true especially for younger students and those who do not know the language well. In Paris, the student comes in touch with many Frenchmen who know English, which may discourage him from struggling to express himself in French. Furthermore, the hordes of American tourists, businessmen, and other students make it doubly difficult for the shy beginner to stick to the French tongue. When he tries in his stumbling way to order a meal in French the Parisian waiter may tell him, in flawless English, what he ought to order and why. Another problem is that the classic European respect for students is diluted by numbers; younger ones especially may be dismissed as dilettantes, *pas sérieux*. In the provinces, on the other hand, English is not so widely spoken, and there are fewer American and British visitors to tempt the student into doing what comes naturally (what comes naturally in this case being wrong). "It's definitely an advantage, there not being many English-speaking people here," a student in one provincial city explains. "There are thirty-four nationalities here—we simply *have* to speak French."

Paris is an especially poor choice during the summer, for then hundreds of thousands of Parisians depart from the city *en vacances*. Visitors have the place to themselves, and while it is still beautiful it is scarcely typical of France. During this season it is almost impossible to walk along any major street for five minutes without hearing English spoken. Yet a careful study of the problems faced by foreign students in Paris leads to the conclusion that it is more the concentration of Americans than the size and character of the city that makes it desirable for students from the United States to go elsewhere.

Small university towns like Heidelberg, with dense concentrations of foreign students, are also better avoided. When foreigners make up from 15 to 20 per cent of the student population (as they do in these places), they cannot expect much attention to be paid them as individuals. Too often the stranger is lost in the crowd; local people quickly find their curiosity sated and their hospitable instincts smothered by the hordes of potential guests. Commercialism invades the student housing market, and the danger of gravitating toward the nationals of one's own country increases. A German at the University of Heidelberg advised: "Having 20 per cent foreign students here is good for *us* but not for *you*. You will fall in with your own group. Go to Tübingen, for instance, where you will have to speak German." An American at Munich, another university with a large foreign enrollment that includes many Americans, confirms the accuracy of this statement. "I try to speak German, but it's hard not to follow the path of least resistance."

But, one will argue, the reason students flock to such places as Paris, Munich, and Mexico City is that these are the interesting places to know and see, the centers of both art and culture, fun and frolic. True enough; but that does not mean that they are the best places for students. There is only one Louvre and one Notre Dame, but all France is filled with art treasures and Gothic churches. Munich's beer is justly famous, but the local brew in Marburg, Tübingen, and Göttingen is also excellent. Paris restaurants are the best in the world, but there are magnificent ones in every French university town, and the food is much cheaper too. Especially in Europe, one is never more than a few hours' journey from some great metropolis where students can go on week ends and during vacations.

The best advice for the student is that he should try to avoid being influenced by fads and fashions in his choice of a place to study abroad. Keep away from the crowds, especially the crowds of Americans. If you must live in a big city, choose one like Hamburg, which has a bustling, growing university with few American students, or even better—if you do not mind living on a powder keg—like Berlin, which has magnificent cultural opportunities and a gay social life, but where there are only about five hundred non-Germans in a university student body of over 10,000.

Dormitory, Pension, Hotel, or Hostel?

Having decided on the location, the student must determine what sort of quarters to seek out. Some will live in dormitories, others in private families; many more will rent furnished rooms or find a place in a pension. There are even students who live in hotels. Almost everywhere abroad student housing is tight, and foreign visitors often have little choice of accommodation. Nevertheless, the advantages and disadvantages of various types of housing should be carefully investigated.

Living in a hotel is obviously the poorest choice, unless one is thinking only of personal comfort and the avoidance of every possible inconvenience. Hotels are expensive, impersonal, lacking in much of the spirit of the local community; in short, they are not designed to house long-term residents. A pension provides something more closely approaching an authentic slice of the local life at reasonable cost, although superficially pensions seem much like hotels. They offer the student independence, but also membership in a group; possibly he will make friends among the boarders over meals or sitting around the common room in the evening. Such places, however, vary widely in comfort and general atmosphere. Often students in pensions complain of being ignored by the other lodgers, or of being nagged by the landlady if they fail to extinguish a light after use, or if they inquire timidly about the possibility of a little hot water for a bath. Furnished rooms have the same good and bad aspects that pensions display, except that the absence of the common dinner table greatly reduces the chances of getting to know one's fellow lodgers very well.

Far more satisfactory than any of these arrangements is the university dormitory or student house, almost without exception cheap, clean, and comfortable. Certainly one can count on a decent minimum standard not always available in rooming houses and third-rate hotels; a student can safely sign up for a proferred room in a dormitory sight unseen, whereas to do so for a furnished room or pension might be risky. Dormitories have the obvious additional advantage of being full of students; thus opportunities for making friends with persons of similar age and interests are great. Unlike most American college dormitories, those abroad impose few restrictions on the comings and goings of residents—another advantage. Finally, the student in a dormitory is an integral part of the university community.

However, because of these advantages the dormitories at universities abroad are always crammed. Most, therefore, have quotas for foreign students and can perforce house only a fraction of those who apply. This is not the case during the summer, however, when regular classes are over, and so large numbers of American students attending foreign summer courses can then be accommodated. But a new difficulty then arises: there are seldom more than a few local students about during summer sessions! Do not expect to meet Frenchmen, for example, in the dormitories of the University of Caen during the summer; there'll be foreign students aplenty, but they will not "speak French like natives," and this, of course, is an important disadvantage for anyone trying to learn the language. On the other hand, a mixed group of foreign students, all eager to meet new people, to discuss world problems, to discover the attitudes and ideas of students from other lands, can provide an extremely stimulating and profoundly educational environment for any student abroad. Indeed, the student abroad who is offered a chance to live dormitory-style at *any* time of the year ought to jump at the opportunity.

What About Family Living?

Living with a local family can be an equally valuable experience, and a number of organizations like the Experiment in International Living make "family stays" the very center of their work. *Students* must look upon this type of housing from a slightly different point of view, however: except for hotels, you can choose no more expensive type of housing. Yet under the best circumstances there are unique advantages to living with a family. The guest becomes a functioning part of an authentic social organization and cannot help but learn a great deal about the culture and customs of the country. Nor can he help but improve his facility with the language, for the family situation complements the classroom situation perfectly: the stress is on natural rather than artificial communication, on everyday vocabulary and idiomatic speech. Aside from these advantages which apply directly to the education of the student, family life offers important practical and psychological rewards. The visiting student can depend on his family when he wants to know where the post office is, what kind of store sells pocket knives or shoebrushes, or where to turn when his teeth need attention. The family also provides an entree into a larger society and thus offers the student a way to make new friends easily and naturally. It also gives him a sense of security quite valuable when one is thousands of miles from home. He is assured proper care when sick, moral support when troubled.

Students fortunate enough to have lived in a true family situation almost always insist that this is the best of all possible arrangements. There is room here only for one fairly extensive expression of opinion, but it could easily be replaced by a dozen others. The speaker is a young man from a midwestern university studying in Germany. He has experienced both family life abroad and the more independent life of a Munich rooming house. "If you want to learn about Germany you must live with a family," he says. "In my rooming house here I learn something about Italy, something about France and other countries—but the landlady is the only German around, and there's never much to be seen of her." On the subject of his stay with a family in a small German town he finds it hard to express himself. Finally, when asked simply to think about the experience and say whatever enters his mind, he says: "My German family has very little money, but you should see how happy they are. When you compare their life with what we have in America it really hits you over the head. . . . When I arrived I was worried that they wouldn't like me, but you know, they were worried too— they thought I'd have a hard time getting on without modern conveniences. What dopes we all were! . . . You know what being a member of a family means? It means sitting in the same chair every meal. It means taking a walk in the evening after the dishes are done. (In America I never washed a dish in my life.) . . . I was closest to the youngest son—he's two years younger than I am. I gave him a Wagner record for his birthday."

The student paused at this point for a long moment and then

added one more comment. "Here's a good example of what it means to be in a family over here. In Germany when two people get to be really close friends, it's up to the older one to suggest that they drop the formal mode of address, *Sie*, and go on a *du* basis. I'll always remember the pride I felt when I realized that it was *my* responsibility to suggest the change to that boy."

The student offered a place in a "family" should, however, make sure that it is a real social organization and not a mere rooming house. Also, some students consider the very intimacy of family life a disadvantage, preferring to be on their own as much as possible. For many, the restrictions and the emotional involvements inherent in living in a family seem disadvantages. And all this again points up the central fact that every individual must make those choices which best meet *his* needs, *his* wants, and *his* tastes.

Keep a Balanced View on Credits

The student planning to study abroad must also give careful thought beforehand to the question of transferring credit. If he is matriculating at a college that runs a foreign program, this presents no problem, except, perhaps, that he is then restricted to the kind of program his college operates. In any other case, the student should clear his plans with the authorities of his own college before committing himself, since foreign universities are seldom prepared to handle the problem. "The first question Americans always seem to ask is: 'How can we get credit?'" the executive director of the Fulbright Commission in Madrid told us. "Of course, this is ridiculous in the Spanish system, where the professor scarcely knows of the existence of any individual student." Most college advisers listen sympathetically to the student who wants to earn credits in a foreign country, but all of them are becoming increasingly aware that some of the special programs for Americans have very low academic standards, and they may not approve of those which blithely announce in their catalogues that their credits are accepted at "most" American colleges. Find out before you sign up!

If the student wishes to study independently he should go to his adviser with a carefully worked-out scheme for using his time abroad. He ought to know the university at which he hopes to work and be able to justify his choice. Foreign catalogues and bulletins are not very helpful to the person seeking a precise description of what actually will be taught at a given place and time, but that does not matter. The student *can* discover from a catalogue the professors under whom he would like to study, and he can learn when the university semesters begin and end; and having done that, probably he's done as much as he can before arriving on the scene. Next, instead of hoping to persuade some overseas university administrator to give him a special examination or a certificate or diploma that more often than not will be meaningless, he ought to arrange with his own college for the supervision of his work. No complicated or time-consuming system of administration is required. The student can agree to take a special examination upon his return, or, perhaps, be asked to turn in an extensive paper in which he demonstrates the results of his foreign studies. In other words, through some such arrangement he conforms to American regulations and yet does not try to mold the European system in the American image. His job is to *learn* something, not to get a grade in a particular course. If he can convince the authorities that he knows what he wants to do, that he is mature enough to get it done and capable enough to grapple with the problems of adjusting to the foreign environment, they will probably devise a way for him to obtain "credit" for his work abroad.

But there is still another way of dealing with the credit problem. Ignore it! Consider what being educated really means. Piling up credits, fulfilling requirements, winning A's and B's—such things have little to do with real education. To spend a year, or even a shorter period, living and studying in a foreign country only to *learn* has much to recommend it. For those who can afford the time (and actually, it is the cheapest way to study abroad!) this approach comes closest to the "European system." It has great psychological advantages because it liberates the student from many worries: about his troubles during his first weeks as a student abroad, about obtaining formal recognition of his accomplishments, even about being "different." Instead he can concentrate on what he is doing without regard for the consequences.

One drawback to studying this way is the risk of failing to work hard, of falling into the comfortable error of believing that "life" abroad is itself educative without regard to how the life is spent. An afternoon passed idly in a foreign café may be pleasant enough and even instructive; certainly there is no harm in it. But it is not getting an education in the sense in which we are using the word in these pages. Credit or no, the library and the lecture hall must come first, whether one is studying abroad or at home.

To a college student, taking courses abroad without the hope of winning credits toward graduation may be a temptation to laziness. For the person whose formal education has been completed—most typically the teacher on summer vacation or sabbatical leave—it is far more likely to have the opposite effect.

Learn the Language

Having decided where to go and what to do there, the student should use as much as possible of the interval before departure, be it a matter of weeks or years, in readying himself for what lies ahead. Language training is probably of first importance. "Learn the language of the country where you are staying," writes one student who participated in the Stanford University program in France, where the courses are taught in English. "Chances are you'll regret it for the rest of your life if you don't, just as so many of us regret having given up those piano lessons which once seemed such a bore."

If you are a freshman with two years, say, of high-school German, press forward with the language as intensively as the department will permit. Certainly take advantage of the language laboratories of your college, for this is perhaps the best way to train the ear and tongue for conversation. But it is by no means clear that exclusive dependence on this kind of preparation is best when there is sufficient time. Thorough mastery of grammar and practice in writing and reading are sure to pay large dividends in the long run, especially for a prospective university student. It is one thing to be able to say "good morning" in the native tongue, to order a meal with a good accent, and to understand the dialogue in a foreign movie without looking at the subtitles. It is another to be able to follow a complicated lecture and to read scholarly books. The latter call for deep intellectual understanding of the language and a wide vocabulary, not merely an ear for sounds and a feeling for idioms.

But if time is short—a few months or less—stress should be placed on conversation. A quick course at a special language school and practice with language records are bound to be useful. No one should expect to master a language in this manner or to achieve even moderate proficiency by any method in a matter of weeks. That is why it would be unwise for anyone lacking a solid background to try to study in regular university classes abroad. But even if one knows nothing and is planning to take courses only in English, a little grammar, a small treasury of words, a glimmering of understanding of the structure and cadences of the foreign tongue, will be of immense helpfulness abroad. A junior from Kalamazoo College studying at the University of Bonn made an interesting point in this connection: "It is wrong to count on learning German after you get here. If you don't feel at least a little at home in the language at the start, when everything is strange, you'll tend to get discouraged and to escape into the company of Americans. Before you know it you won't have any contacts at all with the local people. Then you'll just throw in the sponge—give up."

This warning is well made, but at least for the student who is planning to spend considerable time abroad, the *best* language training can be had on the scene itself. A couple of months of practice and study in the country before trying to follow a university lecture there is bound to pay off handsomely. The better junior-year groups spend their first weeks abroad in intensive language study. Leaders consider it vital to "force" the students' training in the crucial period between arrival and the beginning of the academic year, and students who have been through the experience are almost unanimous in stressing its importance. "I never worked so hard in my life, but that's where I learned French," says one. "You know you will have to speak," says another, "and therefore you plunge." Programs that do not provide at least six weeks of this "orientation" are generally weak academically.

The junior-year groups run their own preliminary language-training programs abroad, but there are inexpensive language classes open to all in every country where large numbers of foreign students congregate. The American should try, at least in this period, to live with a family where no English is spoken. And he should keep away from friends! It is reassuring to be near someone from home when first facing the challenges of life in a foreign country, but it interferes with the learning of the language. By temporarily forsaking old friends, one forges the tools for making new ones.

Who Was Cortez? Where Is Medina?

Beyond acquiring language competence, a student ought to ready himself by learning everything he can about the country he is going to visit. It is amazing how few American students make any real effort in this direction. Many depart for their destination with almost no knowledge of the history of the region, with only the sketchiest understanding of its geography, and in utter ignorance of its educational system. There are American students who arrive in Spain without knowing the location of Seville or Barcelona. Others in France cannot estimate that country's population accurately within ten million. Many in Mexico are unable to identify names like Juarez, Huerta, Cárdenas, or even Cortez and Montezuma. Naturally students like these have little understanding at all of the subtle shades of feeling and temperament that make up the national character of their hosts. While abroad they know neither what to look for nor what to make of what they see.

Many Americans are well prepared, of course; but too many are not, and these are the people who give foreigners a poor impression not only of American students but of the educational system that permits such ignorance to flourish. The problem is the more noticeable because students from other countries generally make much of readying themselves for the experience of studying abroad. A Dutch law student decides to go to Greece, not for formal course work, but merely as a casual tourist. For six months before leaving, he devotes all his spare time to reading about the places he intends to visit. A German lad wins a scholarship to study in the United States. "When I went to Stanford," he says with just pride after returning to his native Berlin, "I knew Stanford like the inside of my pocket. When I reached the campus for the first time I knew exactly where the administrative offices were. When I entered the building I knew which way to turn to reach the office of the adviser of foreign students."

Perhaps such meticulous preparation destroys a little of the romance and adventure of visiting new places, but it is certainly to be preferred to the cavalier approach of some American students abroad.

Most organized foreign-study plans include what is usually called an orientation program in their schedules, but no single course can do the job adequately. Ideally, the student should be learning about the country he is going to visit while he is learning the language. Thus he might read, for example, the history of Mexico in Spanish, accomplishing two tasks at the same time. A long period of gradual absorption of information gives the only true basis for knowing a country well.

The student does not have to be an expert. His head need not be stuffed with facts. He need not be familiar, to refer to examples just mentioned, with the latitude of Seville or the date of birth of General Cárdenas. But if he is going to study in Spain, he ought to know that Seville is in Andalusia, and he should find out a little about its rich and colorful history. Or if he is to live in Mexico, he should know the name of the current President and something of his program. In any country the student ought to know how the people earn their living, what their political parties stand for, their religious traditions, their national heroes. This is a large order, but it is important. The informed student profits far more fully from his time abroad and makes a far better impression on his hosts than the brightest and best-intentioned student who is uninformed.

But suppose it is too late? Suppose you have *not* devoted long hours over a period of years to reading about Japan, or England, or Italy. You are leaving in three weeks. What can you do? First of all, get a detailed map of the country and study it until you can draw it from memory, marking down accurately all the chief geographical features—rivers, mountain ranges, the principal cities. Second, begin to follow events in that country carefully in a newspaper that deals at length with foreign news—the *New York Times*, for example. Third, spend an afternoon with a good encyclopedia, noting down whatever seems important in the articles dealing with the country and its history. Then study these notes as if you were preparing for a stiff examination. If you can accomplish these three things, you won't yet be well informed, but at least you won't be totally ignorant.

Let us imagine how a little rudimentary but throughly mastered information can save a student from embarrassment and do its bit toward restoring luster to the tarnished reputation of American education overseas. An American is spending the summer studying in Madrid. He meets a Spanish student. They chat. The Spaniard asks the American where he comes from. "New York," the American replies; "where do *you* come from?" "Oh, you never heard of it," the Spaniard answers. "A town called Medina. It's in Andalucía."

Of course he is correct. Our American cannot be expected to have heard of Medina, a town of around 15,000 souls. But he *has* studied his map of Spain. "In Andalucía," he muses. "Is it near Sevilla?"

"No, much further south."

"Then it must be in the neighborhood of Cádiz."

"That's right! It's about forty kilometers to the southeast."

Now if the American knows *a little* more he may be able to ask an intelligent question about the Duke of Medina Sidonia, who commanded the Spanish Armada, or at least be able to turn the conversation to another nearby town, Jerez de la Frontera, where sherry is made, or to the Strait of Gibraltar, or to cattle raising, or to something else related to the area. In any case he has shown that he is not an ignoramus. And probably he has also made a friend.

And Who's Our Secretary of Agriculture?

The American who knows nothing of the land he is visiting is not, however, as much to be deplored as the one who goes abroad ignorant of the United States. If he is uninformed about Spain, for instance, the Spaniards will think he has been poorly educated. But if he cannot answer questions about his own country, they will write him off as a complete idiot. And surely he will be put to the test. Almost all foreigners are interested in the United States and eager to increase their knowledge of the country. Educated people in other lands know a great deal about America, although they do not always understand the significance of the facts they have collected. Naturally, every American they meet is looked upon as an authority or at least as a source of knowledge. When the authority makes obvious mistakes, a bad impression always results. "Learn about social conditions in the United States because you will be questioned about them—about little things, like what people do on

Sundays, and big things—what you think about integration." This is the warning of a bright girl from California after some months of study in France.

Many of our students cannot clearly explain the difference between the Senate and the House of Representatives, and even more are baffled when asked to explain how a state legislature differs from Congress. They do not know how to describe the role of the Supreme Court in the federal system or the names of prominent public officials. "The other day," a student in Germany told us sadly, "the father of the family I am staying with asked me who the Secretary of Agriculture was, and I couldn't remember. He was polite enough about it, but I sure felt like a fool."

Current affairs are equally important, and here also some of our students too often fail the test. It is bad enough to be unclear about French politics when living in France, but not to know about what is going on at home is much worse. The Communists are bombarding people all over the world with criticisms of American policies. Americans abroad are expected to be able to answer these charges. If they are unable to do so, how can we expect the local people to believe that the charges are false?

Everywhere abroad, American students report that they are called upon to explain and defend American policies and American institutions. Alas, far too often they are unable to do so. Here are some random examples of their reactions when asked about this:

"The trouble is that Americans come over here with strong impressions, strong feelings, but without the facts to back them up."

"Know your own country! Know the facts! Otherwise you'll be nailed to the wall in discussions with Europeans."

"Evening discussions tend to turn to political questions. You've got to be on your toes."

"Of course students here like to talk about clothes, movies, sex, and all the other subjects we gossip about back home on campus in Ohio. But honestly, world problems are the main topic of conversation. I wish I knew more than I do about where we stand."

"People over here know about what's going on in the world. They don't sit in front of TV as much as we do, and when they do, they don't just look at cowboy and Indian shows."

The American who is planning to study abroad must realize that he is—as the State Department tells him when he applies for a passport—an ambassador of his country. He has plenty of "homework" to attend to before departure if he is going to be a good emissary. The propaganda-conscious nations behind the Iron Curtain make much of this ambassadorial function of students. When asked about it an official at the Czech Ministry of Education and Culture seemed taken aback that the question was even raised. "They are citizens of Czechoslovakia," he said. "Their country is going to be judged abroad by their actions." All Czech students heading for foreign countries, according to the Ministry, are given orientation courses lasting from one to three months to prepare them for the experience.

Even three months of intensive study, however, is pitifully inadequate if one does not begin with a solid understanding of America. Not much can be done about the student who is unfamiliar with his own country and its role in the world (short of tightening up our whole educational system, a long-term proposition), but at least a student headed abroad can be prepared to answer some of the more obvious questions.

Since he is bound to be asked about whatever is in the news from America, the student ought to keep up as best he can with the American point of view. The Paris *Herald-Tribune* is available all over Europe, and the weekly American news magazines can be found in every corner of the globe. The better European papers, like *Le Monde* in France and the *Frankfurter Allgemeine* in Germany, quote American editorial opinion profusely in their pages.

Furthermore, it does not take too much effort to anticipate the questions that are likely to be on everyone's mind abroad. What is meant by the term "The American Way of Life"? Are Americans imperialist warmongers? Why are Americans against increased immigration? The race question is one of the most obvious; think before you leave America how best to reply to queries about it. What would you have said if you were the American girl we met abroad who showed an air-mail stamp bearing a picture of the Statue of Liberty and the slogan "Liberty for All" to a Moroccan student of her acquaintance. He looked at it, sneered, and said in French: "It's not true, is it?" This particular Moroccan was deliberately hostile, but even friendly foreigners—the vast majority—will want to know why prejudice against Negroes exists in the United States (and it is no answer to point angrily to prejudices of their own). Other perennial questions range from the structure of the government to the influence of Hollywood and TV on everyday life, from our thermonuclear policy to the difference between football and soccer, from our policies in Southeast Asia to the supposed plot behind the assassination of President Kennedy. What counts is not pat answers that will magically bring agreement, but the ability to explain and back up your viewpoint clearly and sensibly. And to do this you must know what you are talking about.

Planning, then, consists of deciding beforehand where to go and what to do and then preparing for the task ahead. Each student's program should be realistically attuned to his capabilities, but it should also be a challenge. Those who wish to go abroad primarily for enjoyment should join the tourist hordes and not trouble themselves with academic activities. To achieve maximum profit from study abroad, understanding the foreign language is vital; even a little knowledge is a tremendous asset. Some familiarity with the foreign country and the culture and character of its people is equally important. So, finally, is knowledge of the United States. The sooner plans are made and proper preparations undertaken, the better the results will be. But even a few weeks of preliminary effort, if well conceived and conscientiously executed, will set the student in the right direction as he embarks on his voyage of intellectual exploration.

CHAPTER 3

Before You Leave: Practical Problems

*A million details to remember . . . all about passports and shots . . .
helpful packing lists . . . the ins and outs of foreign currency and
banking . . . you'll surely want to bring home a few gifts . . . tem-
peratures, telephones, and tips*

In addition to preparing himself intellectually for
the experience, anyone who is going abroad to study will have to
attend to a large number of practical details before departure.
Most of these details are no different from those that any tourist
or businessman traveling outside the United States must take care
of, and many of them are obvious. Some, such as obtaining a passport, are essential. Others are merely convenient, but the advantages
of making them can be enormous, especially for a person who is
going to remain abroad for more than a few weeks. This chapter
deals with these practical considerations. Even the student who
has already been abroad and believes he "knows the ropes" should
use it as a kind of checklist or mental refresher.

Don't Forget Your Passport!

All United States citizens traveling abroad must have a valid
passport. This essential document may be obtained by filling out an
application form available at any federal or state court with
naturalization jurisdiction or at one of the passport agencies located
in the following cities:

Boston. Passport office, J. F. Kennedy Building, Government
Center, Boston, Mass. 02116.

Chicago. Room 244A, Federal Office Building, 219 South Dearborn Street, Chicago, Ill. 60604.

Los Angeles. Room 1004, Federal Office Building, 300 North Los Angeles Street, Los Angeles, Calif. 90017.

Miami. Passport Office, New Federal Office Building, 51 S.W. First Avenue, Miami, Fla. 33130.

New York. Passport Office, Rockefeller Center, 630 Fifth Avenue, New York, N.Y. 10020.

San Francisco. Room 1405, Federal Office Building, 450 Golden Gate Avenue, San Francisco, Calif. 94102.

Seattle. Passport Office, 1410 Fifth Avenue, Seattle, Wash. 98101.

Washington, D.C. Passport Office, Department of State, 22nd and E Streets, N.W., Washington, D.C. 20524.

Honolulu. Special Passport Representative, Room 304, Federal Building, Honolulu, Hawaii. 96813.

Proof of United States citizenship must be submitted with the completed passport application form. A birth certificate or certified copy of birth record obtainable from the Registrar of Vital Statistics of the locality in which the birth occurred is the usual type of proof for native-born citizens, but if such a record is not obtainable, a notice by a local authority indicating that no birth record exists should be submitted along with either of the following items of secondary evidence: a baptismal certificate, or an affidavit of date and place of birth (executed by a parent, older blood relative, or some other individual having personal knowledge of the date and place of birth). A naturalized citizen should present his naturalization certificate. In all cases a previously issued passport, even if expired, will be accepted as evidence of United States citizenship. An applicant may also be required to establish his identity to the satisfaction of the Clerk of Court or Passport Agent, either through personal knowledge, by the presentation of an acceptable document of identification, or by an identifying witness. An identifying witness who has known the applicant for at least two years is required only when the applicant cannot satisfactorily establish his identity through other acceptable methods. Two duplicate photographs, both signed by the applicant in ink on the back and taken within the two previous years, should accompany the passport application form. These photographs must be full-faced on thin, unglazed paper with a light background. The size of the photographs must not exceed three inches by three inches or be less than two and a half inches by two and a half inches.

The fee for a new passport is $9.00. The execution fee is an additional $1.00, unless the application is executed by clerks of state courts authorized to collect $2.00. The fee for renewing a passport is $5.00. These passport fees may be paid in currency or with a check or money order made payable to the passport office.

As soon as the passport is received, it should be signed as indicated. Until this has been done, it is not valid. All the information requested on the inside front cover must also be filled out. A passport is a highly important and valuable document; it should be carefully guarded and kept in good condition, for its loss or theft while abroad can cause considerable difficulty and expense. When traveling abroad, it is best to keep it on hand at all times. If it is mutilated or altered in any way, it is rendered invalid.

The loss or destruction of a passport must be reported immediately to the Passport Office, Department of State, Washington, D.C. 20524, or to the nearest American consular officer if the loss occurs abroad. When applying for a new passport to replace one that has been lost, destroyed, or mutilated, it is necessary to present a detailed statement, in the form of an affidavit, explaining all the circumstances under which the loss or mutilation occurred. As a rule, a thorough inquiry must be made before a new passport can be issued.

Passports are valid for three years and may be renewed once for an additional two years. Passports may be renewed by forwarding a completed passport renewal application (Form DSP-17), the passport, and renewal fee ($5.00) to the Passport Office, Department of State, Washington, D.C. 20524, or to one of the passport agencies. Other officials authorized to renew passports are American diplomatic and consular officers abroad.

Many people confuse a passport with a visa when they are arranging for a trip abroad. A passport identifies the bearer as a United States citizen. It is issued by the United States government and is required for departure from or entry into the United States. A visa is a document issued by a foreign government to visitors giving them permission to enter that country for a specific purpose—usually for work or study. Most countries in Europe do not require visas for short periods of residence, usually up to three months. However, nearly all countries require visas for longer periods of residence. Students should contact the consul or embassy of the country in which they are going to study for detailed information.

Getting Your Shots

All students traveling abroad are urged to immunize themselves against certain contagious diseases before departure from the United States.

Smallpox. The United States Immigration Service requires proof that anyone entering the country has been immunized against small-pox. Travelers must have an international certificate of vaccination card, validated within three years of the date of arrival. These cards are available at Public Health Service Offices, passport offices, and travel agencies. Take this card to your doctor when you go to be vaccinated and have him sign it. Then present the signed card to your local Board of Health to be stamped and validated before leaving the United States.

Typhoid and Paratyphoid. A combined vaccination against both these fevers can be obtained in three inoculations, which must be taken 7 to 28 days apart.

Tetanus. Immunization can be obtained by two inoculations 3 to 6 weeks apart.

Poliomyelitis. This vaccination, recommended for all travelers under forty years of age, is administered in two inoculations about 3 weeks apart.

Some of these shots can cause unpleasant aftereffects for a day or so; you should, therefore, schedule them at a time when you have no important engagements. Students traveling to countries outside Europe may be required to obtain other shots. Information about these inoculation requirements may be obtained from the nearest representative of the United States Public Health Service, or the Division of Foreign Quarantine, Public Health Service, Department of Health, Education, and Welfare, Washington, D.C. 20201.

Other Medical Reminders

Glasses. Persons who wear glasses should take along an extra pair, together with a copy of their lens prescription.

Special medical needs. Anyone suffering from diabetes, or who is allergic to penicillin, or who has a chronic physical problem that may require special emergency care, should prepare a statement of his condition and the treatment required in the language of the country where he will be residing. This statement should be carried in the wallet or purse at all times.

Water. Nearly all major cities abroad now have safe tap water. However, students should always exercise caution when drinking water from wells or streams in country areas, even in Europe. Water in the rest rooms of trains or ships is normally not suitable for drinking.

Uncooked Food. In some areas of the world, caution should be exercised about eating uncooked fruits and vegetables, milk and dairy products, and other easily perishable food.

Medicines. Most ordinary medicines are readily available in Europe. However, students requiring special American patent drugs or pharmaceutical products should take adequate supplies with them. Those who frequently take special non-prescription drugs for simple but recurring ailments (such as colds, indigestion) may wish to do likewise, but suitable substitutes are available nearly everywhere.

Clothing Tips

The experienced traveler always gives a lot of thought and time to selecting his wardrobe for a long trip. The following hints may be of use in planning your wardrobe.

Even students planning to remain abroad for a long stay should avoid taking a large amount of luggage. Most student dormitories in Europe offer quite limited wardrobe space, and storage space is usually at a premium. Those who travel by air will usually be limited to a maximum of 44 pounds of luggage. While there is usually no limit when traveling by sea, the inconvenience of moving heavy trunks to and from port areas is such as to militate against too much baggage.

Students in Europe dress much the same as American students, with certain exceptions. European men do not wear sneakers except on the tennis court, and to avoid being conspicuous you should do the same. Dress for class is often informal except in certain bastions of formality such as Oxford and Cambridge, where coat, tie, and academic gown are still required. However, when invited to dinner with a family or when attending the theater, opera, or concerts, a student should wear a dark suit, white shirt, and tie. Sportswear on such occasions is in bad taste.

For the girls, there are rather more differences between campus dress abroad and at home. Tennis shoes are not à la mode. No matter how informally a Sorbonne coed is dressed—usually skirt and sweater—she will generally wear shoes and stockings. In the summer she might wear sandals or flats with no hose. Also girls in Europe rarely wear slacks or shorts on the street. These should be kept strictly for the dormitory or the beach. The same caution applies to hair curlers: Europeans believe strongly that even for short trips, girls should complete their hair preparations before leaving the house or dormitory.

Europeans are also surprisingly formal about sportswear, from the American point of view. For example, tennis players are usually required to wear whites. In addition, it is the custom when going to or from the swimming pool, beach, or tennis courts for the European to wear street clothes and change in dressing rooms provided at sports areas. Though Europeans are not shocked by the most minuscule bikinis on the beach, they consider tennis shorts or bathing suits highly improper on the street.

In order to derive the greatest number of different outfits from a limited wardrobe, it is essential that clothing be interchangeable. Girls, for instance, should see that blouses and sweaters combine well with several skirts and dresses. The easiest way to solve the laundry problem is to take dacron or other wash-and-wear clothes, which the student can launder himself. Dark colors and prints will help camouflage spots or wrinkles. Knits hold up well. Professional laundering in Europe and most other places is slower than in the United States, and the student should be careful to use only reputable dry cleaners. For students residing in dormitories, community living makes imperative the identification of all clothing with name tapes.

Although factors of climate, length of stay, and personal taste will influence the make-up of each student's wardrobe, the following checklist, for students going abroad for a summer to a western European country, provides a useful guideline. Those going abroad for a longer period must naturally make revisions, as must those going to countries with very hot or cold climates.

ESSENTIALS FOR MEN

Wear: Sports coat (conservative color); dress slacks; white shirt and tie; black or cordovan shoes and socks; all-weather coat or raincoat; hat or cap (if desired).

Pack:

2	suits
2	pairs of casual slacks (washable)
1	belt
2	sweaters (one lightweight, one heavy)
4	sport shirts (wash-and-wear)
2	dress shirts (wash-and-wear)
12	handkerchiefs
1	pair of good walking shoes
1	extra pair prescription glasses (if required)
2	ties
6	pairs of socks
6	undershirts, 6 shorts (cotton or synthetic)
2	pairs of lightweight pajamas
1	robe (double for beach robe)
1	pair of slippers
1	pair of bathing trunks
2	bath towels, 2 hand towels, 2 washcloths
	tennis clothes and shoes (if needed)
1	small traveling alarm clock
1	large plastic bag for wet laundry
1	laundry bag
1	pair of beach shorts
1	copy of birth certificate (necessary in case of loss of passport)
1	washing kit containing the following: safety razor, blades, shaving cream, toothbrush and toothpaste, deodorant, nail scissors, 1 bar of soap in dish (soap is not usually provided), plastic folding hangers

ESSENTIALS FOR WOMEN

Wear: Dark, nonwrinkle suit; comfortable shoes and stockings or sandals; all-weather coat or raincoat; scarf (and hat, if desired); good-sized leather bag (preferably shoulder-strap type).

Pack:		
	2	dress-up dresses (short dinner type)
	2	skirts—cotton or synthetic fiber
	2	sweaters (one heavy and one light)
	4	blouses (preferably drip-dry)
	1	pair of sturdy walking shoes
	1	pair of evening shoes
	4	pairs of nylon stockings
	3	pairs of peds
	2	weeks' supply of lingerie
	1	pair of plastic boots or rubbers
	2	bathing suits
		handkerchiefs and plenty of tissue (removed from box)
	1	pair of bedroom slippers and lightweight robe (should double as beach robe)
	1	pair of slacks (for use in dormitory or on beach; do not take bermudas)
		tennis clothes and shoes (if needed)
	1	pair of sun glasses
	2	bath towels, 2 hand towels, 2 washcloths
	1	bar of soap in plastic soap dish
	1	small traveling alarm clock
	1	large plastic bag for wet laundry
	1	laundry bag
	1	extra pair of prescription glasses (if required)
	1	copy of birth certificate (necessary in case of loss of passport)
	1	cosmetic bag containing the following: clothes brush, hairbrush, shower cap, hair-care needs, nail scissors, razor and blades, deodorant, sanitary needs, cosmetics, toothbrush and toothpaste, sewing kit, and plastic folding hangers.

Money Matters

Students planning to go abroad for a short trip are advised to take nearly all their funds in traveler's checks, which are both convenient and easily safeguarded. Most banks sell traveler's checks. The most popular are those issued by American Express and the First National City Bank of New York. Travelers should also take at least $20 worth of the currency of the country to be visited first, for it is not always possible or convenient to change money at airports or other terminals.

Keep a record of the numbers of all traveler's checks in your luggage; these are required to obtain a refund for lost checks. When leaving a country for the last time, be sure to spend all coin money before departure, because banks will usually only exchange foreign currency held in notes. Change traveler's checks at banks rather than at hotels or restaurants, since banks usually offer a more favorable exchange rate.

Students intending to stay abroad for a considerable length of time should arrange through the foreign department of their banks to open a bank account in a branch of a correspondent bank in the city where they will reside. Since this process usually takes several weeks, it should be done well in advance of departure. Once the account has been opened, sufficient funds should be transferred abroad to take care of all needs. A particular point to note is that foreign universities will not usually accept payment by a check made payable on a domestic American bank and that foreign banks take several weeks to process such a check. In general, when sending funds abroad from the United States, have an American bank air-mail or cable the money to a foreign bank. In no case should personal checks be sent, as cashing them may prove difficult or impossible.

The following brief notes on the currency of countries which are usually visited by American students may prove useful.

Austria. The basic unit of currency is the shilling, which is worth 4 American cents (25 shillings to the dollar).

Belgium and Luxembourg. Centimes and francs form the basis of the currencies of Belgium and Luxembourg, which are of equal value. One hundred centimes equals one franc. One franc equals 2 American cents. One dollar equals 50 Belgian or Luxembourg francs. Note: Belgian francs are accepted in Luxembourg. Luxembourg francs, however, are not usually accepted in Belgium.

France. The French use the decimal system, with the basic unit being the franc, which is worth 20 cents. Francs are divided into centimes, with 100 centimes to the franc. Visitors to France, however, should know of the difference between old francs and new francs. Basically, 100 old francs are worth one new franc. Although the changeover was made a number of years ago, many Frenchmen (especially in the country) still think in terms of the old franc. This habit can be very confusing, since old francs and currency still circulate along with the new.

Great Britain. British currency is somewhat complicated, as it does not use the decimal system. The basic unit is the pound, which is equivalent to $2.40. Pounds are divided into shillings, with 20 shillings to each pound. Shillings are divided into pennies, with 12 pennies to each shilling. A cent is the equivalent of one penny. After 1971 Britain's money will go on the decimal system, with 100 pennies to the pound.

Greece. Greek currency is based on the drachma, which is divided into 100 leptas. One drachma is worth just over 3 cents.

Israel. Israeli currency is based on the pound, worth about 30 cents. There are 100 agorot to a pound.

Italy. The unit of currency is the lira, which is worth a tenth of an American cent (625 lire to the dollar).

Netherlands. Dutch currency is based on the guilder, with each guilder being divided into 100 cents. Guilders are also sometimes called florins and are written "f." One dollar is worth 3.62 guilders. One guilder is worth 28 cents.

Spain. The basic unit of currency is the peseta, which is worth slightly less than 1½ American cents (70 pesetas to the dollar).

Switzerland. The basic unit of currency is the Swiss franc, which is worth 23 American cents (4.28 francs to the dollar). Francs are divided into centimes, with 100 centimes to the franc.

USSR. Russian currency is based on the ruble, which is divided into 100 kopecks. The official rate is 90 kopecks to the dollar, or $1.11 to the ruble. NOTE: No trading in Soviet currency is permitted outside the Soviet Union. Therefore, students must neither take rubles into the country nor bring them out. Students should purchase their Russian currency requirements at the border and exchange any remaining rubles on departure from the Soviet Union.

Tell Your Draft Board!

Any male student who will reach the age of eighteen while abroad must notify his local draft board of his intention to leave the country. Exemption from the draft will usually be given to undergraduate students who have received acceptance for bona fide courses of study abroad. Students who have already registered must also notify their local draft board of their impending change of address. These students should also request a permit to depart from the country. These Selective Service rulings are mandatory, and failure to comply may result in severe penalties.

Gifts, Shopping—and Customs

There may well be many occasions when students will wish they had small gifts for the friends and acquaintances they make abroad. The gifts which are usually most appreciated are those which symbolize America, the student's state or region, or his home town. Thus, for example, Kennedy half-dollars are always immensely popular. Some special picture or handmade product of the student's region may be appropriate, and such items must be taken along in advance, without the assurance that they will ever be needed.

Most students, of course, give more thought to what they will buy abroad than to gifts for persons not yet even encountered. One of the delights of travel abroad is the opportunity to buy native products at local prices. Students should, however, take great care in making important purchases, for prices vary enormously. It is best, if possible, to wait until one has been in a country for some time before making major purchases. Buying impulses sometimes change as one becomes better acquainted with local merchandise.

The following hints may be helpful on what to buy:

Austria. Petit point evening bags, leather goods, wooden handicrafts, ski wear.

France. Perfume, jewelry, gloves, and antiques are the best buys. French high-fashion clothing, while famous, is prohibitively expensive. However, chain stores like Prisunic and Monoprix sell ready-to-wear women's clothing that is both excellently designed and inexpensive.

Germany. Clocks, cameras, cutlery, china, heavy leather goods.

Great Britain. Bone china, woolens, cashmeres, tweeds, rainwear, silver, men's wear.

Greece. Pottery, woven shoulder-strap bags, dolls, jewelry.

Italy. Leather goods, gloves, Venetian glass, jewelry, silk, silver.

Spain. Leather goods, lace, embroidered linens, ceramics, jewelry.

Switzerland. Watches, clocks, typewriters, music boxes.

Major purchases, such as furniture and sets of china, must, of course, be separately shipped. Use a reliable and experienced store to avoid running the risk that the order will be forgotten or so poorly packed that the goods arrive damaged. Check carefully to see precisely what the shipping charges are, as, in many cases, shipments are handed over by the stores to custom brokers and freight forwarders in the United States, who may make extra charges for their service. Parcel post is the cheapest and most satisfactory way to send items back home, if their weight is not too great. Purchases should be insured and the proper customs documents attached.

In making purchases abroad, it is important to remember that many items imported into the United States are subject to duty. The balance of payments problem has resulted in a major review of United States custom procedures. At present the following points should be observed:

1. If you take abroad with you from this country any expensive foreign-made articles, such as cameras, binoculars, or watches, make sure you take with you the receipt from the store where you purchased the items or some other evidence that the item was bought in the United States. Otherwise, you may have to pay duty on it when you return.

2. A resident of the United States who has been traveling outside the country may bring back duty-free articles up to a value of $100. NOTE: There is a limitation on the number of certain foreign products trade-marked in the United States which you can import. For instance, most brands of French perfume are limited to one bottle of each scent.

3. In addition, gifts whose value does not exceed $10.00 may be sent to persons in the United States from abroad without payment of duty. The value of each package must not exceed $10.00, and each parcel should be marked "Gift $10.00 value" in large letters. No one addressee may receive in a single day parcels exceeding the $10.00 limitation.

4. Some items, such as antiques, books, and works of art, may be

imported free of duty in any amount. Other goods, beyond the amount of the tourist exemption, are taxed at rates ranging from 3 to over 50 per cent. It is therefore important to know the rate of duty before purchasing expensive items. Natural pearls brought in loose are taxed at 3 per cent, but permanently strung pearls may be taxed as high as 55 per cent!

5. On arrival back in the United States, travelers must make a declaration of all goods purchased abroad. The goods are assessed at the price paid for them, so it is important to have sales receipts for all purchases and to have these, and the goods themselves, packed together. This will greatly speed the routine of getting through the customs.

Other Things to Know About

Clothing Sizes. In general, foreign countries use clothing sizes based on the metric system. The following table shows how these compare with American sizes for most common types of clothing.

WOMEN'S CLOTHING

BLOUSES AND SWEATERS
U.S.A. and England

32	34	36	38	40	42

Continent

38	40	42	44	46	48

DRESSES AND SUITS
Misses sizes
U.S.A. and England

10	12	14	16	18	20	22

Continent

36	38	40	42	44	46	48

Women's sizes
U.S.A. and England

34	36	38	40	42	44

Continent

42	44	46	48	50	52

SHOES
U.S.A. 4 5 6 7 8 9
England
2 3 4 5 6 7 9
Continent
36-37 37-38 38-39 39-40 40-41
41-42 43

MEN'S CLOTHING

SHIRTS
U.S.A. and England
14 14½ 15 15½ 15¾ 16 16½
17 17½ 18
Continent
36 37 38 39 40 41 42 43 44 45

SWEATERS, SUITS AND COATS
U.S.A. and England

	sm	med	lg		ex lg		
	34	36	38	40	42	44	46
Continent	44	46	48	50	52	54	56

HATS
U.S.A. and England
6⅝ 6¾ 6⅞ 7 7⅛ 7¼ 7⅜
7½ 7⅝ 7¾
Continent
53 54 55 56 57 58 59 60 61 62

SHOES
U.S.A. and England
7½ 8 8½ 9 9½ 10 10½ 11 11½ 12
Continent
41-42 42-43 43-44 44-45 45-46

Electric Current. Voltage varies widely abroad. In general, do not take electrical appliances (except those operating by battery) since their use will probably prove to be a great nuisance, what with converters, adapters, and other apparatus you may have to take with you. The predominant voltage in Europe is 220 or 240, 50 cycle alternating current, as compared to 110 volts, 60 cycle current in the United States. There are also tremendous differences among cities.

Metric System. Except in British Commonwealth countries, all countries use the metric system of measurement. Shown below are examples of equivalents of this system to ours:

1 Kilometer	equals	.62 miles	(To convert kilometers to miles, multiply the number of kilometers by .62)
1 Meter	equals	39.37 inches or 3.28 feet or 10.9 yards	
1 Kilogram	equals	2.20 pounds	(To change kilograms to pounds, multiply by 2 and add 10 per cent)
1 Liter	equals	1.06 quarts or 0.26 U.S. gallons	

Temperature. To convert Centigrade into Fahrenheit, divide the Centigrade temperature by 5, then multiply by 9, then add 32. To translate Fahrenheit into Centigrade, subtract 32 from the Fahrenheit temperature, then divide by 9, then multiply by 5.

Telephoning. Public telephones are found in post offices, cafés, hotels, restaurants, railway and subway stations. In some countries in Europe, it is necessary to have special tokens to make a telephone call. These may usually be bought from the cashier of the establishment where the telephone is located. When telephoning the United States, call person to person from a post office. Most countries have English-speaking operators on their international switchboards. Remember that there is a time difference of between six and eight hours between the United States and Europe. For example, if it is nine in the evening in New York, it will be three o'clock in the morning in Paris.

Tipping. Students going to Europe should make themselves aware of local tipping customs. On the Continent, most restaurants add a standard service charge to the bill, usually 12 or 15 per cent. It is, therefore, not necessary to give the waiter a tip, but it is common practice to leave a few small coins as an appreciation of good service. In England, as in the United States, the tipping is up to the customer. The usual amount is 12 to 15 per cent of the bill. It is customary everywhere in Europe, except in England and Germany, to give cinema, theater, or opera ushers a small tip.

France:	50 centimes per person
Italy:	100 lire
Spain:	2½ pesetas
Austria:	2 shillings

As in the United States, it is necessary to tip cab drivers about 10 per cent of the meter charge. Hotel porters should be tipped for carrying luggage to your hotel room. In addition, in Europe it is customary to tip chambermaids for special services, such as running a bath. An additional sum is left on departure.

Holding Down the Cost

High-level education at low cost ... group rates make for cheap overseas travel ... many travel bargains for students abroad ... some typical costs ... observations about scholarships and other sources of financial aid ... figuring your budget ... student subsidies

While the price of a college education in America continues to skyrocket, the relatively low expense of study abroad becomes increasingly attractive. Even with overseas transportation included, American colleges operating overseas programs do not charge their students appreciably more than for comparable time on the home campus; and students able to go abroad on their own can manage even more reasonably, studying in Europe for a full year without spending as much as they would at Vassar, Yale, Oberlin, or any similar American college.

College costs abroad, like college costs in the United States, consist of four main items: tuition, living expenses (room and board), transportation, and incidentals. We shall discuss each of these items in detail, but in general:

1. Tuition charges are much lower abroad.

2. Living costs are also lower in most parts of Europe (especially for students), unless one insists on duplicating every American luxury and convenience.

3. Transportation charges are naturally higher when one studies abroad.

4. Incidental expenses are attributable to many different factors, some of which are cheaper in Europe, some in America; but for

most people they seem to average out to just about the same amount abroad as at home.

The Biggest Bargain Is Tuition

Many European universities charge no tuition at all. In France, for example, a regularly enrolled student pays a registration fee of about ten dollars for the privilege of attending all the classes he wishes at any French university for an entire year. Special classes for foreigners at the European universities are not free, but everywhere the cost is exceedingly low when compared even to state and municipal universities in the United States.

At the University of Caen, for example, a full academic-year course for foreigners in the language, civilization, and literature of France costs only $45, including registration, library fees, and all other academic charges. Special classes can be organized for junior-year groups for relatively little. One can hire a well-qualified instructor to give a special three-credit course in Franch literature, for example, for about $450 a semester. This works out to $15 a credit if no more than ten students are enrolled; and with larger groups, the cost per point is lower still. At home colleges in the United States, similar courses would cost about $55 per credit. Thus the Sweet Briar program described in detail below (p. 148), which is typical of the better junior-year programs, manages to cover all its overhead and still charge its students for a full academic year's work of thirty credits approximately $35 per credit.*

Living Expenses

The costs of room and board for students in Europe naturally vary with individual requirements, the country, and the district. The cheapest housing can be found in university dormitories, for these are subsidized, but such quarters are in short supply except during the summer. A single room with toilet in a dormitory at Aix-

---

* Branch programs are able to pass on similar savings on their language courses, which are taught by foreigners. The American professors who teach abroad are naturally paid more than they would receive at the home college, but this budgetary problem is handled by requiring all students to take the same courses, thus keeping the required number of American professors to a minimum.

en-Provence rents for under $25 a month. It costs more to live in a rooming house, even though the quarters are sometimes austere. And it is still more expensive to live with a private family, although many experts believe that the care, attention, and language practice gained in the family situation make the cost well worth while, especially for younger students. However, unless one insists on staying at a de luxe hotel, housing costs will be no greater than in American college towns.

It is also difficult to speak with authority about food costs. A student with permission to use a hot plate in his furnished room (such permission is *not* easily obtainable) might conceivably eat very cheaply, but very few attempt this. The cheapest meals are those available in student restaurants, which also are always subsidized. Prices vary from country to country, but a full meal usually costs no more than a dollar. Bona fide American students can obtain admittance to these restaurants, and there is seldom cause for complaint about the food.

The cost of meals for students living *en pension* or with families* cannot always be separated from the room rent. But board is somewhat higher than at student restaurants and a good deal lower than at ordinary public restaurants. For students in organized programs, room and board are usually arranged for in advance by program officials. In Paris, a high-cost area, Sweet Briar is still able to provide decent accommodations *and* meals with private families for its students for about six dollars a day.

Getting There Cheaply

Transportation looms as a very large item in the budget of every student going abroad, despite the fact that the expense varies with the nature of the accommodations and the type of carrier. Round-trip tourist-class travel on an ocean liner between New York and the Channel ports is about $400. Economy jet airplane fare to Europe and back is a little over $500; charges on the "old-fashioned" piston-type airplanes are somewhat less. Icelandic Air-

---

* In the language of overseas education a pension is simply a rooming house that serves meals. A family gives the student friendship, help with the language, and general guidance. In practice the line between the two is often blurred.

lines, which does not belong to IATA, the airlines trade association, flies piston-type equipment to various European cities still more cheaply, and lower fares can be had in the off season. However, most students must make the journey during the summer, when maximum rates are in force.

The Council on International Educational Exchange charters ships and planes for groups at rates somewhat below those just quoted. There is usually room on Council ships for individual students, the fare running about $375 to France and back. The Netherlands Office for Foreign Student Relations also operates "student ships" in the summertime, with round-trip fares of about $340 to $360. This is a considerable saving over regular tourist-class charges, but there is some minor sacrifice of time and comfort.

The airlines also offer special reduced "group rates" to Europe. The round-trip fares by jet from New York for members of such groups run about $300, but vary with the season and destination. The group must make reservations in advance, and during the busy summer season group rates do not apply on week ends; but these are minor disadvantages, considering the savings. Groups of students heading for European schools should surely be able to adjust their plans to conform to these schedules.

The cheapest transportation rates are those available to groups able to charter entire planes. The airlines offer chartered flights that make it possible for a group of about one hundred persons to fly to London or Paris and back to New York for about $225 each. There is much less flexibility when one travels this way (since each chartered flight must leave and return at a specified time, and members cannot switch planes or obtain refunds after reaching Europe). And there is also the danger of disappointment if a proposed flight fails to "fill." Furthermore, only bona fide members of an established organization can charter planes. Colleges and universities qualify under this rule, but students from one institution may not join a charter flight organized by those of another. Thus, only at the larger universities are there likely to be enough students who want to go abroad and can arrange their schedules to fit a common time for departure and return. Moreover, even at such institutions it is only in the summer months that such trips prove feasible. Students interested in spending an academic year abroad will not find charters available except in very special cases. But for those who are able to take advantage of them, charter flights are a "best buy." The pilots, food, weight allowances, and service on these flights are equal to those provided on regularly scheduled flights.

And Traveling Cheaply Once You're There

Of course, the minimum cost of transportation involves considerably more than the ocean crossing itself for most students. One must get from one's home to New York and from the place of landing to wherever one is going to study. But for these expenses and for general travel after arrival (and every student should try to see as much as he can while abroad), there are many ways of shaving the cost. Foreign governments frequently provide special rates for traveling students. In France, for example, a 30 per cent discount is offered to any foreign student between the ages of sixteen and twenty-eight for a round-trip journey by railroad from point of entry to the university where he is going to study.* The Canadian railways offer special low rates for students. There are special chartered flights to a variety of European centers available to students in some countries.† European student groups have organized an extensive network of special low-cost trips between popular points of interest. Students can fly cheaply from Basle to Athens on a plane chartered by the Swiss National Union of Students. They can also take a special train from Rotterdam to Salzburg for a little over $12, under the auspices of the Netherlands Union, or go from Bonn to Barcelona on a bus chartered by the German Student Travel Service. A valuable book, *The Official Student Guide to Europe*—describing these many possibilities in detail, complete with prices and timetables—has been published by the United States National Student Association.

There are many other means of reducing transportation costs, including the well-known European EURAILPASS and the British

---

* These tickets are good for only three months and so are of use chiefly to summer-school students.

† Americans should be reminded that special privileges and discounts are made available to students through subsidies provided by the host countries. These privileges should never be abused by freeloaders or tourists who are not studying abroad.

Railways "thrift coupons," available to all travelers, whether students or not.

In Europe, where one does not have to travel far to get one's fill of interesting and varied sights, a bicycle is a most practical as well as the cheapest form of locomotion. Armed with membership in his local federation of youth hostels—and with an International Student Identity Card issued by the Co-ordinating Secretariat of the National Union of Students, and the above-mentioned *Student Guide to Europe*, or such publications as the *Student Hostels and Restaurants List* published for the National Union by its Swiss affiliate, and the *International Youth Hostel Handbook*, published by the International Youth Hostel Federation—the cycling student can travel widely and live at minimum cost. Accommodations at youth hostels are simple, but they do include washing and cooking facilities, and in some hostels meals are provided at very reasonable rates. Smoking and drinking are not permitted (except in France and Italy, where one may drink wine with one's meals). No one may stay at any hostel more than three consecutive nights. And it is interesting to note that when facilities are crowded, priority goes not to the first arrivals but to the *youngest* travelers. In short, hostels are not very much like hotels so far as service and comfort are concerned, but they do not resemble hotels in price either; and most important of all, they provide a wonderful means for meeting other young people.

There are also many agencies eager to help the student abroad who wants to travel during his vacations. The various National Unions of Students operate low-cost tours to local places of interest, provide lists of good, moderate-priced hotels, obtain very cheap rates for group travel by rail, and run extended tours all over Europe at very modest cost. Typical of the tours are a fifteen-day tour of Scandinavia for $151, a seven-day tour of Israel for $68, and a seven-day cruise of the Aegean Islands (not including meals) for a mere $23. Accommodations are very simple; on the Aegean cruise, for example, one sleeps on the deck. But for economy and a close-up view of foreign students, such excursions are hard to beat.

If one demands speed and comfort and American-type facilities everywhere, the expense of travel while studying abroad can be much higher. Aside from lower costs, the economical type of travel is far superior from an educational point of view. To travel first-class, to live at the most expensive hotels, teaches one little that is valid about the countries and peoples one is visiting. Contact is largely with what Thomas Jefferson called the "hackneyed rascals" whose business it is to prey on tourists, and one moves in a sort of stereotyped milieu that represents everywhere the local concept of what a first-class British, American, or "international" hotel should be. To see foreign peoples as they really are, to understand their way of life, and to get an opportunity to practice their language, it is necessary to travel unpretentiously.

How Much for Haircuts and Theater Tickets?

Certain incidentals tend to be costlier in Europe than in America—laundry and dry cleaning, for example. Clothing, particularly items made of cotton or of synthetics, such as nylon or dacron, is also cheaper in the United States. Tobacco products cost more in foreign countries because they are more heavily taxed than in the United States. Anything made in America that a student feels he cannot do without should be taken with him. To purchase it overseas is sure to be costly. With items like cigarettes and liquor, any considerable quantity of which may not be imported into European countries without the payment of heavy duties, the student should cultivate a taste for the local products.

Most other goods, and nearly all personal services, are more reasonable abroad. Haircuts and theater tickets, trolley transportation and books, are all good buys. Food, except for staples, is not cheap in Europe, although restaurant meals certainly are, so the student accustomed to bedtime feasts in his room had perhaps better change his habits if his purse is thin. A good rule for economy-minded students would be to adopt as closely as possible the way of life of the local students. They are generally careful with their funds and knowledgeable about local prices and good buys. To do so may involve giving up habits and possessions that almost seem necessities in the United States, but aside from savings in money, this is one of the best ways to get on familiar terms with foreign students who, being human, are apt to be somewhat resentful of visitors who are living a great deal better than they can.

It's Cheaper If You're Smart

To qualified students, scholarships and fellowships are other means of reducing costs. Each year in the fat volume *Study Abroad,* published by UNESCO, there are descriptions of numerous grants offered by public and private institutions all over the world for international study. And each year the volume grows thicker! At present more than 100,000 grants are described. These vary greatly in subject, stipend, and period of time. Some are restricted to students of a particular nationality. Some are for college professors and other specialists. Others are for grade- and secondary-school teachers. Nevertheless, there are a very large number of grants for which American students are eligible, beginning with the Fulbright and Smith-Mundt fellowships offered annually. Good grades are important if one expects to win a scholarship, but because the student abroad is something of an ambassador, linguistic ability and a pleasing personality also carry great weight. "A primary factor in selection," the Fulbright authorities state, "is the potentiality of the candidate to further understanding between the United States and the host country."

The best way to find out about these grants is to examine the latest volume of *Study Abroad* carefully.

Another source of information for scholarships and grants is the lists published annually by the Institute of International Education: *Fellowships Offered by Foreign Governments, Universities and Private Donors* and *United States Government Grants.* The student who needs financial help would be wise, when inquiring about any of the programs listed in this book, to indicate his interest in applying for a scholarship if any are available.

Just How Much Will It Cost?

Exactly how much will it cost to spend a year studying abroad? The answer to this question depends, of course, on where one studies and how one lives. All the organized programs have figured expenses carefully, and the figures are dependable. But, as we have seen, participating in an organized program, whatever the advantages, is by no means the cheapest way to study abroad. Let us, therefore, try to arrive at estimates, realizing that one must make allowances for differences in the cost of living in different parts of the Continent. We assume fourteen months of study and travel, since it is actually uneconomical to stay for a shorter period; the longer you remain abroad, provided you are using the time efficiently, the longer the period over which the high transportation costs may be prorated. Further, our estimate does not attempt to reduce expenses to the bare minimum. We assume that the student will want to travel, buy souvenirs, write air-mail letters home to friends and relatives, spend a modest portion of both his time and money in cafés and theaters, and so on.

The first item is for transportation from the student's home to the place where he is going to study: $550. This must naturally be an average figure; a New Yorker studying in Dublin will get by for less, while a Californian studying in Athens will find $550 considerably below his actual needs.

The next item is tuition—ten months in residence at a university (two months while taking a language course for foreigners and eight months of the regular academic year), plus a summer-school tuition, regular university fees, and books. Not more than $150.

Living in a student dormitory or a simple furnished room and eating in student restaurants, the basic room and board will run at most to $150 a month, or $1,500 for ten months.

One month during the second summer abroad at a student vacation center, such as that as Saint-Aygulf on the French Riviera—about $120.

For the remaining three months, although presumably not all at one time, the student would be traveling. Assuming that he divided his time equally between bicycle, bus, and rail transportation and that he stayed mostly at student hostels, he should be able to manage this at a cost of about $200 a month—$600.

If we then allow $100 for postage, gifts, and souvenirs, the total comes to $2,920. Students who must count their pennies and are willing to tax their ingenuity can get by on much, much less.

Foreign Government Subsidies

The subject of costs must not be dropped without the inclusion of one important reminder. Nearly every special privilege and low-cost service offered to American students in foreign countries is made possible through subsidies provided by foreign taxpayers. These subsidies exist because the people and their governments value education highly and believe that they and the rest of the world will somehow profit if students from different countries are encouraged to live and study together. Anyone who takes advantage of the special treatment thus provided obviously assumes a moral obligation to make the most of the experience and to devote his primary attention to serious intellectual activity. As President Thomas Mendenhall, of Smith College, said at a recent conference on study abroad: "We shouldn't inflict our students on crowded foreign universities unless they are prepared to do serious academic work."

Some students, unfortunately, are willing to accept special privileges without fulfilling their part of the bargain; indeed, some become "students" merely to obtain the privileges. In Paris, for example, uncounted numbers of "freeloaders" (both French and foreign) have signed up as students simply to gain access to low-cost housing and student restaurants. Some years ago authorities tracked down three French post office employees who had been eating lunch for years at a student restaurant near their place of work. They had enrolled at the university as "law students," but had never attended classes. Among the American cheaters, there are, according to one local report, "legendary figures who claim to have been living in Paris as students since they arrived here on the G.I. Bill at the end of World War II. They have their cards to prove it, but claim they don't even know where the Sorbonne is."

As a result of such misuse of student privileges, the University of Paris has been forced to crack down, limiting the classes of persons who are entitled to student cards. But the point is that no individual ought to accept benefits intended for students if he is merely a loafer or dilettante masquerading as a student.

Making the Most of It

*The precarious balance between formal and informal education...
Thomas Jefferson's advice on sightseeing ... learning the local customs is education too . . . a well-kept journal may bring rewards
in later years ... friendship ... how to answer the hard questions
about America ... there may be some sore points, and you'll just
have to face up to them*

Unlike the usual college routine in the United
States, study abroad is inevitably combined with travel, sightseeing,
serving as an ambassador of good will, making friends of a different nationality and race, learning a new language, and "soaking"
in a different culture. How to get the most out of a short year or
two involves a delicate balance between burying one's nose in the
books and getting to know the country and the people. The more
conscientious the student, the more he is likely to feel frustrated
about not being able to do both every waking moment of his time.
"A year in Paris sounded like a long time," one intelligent and
thoughtful student observed, "but I sailed home as much aware of
all I had not seen and not done as all that I had."

This feeling is a healthy one. It means that the particular student
was conscious of his objectives and had undoubtedly accomplished
a great deal. He should certainly not have been discouraged; and
he was not. But even for the most willing and thoughtful, the excitement and upheaval, the delightful confusion, and the constant
stream of new impressions can sometimes make for inefficient and
ineffective use of time. So let us review our objectives to see how
we can make the most of our limited time and energies.

Even a Beer Hall Can Be a Classroom

Putting aside for the moment the difficulties in the way of *academic* achievement in an unfamiliar educational system, the question here is not how much the student learns, but how hard he tries, how many of his precious hours he ought to devote to the classroom and the library. If a student is to spend every moment with his books, he might just as well remain in America. Furthermore, in a foreign country even the most trivial forms of amusement may have an educational value. In the United States, a student who spent the afternoon drinking beer with students in a local bar and the evening watching a grade B movie could justly be accused of wasting his time. Transport him to Germany, and the same number of hours in a Munich beer hall will teach him a great deal about German society, while watching the shallowest German film in a local *Schauspielhaus* will provide him with valuable linguistic training. Of course this would not do as a day-in, day-out regimen; if one goes abroad as a student, study must still be his major occupation.

Adjusting to a foreign system of education requires that the American student make a greater than normal effort simply to accomplish as much as he would were he studying at home. After long experience supervising the excellent Smith junior-abroad programs, Dean Helen W. Randall came to the conclusion that except in language courses, her girls did not achieve as much in a purely academic sense while abroad as they did at Northampton. This being the case, it behooves the conscientious student to make a special effort.

Second, the student in a foreign country should, as much as possible, adopt the way of life of the local students. If he considers his stay a mere lark, or a kind of sociological sightseeing expedition—if, in other words, he looks upon himself as an outsider viewing the system, but not participating in it—he will not make the most of his time abroad.

How then do the local students treat their academic responsibilities? In a word, they take them very seriously; their careers, economic well-being, and social status hang in the balance. They cannot afford to be casual about their work. If the visitor is truly to understand what it means to be a student in Spain or Sweden or Japan or anywhere else, he must try to share, at least a little, this intensity of purpose. If he succeeds he will inevitably increase his own sense of accomplishment and satisfaction and will also profit in the direct academic sense. Moreover, he is sure to soak up intuitively the very understanding of the alien society that the lazy or unthinking student only imagines he gets when he abandons his books in order to see "life" from the terrace of a local café.

One way to stay in touch with student life in any country is by taking advantage of the services provided by the local National Union of Students. Everywhere these organizations are powerful and active, and any student can profit from using their facilities. For example, the British group publishes and distributes a pamphlet, *Overseas Students in Britain,* a travel guide called *The Long Vacation,* and a fat *Student Guide to London.* It also runs tours, sponsors a student drama festival, organizes conferences and debates, operates a student hostel and an extensive system of work camps, and publishes a long list of names of British firms that offer special discounts to students on items ranging from camping equipment to sewing machines, from dancing lessons to secondhand books. The French union will literally load down the inquiring visitor with mimeographed material, all designed to help him in one one way or another. Many American students do not seem to know about these useful services, for student officials repeatedly tell us that they seldom see Americans at their headquarters. But they insist that they are eager to make their services available to all students and will certainly welcome Americans.

The student must be careful of the impression he is creating in the minds of foreign observers. Everyone is familiar with the stereotype of the uncouth American tourist in the garish sport shirt, insensitive to his surroundings, convinced that every foreigner he meets is trying to cheat him, and devoted to the principle that since money talks there is no need for him to learn what he calls the local lingo. Fortunately, few students have either the means or the attitude of mind to behave in this manner, but the student who wastes his time or displays an indifferent attitude toward his studies is a bad ambassador nevertheless. Such a student is not only injuring the national interest of the United States in his small way but also injuring himself. Busy people naturally resent idlers; dedicated people are contemptuous of those who are mere dilettantes.

We have emphasized that no one should travel thousands of miles merely to bury his nose in a book; fortunately, however, the apparent conflict between the student's obligation to his books and his desire to be a part of the local community is somewhat illusory. To begin with, it is impossible for the most devoted scholar to spend all his waking hours in intensive mental activity. But in any case, the student abroad will find that he can actually study as hard as or harder than he did at home and still have *more* time for other things. This is true because so many activities that occupy the time of students in American colleges will not require his attention in universities outside the United States. There are no fraternities, no football games, no obligations to family to fulfill. No class time is given to gym, or to ROTC, or to numerous "required" courses unrelated to the student's major interest. In short, the student has shed many of the time-consuming obligations of everyday living. For the moment he can participate more directly and intensely in the world around him. This, of course, is one of the chief advantages of his situation.

Systematic Sightseeing

Wherever the student has settled, he should make a systematic effort to know that place thoroughly. He will also want to travel widely, but part of his purpose while studying should be to develop an intimate understanding of at least one foreign community. "To pass once along a public road through a country," Thomas Jefferson wrote in a letter to the German scholar Christoph Ebeling, "and to put up at its tavern and get into conversation with the idle, drunken individuals who pass their time lounging in these taverns, is not the way to know a country, its inhabitants or manners."

Jefferson, by the way, has left us an excellent description of how to study a new town. One should first purchase a map of the place and a guidebook describing its major "curiosities." Then it is best to go to some high place (Jefferson suggested a church steeple), from which the entire region can be seen. Having gained this *Überblick*, begin to examine the points of interest carefully. "When you are doubting whether a thing is worth the trouble of going to see," he advised, "recollect that you will never again be so near it, that you may repent the not having seen it, but can never repent having seen it."

The main point to keep in mind in this connection is to be systematic. Especially for the student in a large city this is very important advice, since it is easy to slip into a routine of living wherein only a narrow segment of the community is ever seen. In Jefferson's day there were no glass-topped busses to whisk the sightseer all over a great city in a few concentrated hours. Had there been, he would probably have urged every traveler to make use of them. A bus tour is usually a first-rate way to orient oneself quickly and learn what must be really seen. But these tours are no substitute for careful observation and study; to take two or three four-hour tours of Paris or Rome and then think you have "seen" either of these cities is simply foolish.

The student should plan a series of expeditions, on foot, to the interesting quarters of "his" city. For all the major cities of the world there are detailed guidebooks which suggest particular routes suited for the study of the place in this manner. The Michelin guide to Paris is an excellent example. Once his routine has been established and he has settled into his studies, the student should set aside one afternoon a week for exploring. Guidebook in hand— local citizens everywhere respect the visitor who cares enough about their community to study it thoroughly—follow the prescribed route for the day. Do not be afraid to stop a stranger to ask a question. Even if he cannot answer it he will be grateful to you for having asked it, and perhaps, his own curiosity aroused, he will join with you to stop other passers-by until the answer is found.

On these expeditions, the student ought to travel alone, or at most with one other person. Traveling in a group is not recommended, for several reasons. The group is conspicuous and therefore a possible source of distraction and annoyance to others; it makes for interruptions in the normal flow of traffic. It is inhibiting, for one must submit to its discipline and cannot turn aside to look in a shop window or explore an interesting side street. Any group tends to turn in on itself instead of looking at the surroundings; merely in order to remain a group, its members have to pay attention to one another at the very time when their attention should be directed outward.

"Plan to do some traveling alone," advises one American student. "One is free to observe without distraction and to fall into conversations with persons who might not feel any strong desire to break into conversation with a compact group."

Looking at a community from the outside is only the beginning of getting to know a place. The student should try to experience the many facets of its life. If the town is fairly small, daily reading of the local newspaper will soon enable him to understand its politics and society, and this understanding will lead to countless insights into everyday affairs as they occur. In a big city the student should sample all the newspapers, familiarizing himself with their differing viewpoints toward the news. Then, like any citizen, he should settle down with whichever journal best suits his tastes and read it as he would his favorite paper in America.

Whatever his resources, every student should make a fair trial at living as much like the local students as possible. A young man from the University of Pennsylvania studying in Germany provides a good example of a student who did so. Here is his account of a typical day in his life at the University of Bonn:

> My roommate (a Norwegian) and I start our day at 7:45. We buy what we need for breakfast, eat, dress, and are at the University by 9. We walk the 15-minute stretch to school. At noon, I go to eat either at the Mensa (the central student center and mess hall) or cook my midday meal at home. Afternoons are generally free. . . . I always make my own supper. Evenings I read, talk with friends, study some, perhaps go to eat a snack, or write letters. . . . I've been to one movie in more than a month since I've been in Europe. We usually go to bed rather early.

"Don't be part of a little group of Americans who always stick together," he continued. "Be ready to expect anything; things are done differently in Europe."

A life like this, quite obviously, may not be one continuous round of fun and excitement. There will almost surely be moments of loneliness. "Be prepared for being away from home for a long time," this youth warns, somewhat sadly.

Tripe for Dinner

To live as this young man lived will mean avoiding American products not available to persons of modest means on the local market. It may involve changing one's tastes in food, clothes, amusements, and study habits, the object here being not the slavish imitation of others or the adoption of the expatriate's contempt for everything which symbolizes his native land, but rather an attempt to experience the local life from within. An American girl at the University of Caen sits down to a meal at the student restaurant. "We are having a great treat today: tripe," a French student tells her. "What's that?" she asks innocently. "Tripe" the Frenchman replies. "Don't you know what tripe is? It's the lining of a cow's stomach. *Tripe à la mode de Caen,* a great delicacy." The girl turns pale—but when the tripe arrives she eats it. "I wouldn't have had the courage," she later recalled, "but everyone else was gulping it down and saying how good it was." She added that she was not exactly captivated by the taste of tripe, but felt that she was certainly the richer for having sampled it.

The student ought to consider such things as a sort of experiment, a search for objective understanding arrived at through the most subjective kind of submersion in the local culture. An observer who is at the same time a participant, he will be ready to bear occasional petty inconveniences cheerfully. His position ought to be that of the anthropologist who lives with a people of different culture, copying native customs in order to understand them. Differences, he must realize, are neither good nor bad in themselves. They *are,* however, wonderful guides toward understanding not only the local culture but one's own. The student who can learn to look at his environment this way will surely increase the rewards of his stay abroad.

Two Styles of Travel

Most students abroad for any considerable period do manage to travel fairly extensively during their stay. There are two basic ways to make a tour, each with its particular advantages. One is the bicycle or walking trip; students who travel this way cannot cover great distances, but they do see the regions they visit close up. For such travelers youth hostels are convenient, but it is also possible and desirable to stop at farmhouses along the route for meals and lodging and simply to meet people and learn something of how they live. Farm families almost invariably greet the friendly traveler warmly, especially if he makes it clear that he is a student.

It is a good idea, while traveling in this manner, to keep a diary or notebook and record all the miscellaneous information and impressions that one collects. Jefferson did this religiously while exploring Europe, and his journals are models that every student should examine. Here is a sample:

> March 7 & 8. From la Barque to Chagny. On the left are plains which extend to the Saône, on the right the ridge of mountains called the Côte. . . . The plains are in corn; the Côte in vines. The former have no enclosures, the latter is in small ones or dry stone wall. There is a good deal of forest. Some small herds of cattle and sheep. . . . A vigneron at Voulenay carried me into his vineyard, which was on ten arpents. . . . An arpent rents at from twenty to sixty livres. A farmer of ten arpents has about three labourers engaged by the year. He pays four louis to a man, and half as much to a woman, and feeds them. He kills one hog and salts it, which is all the meat used in the family during the year. Their ordinary food is bread and vegetables.

Information jotted down like this is seldom of earth-shaking importance, but collecting it fixes in the mind not only the facts recorded but hundreds of associated impressions and ideas that might otherwise soon be forgotten. Few travel journals will ever be as full and interesting as Jefferson's, but any traveler's account of his adventures will be a source of recurring pleasure in later years—at least to him.

There is also much to be said for the student who wants to see all the traditional high spots; travel for him will mean hopping from one metropolitan center to another, concentrating his efforts on sightseeing, museum tours, and the like. With modern means of transportation, huge areas can be covered in comparative comfort in a short period of time. When touring this way the student ought to prepare himself first by boning up on each city before he gets there. He ought to know something of the history and principal attractions of the place. He should study a simplified map so that he will be able to orient himself quickly when deposited at the door of his hotel. In this case, it might be wise to join an organized tour, since the savings in time and money involved will outweigh the disadvantages. It is wasteful, when one has but two days to see Naples, say, or Copenhagen, to have to spend precious hours finding a hotel room or pondering over a timetable.

Casual tourists are generally well cared for by the dozens of organizations that run tours all over the world with great efficiency, but the serious American student ought to consider joining a group made up of foreign students. These tours will be the cheapest, and they will bring him in close touch with persons like himself from other lands. He will learn a great deal while hurtling across the countryside in a bus, as well as while roaming the streets as a sightseer. But in any case, he should try to spend some time in each place exploring on his own. Even an hour or two of aimless wandering (after the great cathedrals and museums have been covered with the group) will enable him to soak up some of the local atmosphere.

Leave the Photography to Professionals

A word of advice is appropriate here for the amateur photographer. It is seldom profitable to take pictures of the great sights themselves. One can always buy excellent post-card photos of the cathedrals, monuments, castles, and landscapes that one will want to remember. These pictures cost no more than a dime or so each and are far superior to those snapped without preparation by even the most gifted amateur. A good idea is to collect these photographs at each place of interest and to use the backs to keep a journal account of one's travels and impressions, saving the camera shots for things that have some personal significance that cannot be found on a post card: the restaurant where one has had a particularly enjoyable meal, the flower seller in front of one's hotel, one's companion asking directions of a policeman, and so on.

Making Friends

The area where students most commonly fail to take maximum advantage of their opportunities while abroad is that of personal relationships. From long and intimate experience Professor Angel del Río, of Columbia University, a former dean of the Middlebury College Spanish Summer School and founder of the Middlebury graduate program in Madrid, learned a great deal about the problems of students in foreign countries. He saw hundreds of them on both sides of the Atlantic grappling with a strange culture and an unfamiliar tongue. When asked for the benefit of his observations about their problems, he ranged at length over many facets of foreign study, but then suddenly dismissed what he had already said with an impatient wave of his hand and remarked: "The first thing you need, above all else, is a friend."

There are many reasons why Professor del Río considered friendship so important in foreign study. Students abroad are cut off from their normal social relationships. Separated from friends and family, removed from familiar faces and landmarks, even the most self-sufficient need to develop new human contacts. Then, too, a student needs friends for purely academic reasons. In getting to know other students, he finds his adjustment to the new environment hastened and smoothed. From simple tips about how to navigate the complex red tape of registration, student cards, university catalogues, and the like to philosophical discussions on the nature of higher education, friends among the local student body can ease the path of the visitor and deepen his appreciation of his academic experiences.

Furthermore, intense intellectual effort calls for periods of relaxation. The scholar must plunge into the gregarious world of the café or the beer hall from time to time or he is sure to go stale. Students need also to discuss what they are learning with their fellows. What Americans call the "bull session" is actually an international phenomenon and a necessary part of the process of education.

The development of friendships is also important from the point of view of international relations. Personal benefits aside, every student, simply because he is considered representative of his country, ought to get to know people abroad and give others a chance to know him. Of course, no one can fairly accuse a student who deliberately wishes to avoid people of being unpatriotic, but students in general do have an obligation to try to develop international understanding while overseas. For most, this can best be fulfilled on the personal level in man-to-man relationships. Other governments as well as our own spend large sums subsidizing (directly and indirectly) the education of foreigners for this very reason: they feel that their national interests and the best interests of the world at large will be served if intelligent youths of different lands are given a chance to come together to learn. Any student who partakes of such largess really ought to play the role expected of him, especially in view of the fact that this coincides with his own best interests.

To take an obvious example, the United States and the Soviet Union have set up an exchange of students program. Any American who accepted a scholarship in this program would be morally obligated to try to understand the Russians' point of view and to explain his own to them as forcefully as he could.

Defending America

Because of the sensitive position of the United States in world affairs, the American student is particularly exposed to questions about his government's actions and policies. A special problem is posed by the malicious question, the point raised not to obtain information but to embarrass. Dr. Paul R. Conroy, Chief of Professional Training at the United States Information Agency (USIA), after long experience with this type of questioning, worked out a system for teaching Agency personnel how to cope with it. Students are less likely to be baited by "agitators" than are professional diplomats and other official representatives of the United States, but they are not immune to such attacks and can profit from the advice which Dr. Conroy offers. Here is his description of the USIA training program, drawn from an essay in the *Antioch Review:*

> In the Training Division of the Agency a small group of persons preparing for overseas service meet regularly with me and others. One of them is invited to join us in front of the group, and the scene is set in the country, and the occasion is either a press conference or some less formal gathering. We try to keep the situation as realistic as possible, misunderstanding his American colloquialisms, expressing irritation at any patronizing remarks, and responding warmly to an expression of genuine interest and reasonable discussion of the problems we raise. . . .

The questions we use are current, drawn from news developments or from common criticisms of America in the given country. To these are added the perennials: why do you hate the Negroes so? why are you so materialistic? why is the level of your culture so low? why is juvenile delinquency so prevalent? why are there so many divorces? why do you keep the Indians in concentration camps? why is your government such a threat to world peace? A large group of additional questions probe for an explanation of American foreign policy in various areas of the world.

The first time the trainee encounters such questions he all too frequently displays his ignorance by lamely conceding the points of criticism or by trying to bluff his way through, only getting into deeper and deeper water. He may try to play safe with laconic and non-committal answers which actually arouse suspicion as to his mission in the country. Or he may be overly defensive and allow the "nationals" to push him from one embarrassing admission to another. Worst of all, he may become emotionally argumentative and make statements which give the questioners more ammunition against him.

When the conversation has gone far enough to illustrate the point, it is broken off, and the whole group engages in a post mortem. Every trainee has identified himself all along with the American representative, second-guessing him at each exchange of views, and now the issues are discussed while they are hot. It is a down-to-earth experience for all concerned, and the trainees emerge from the discussion with a keen incentive to study both the problems of America and those of the country of their assignment so as to do better next time.

In additional sessions, the trainee becomes more skilled and the "nationals" become more and more difficult. In the later stages we apply as much pressure as he can take, even becoming more cantankerous and offensive than any national he is likely to encounter. Thus on the job overseas he will gain more confidence when he discovers that the simulated conversations he learned how to handle were far worse than anything he now faces.

Dr. Conroy has also allowed us to print the following suggestions on methods of answering foreign critics, pointing out, however, that these are his personal views and not necessarily those of USIA:

Most of us are accustomed to thinking of things American as generally good, and certainly of our intentions as good. While we are aware that there are people who are critical of our actions, our culture and way of life, and who question our motives and intentions, this has been a matter of only vague concern to most of us. However, anti-American attitudes and criticisms, the reasons for them in various parts of the world, and how to answer these criticisms become a matter of major concern when one becomes a representative of the United States abroad. It may be unfair but it is natural for people to assume that an American representing his country abroad should have the answers to any problem they may have about the United States, its actions, its policies, its way of life, and its culture. Communication is an art, so the suggestions which appear below are along the lines of good practice, which, if consistently applied, will help anyone to carry on a useful discussion with an anti-American critic and develop skill in the art of finding a common ground which will serve as a spring board for changing the critic's attitude of mind.

DON'T ARGUE. Most of us know from experience that no one ever "wins" an argument. When a discussion becomes emotional and feelings of pride are aroused, it becomes a matter of pride to hold up your end of the argument. The point is soon reached when neither disputant is paying much attention to what the other is saying, for each is too busy thinking up his next crushing retort. You know that this has happened when you see in the expression of your "listener" that he is no longer really listening to what you have to say. True, if one of the disputants happens to be louder voiced than the other and creates a distasteful scene, the other may drop the argument merely because he does not like such scenes. But this certainly does not mean that the loud mouth has "won" the argument in the sense that he has convinced his opponent that he is right; the most he has accomplished is to convince his opponent that he is loud-mouthed and opinionated. Since your purpose in carrying on a discussion with an anti-American critic is not to convince him that you are that type of person, but to try to change to some degree his attitude toward the U.S. and things American, you must avoid any action which will turn the discussion into an argument.

ANSWER WITH A "YES, BUT." Probably there is no more sure-fire way to get a person's back up than to contradict flatly some statement he has just made. If someone says to you: "You're wrong; you don't know what you are talking about: just listen to me and I'll tell you the facts," your pride is stung, and almost automatically you are going to be determined to show this so-and-so a thing or two and prove that you are right. Wild horses could hardly get you to concede defeat after this, and a fruitless, ill-tempered argument is under way, or you may simply drop the whole subject in disgust. On the other hand, if someone says: "Yes, I can understand how you feel, but have you thought of . . . etc.," your feathers are not quite so ruffled and you are at least willing to listen to what he has to say with a reasonably open mind. . . .

FIND OUT WHAT THE CRITIC REALLY HAS IN MIND. This is essential when the critic comes up with a sweeping general statement such as, "Americans have no culture and are nothing but materialistic dollar chasers." Admittedly, one is naturally inclined to bridle at this and come back with some strong retort. This may be exactly what the critic wants, to needle you enough so that you will make a hasty and ill-considered reply. However, if you do not rise to this bait, but simply pleasantly inquire as to what type of culture is in question by saying something like, "Well, culture is a word which has a lot of meanings. Perhaps we could discuss this a little better if you could tell me just what aspect of culture you were thinking of." This may elicit the reply that most of our music seems to be rock and roll, and that when good music is programmed on our radio or television stations, something like a Beethoven Sonata is interrupted every five minutes for an advertising commercial in very bad taste. Now, however, you have something definite to talk about, music in America, and you can take up the theme from there. On one occasion an American spent a long time trying to explain various phases of the school integration problem in answer to the question, "Why wasn't Autherine Lucy permitted to go to school," only to discover that the questioner meant his query literally, and thought that Miss Lucy was not permitted to go to *any* school. One is likely unconsciously to assume that the questioner knows more about the subject than he actually does, when often his question may come from rather vague and fleeting impressions he has picked up. It is good to ask questions and use other means to be sure that you know what is actually bothering the person. It may take some time to do this as people often are inclined to conceal their real gripes behind broad generalities. Often it takes time and patience to find out what the "hidden agenda" of the discussion are.

DRAW ON YOUR OWN EXPERIENCE. What you have seen and observed is your own. You should consciously plan to make the most of it. Getting the discussion down to personal experiences helps to escape the pitfalls of talking in broad general principles. In the case of the criticism of commercialism in radio, you could easily say that you agree that sometimes these commercials are irritating, but that you have listened to many programs of good music such as complete operas from the Metropolitan or symphonic concerts by the New York Philharmonic, and that you have never heard a commercial interposed except at intermission, between acts or after the performance of all movements of a symphony. Then you can go on to discuss the fact that there is a small amateur symphony in your town, if this is true, and remark that commercial sponsorship has brought good music to millions of people who might not otherwise have a chance to enjoy it, and that most Americans feel that the advantages of this outweigh the disadvantages—but, after all, all peoples have their own ways of trying to provide for themselves opportunities to enjoy the better things of life, and our way seems to work out pretty well for us. In this type of response, you are not trying to prove too much, but are establishing the basis for a pleasant discussion of music and the enjoyment of it, which is almost certain to end with the questioner feeling that he may have been a little hasty in coming to the conclusions he had before he talked with you.

TRY TO GET THE DISCUSSION OUT OF AN EXCLUSIVELY AMERICAN CONTEXT. Often the critic will bring up items which are rather universal problems of human beings the world over, such as racial prejudices or discrimination, and present them as though they were something upon which Americans had a monopoly. Failure to take the obvious steps to get the issue into proper perspective can make it extremely difficult to carry on an intelligent discussion of the problem and the steps we are taking to deal with it. This certainly does not mean that you should make invidious comparisons with the situation in the questioner's country, in which you are a guest. However, you are likely to find yourself very much on the defensive if you do not do something about getting the matter into perspective as a human problem which has a definite manifestation in America. In the midst of doing this in the early phases of the discussion, you will also have a good chance to size up the questioner and come to some conclusions as to whether he is genuinely and honestly seeking information and enlightenment or whether he is a professional needler. If the latter, your answers will primarily be directed to whatever group of people, large or small, may be listening to the conversation. However, again it is well to remember that questions which may seem to you to be highly provocative and irritating may not be intended that way by the questioner. They may have been directed to him in that form and he is honestly trying to find the answer.

BE REASONABLE. Your manner will be remembered long after your words or discussion points. If you show that you are willing to give courteous consideration to the critic's point of view, you will leave a favorable impression on the critic and other participants in the conversation. Candor is often most useful; if you don't know very much about the subject, say so frankly and try to steer the discussion to a theme upon which you can offer something constructive having some relation to the subject brought up by the questioner. Never forget the resources you have available in the USIS library, where reference material on virtually every subject can be secured quickly and without research and extensive study on your part. Where feasible, offer to get more information for the questioner, and arrange a definite time when you will have the data for him. Even where the question is on something very specific, on which you may not be informed in detail, you can carry on an intelligent, reasonable, and rewarding discussion if you have a good grasp of general background factors connected with the subject. Often it is useful to seek the questioner's point of view in detail and his reasons for it. This shows a flattering interest in his opinions and will usually yield clues to items which you can discuss with him. Quite often you will be able to say that there are many people in the U.S. who agree with his point of view, but on the other hand others feel differently for the reasons you then list. This device of taking the discussion over into the realm of opinion of various groups in the U.S. can be very helpful at times. Expression of appreciation of things which are good in his country should be inserted judiciously into the conversation to establish rapport and your breadth of view. While you may consciously resort to a tone of righteous indignation purposefully, you must remain in control of the discussion and present an appearance of confidence and aplomb. Sometimes you will disarm the critic by candidly admitting that the problem he presents poses a dilemma for the U.S. as to the most useful approach to its solution, and you may even ask whether he has any suggestions as to what should be done. People again are flattered by being asked for their views. The ensuing discussion will enable you to get in the points you have in mind. Remember that you are not always going to convince everyone in one setting, but you will have gone far if you leave the impression that there is something in the U.S. point of view.

Dr. Conroy's advice is sound, but no matter how carefully an American responds to a question, whether it be malicious or honest, he must know what he is talking about if his answer is to be effective. The Council on International Educational Exchange, an organization that helps groups and individuals going abroad for educational purposes to find low-cost transportation, provides a useful orientation program on all the ships it charters. It is called the

Travelers' Recreation-Information Program—TRIP for short—and offers shipboard lectures and discussions designed to help the student "clarify his own thinking about the U.S.A." This sort of thing can be very helpful, and so can the rest of the TRIP shipboard educational program,* but it is *never* justifiable for a student to wait until he is actually en route to begin preparing for living abroad.

A Six-Inch Library

Fortunately, the student can take a great deal of concentrated information along in his baggage even if he cannot cram it all into his head. Then at least he can say: "Wait, I don't know—but I'll look it up," when he is asked a difficult question. A few carefully chosen paperback books will prove immensely useful in this connection. With modern air-travel weight limitations, the student cannot tote along a five-foot shelf of classics, but a "six-inch shelf" can be carried aboard weight-free, as hand luggage or stuffed into odd pockets.

This "six-inch shelf" should contain the *World Almanac* and a history of the United States. The *Pocket History of the United States* by Allan Nevins and Henry Steele Commager (Pocket Books) and William Miller's *History of the United States* (Dell) are both excellent. Add to these Richard B. Morris' *Basic Documents of American History* (Van Nostrand) and a work such as D. C. Doyle's *The United States Political System and How It Works* (New American Library). Bring also a detailed map of the United States—a wonderful conversation piece in any student café—and a copy of your college catalogue. Include the latest edition of *Paperbound Books in Print* (Bowker), which will serve two purposes. It provides clear and concrete refutation when a foreigner claims that the average American is without cultural interests, and it is also a marvelous boon to those interested in purchasing cheap American books. Finally—if you want to be a really well-armed ambassador—carry along a collection of your own favorite paper-

---

* In addition to daily classes in the principal European languages featuring such things as academic terms, slang, food words, and "etiquette," TRIP offers lectures on student life, European culture, foreign educational systems, and other useful topics. Council-chartered sailings, with upward of a thousand students aboard, are also, according to universal testimony, marvelous fun.

backs to lend or give to people you meet. Take books that have some literary stature, of course, but not simply those you know are highly regarded. There is no better way to gain the respect of foreigners both for yourself and for your country than to talk about a good book that you know well and about which you are enthusiastic.

Some Difficulties in Adjusting

Students abroad are quick to recognize the importance of making friends, but many report that it is difficult to do so. It is not hard to see why. The visitor is a rootless stranger in a new country, a mere bird of passage suddenly settling into a community of busy people. Everyone's natural tendency is to pass him by. Language problems exaggerate his isolation. A reasonably good command of a foreign language will be adequate for the tourist, but it is not enough for anyone who hopes to develop real friendships. "Even when you understand everything and can get across your own ideas, it is still hard to make close friends," one student told us. "There are always slang expressions that have to be explained, and the general ease of expression that you need with a true friend simply cannot come in one year." The strain of trying to communicate itself acts as a bar to friendship. "Sometimes," another student reports, "it is not worth the trouble to say it in French. As a result, all your relationships with other people are affected. To the French, I know that I don't appear as I really am."

Here is a story—told us some years ago when we were working on *From Main Street to the Left Bank*—that shows how the language barrier can hinder the development of friendships:

Older Man: "Jenny, are you going out with Henri again this evening?"

Jenny: "No, I'm not. I won't walk with him ever again."

Older Man: "Why not? I thought you liked him."

Jenny: "Oh, I like him all right. But every time we go walking he stops somewhere along the road and relieves himself in the ditch. It's very embarrassing."

Older Man: "Now, Jenny, that's not very reasonable. You ought to realize that's the way the French are about things like that. If it really bothers you, why don't you ask him not to do it?"

Jenny: "I can't. I don't know how to say it in French."

Another problem is money; most Americans abroad have much more of it than local students, many of whom are made to feel either resentful or shy as a result. An American girl's experience in a French dormitory illustrates this: "Our room has two closets. Mine is full of clothes; . . . my roommate's closet is half empty. Every time I open mine I feel bad, because I know she envies all that I have."

The American with greater resources and limited time is led into types of activity beyond the reach of local students. Some buy automobiles; this expands their scope enormously and is a good thing, but since few foreign students have cars it acts to keep the two groups apart. "Your students have more money than most of us," a German student comments. "They drive cars, get around, and we can't do these things. Thus they form a group of their own." The poor student scraping along on a tight budget may actually have more friends among his local colleagues than the well-to-do, no matter how hard the latter tries.

Foreign students are very busy and have relatively little time for social activities. Aside from their academic obligations many are forced to work in order to support themselves. According to one authority, more than 40 per cent of all French university students fall into this category. Foreign students are also, by and large, rather formal and are slow to develop close relations with anyone. "People are hard to get to know here," an American in Munich complains. "They are always nice but distant. I'm used to real friendliness, and here it is strained. People just don't talk to someone they don't know."

This, however, is a one-sided view of the problem. It is difficult for American visitors to realize it, but there is little that they can really offer their hosts in the way of friendship. Why *should* people who are busy, who already have friends of their own, bother themselves with strangers whose knowledge of their language is limited and who will soon be returning to their own country in any case? Furthermore, many American students look upon foreigners as curiosities; they collect "friends" the way some people collect postage stamps. Naturally the discerning foreigner will resent and reject advances made in this spirit.

And shyness has much to do with the problem. While Americans tend to claim that foreign students reject their advances, many foreigners argue that it is *the American* who is clannish, cold, and unwilling to make friends. No doubt both are correct in describing behavior and both wrong in ascribing motives.

All these factors, plus the size and impersonality of university lectures and the lack of a "campus atmosphere" at most foreign universities, increase the difficulties of the student abroad who is trying to find new friends. One result is that the American students in any foreign university are pushed together. All foreign groups tend to hang together, but Americans seem to be more prone to do so than most. The temptation ought to be vigorously resisted. No one who associates only with his compatriots can expect to understand a foreign country and its people. Furthermore, when Americans habitually stay together abroad they are bound to cause bad feeling. Cliques, even if well behaved, always cause resentment; and when their members talk in a foreign language, they may cause suspicion as well.

It would of course be unnatural and undesirable for American students abroad to refuse to have anything to do with their fellow Americans. As an administrator of the Summer Course at the Alliance Française pointed out, students who are forced to speak and think in a foreign language all day must relax occasionally simply to avoid overfatigue. Furthermore, it is good to have someone with whom to compare notes, review one's experiences, try out new ideas. People with common interests are sure to be drawn together and ought not to be discouraged from doing so at home or abroad. But at least until the student has achieved a reasonable competence in the local language he ought to keep his contacts with other English-speaking people to a minimum.*

Meeting People

Educators everywhere realize how important it is for students to make local friends while abroad, and they have done a great deal to help the visitor make contacts. Practically all universities have special offices or committees that try to help foreign students meet

---

* Most students report that it is impossible for learners to avoid lapsing into their native tongue when together, no matter how strong their resolution to avoid it.

local people. France, for example, has a national welcoming committee for foreign students with branches at all her universities.
Germany has an academic exchange service on the national level
and special officers for foreign student affairs at each university.
There are similar organizations and clubs for foreign students in
most universities the world over. Within their often-limited means,
they all try to aid the visitor in his search for friends.

Students participating in organized programs can always count
on special help in meeting people. The junior-year groups give
teas, dances, and even an occasional cocktail party to which local
students are invited. The Fulbright Committees run similar functions. Gatherings of this type are frequently excessively formal
and artificial; nevertheless, they are sometimes helpful, especially
if a skilled host can break the ice and get people talking.

Local excursions are excellent means of bringing students together, and fortunately their number is legion. One may feel un-
comfortable at first with a stranger, but after jouncing across the
countryside for a few hours with him in a bus, the awkwardness is
almost sure to disappear. These affairs are more purposeful than
the traditional tea party or dance. No one participates only to meet
people, and all concerned are more likely to be natural and at ease.

Students might try seeking out people and organizations with
special interests like their own. Even if one knows the language,
the cultural barrier may make it hard to converse when first he
meets foreign students. But if the student's hobby is radio, for
example, association with other "hams" will be relatively easy and
mutually interesting. Modern linguists have discovered that a person can master the vocabulary in an area where he has a special
interest with remarkable rapidity. A novice who might be tongue-
tied trying to make general conversation at a tea party can often
communicate fluently when the subject is chess or skiing. There
are far fewer student clubs in most foreign universities than in
America, but they are not nonexistent. The American abroad ought
to track down such groups whenever he can.

In the last analysis, it is up to the student himself if he is to
make friends. If he insists on maintaining the fiction that he is a
guest and waits to be entertained by his "hosts," he will usually
wait in vain. This point came up repeatedly in our conversations
with students. An American student in France said: "You have to

realize that foreign people are not going to be climbing all over you to make friends." Another in Spain agreed. "You have to go out of your way if you want to make friends in Spain. You can't expect the Spaniard to seek you out."

A young German studying at Heidelberg offers this advice: "If an American really wants to get to know German students, he can. He should go to one of our student hangouts. Not to the 'Red Ox' or other so-called student cafés on the main street, but to the small places. All he has to do is ask a German girl for a dance. She will surely introduce him to her friends, and he can go on from there. But you've got to try. For example, if you asked me to take you to such a place I would, but you shouldn't expect *me* to look *you* up."

Friendship Do's and Don'ts

Again we emphasize that it always pays to try to speak the local language. Two Americans studying in Norway went camping between semesters. Whenever they stopped at a village in some isolated mountain valley they attempted to communicate in their halting Norwegian. Everywhere, these young men reported, people greeted them warmly. They were treated to drinks, queried eagerly about America, invited to dine at many private homes. "If we'd spoken English, people might have understood us, but we wouldn't have seen anything but the sights," they said. A word of caution, however, about the manner of seeking friends: don't go up, slap a European on the back, and start asking him questions. And go slow on addressing casual acquaintances by their first names.

Abroad as at home, sex is a powerful stimulus to the development of friendships. A pretty girl will find it easy to know as many young men as she wishes to know in a foreign university, just as in the United States. Sex, indeed, is a universal language and often a substitute for language. "If we don't know [French], what else is there to do?" an American girl at Grenoble confesses frankly.

On the other hand, ignorance of the local language and of local standards of behavior can lead a student into unfortunate emotional relationships. For many students, a member of the opposite sex, when of a different nationality, seems to have a special charm. Unscrupulous foreigners, trading on this foolish romanticism, sometimes take advantage of naïve American visitors, having convinced them that certain forms of behavior unacceptable in America are à la mode abroad. Not necessarily so, of course.

Some American girls, conditioned by kissing games at adolescent parties, consider osculation a casual and mildly enjoyable game or part of the ritual of thanking a boy for taking them to the movies. When they submit to the embraces of a young man abroad who has never played "post office" or "spin-the-bottle," they are sometimes rudely shocked by what follows. Professor Elbert Dobert, a former director of the Wayne State junior-year group in Munich, once suggested a simple way of explaining this danger to American girls in his charge. He constructed two diagrams:

A X B	A X B
U.S.	Germany

These diagrams illustrate the significance of kissing in the two cultures. In each figure X is the first kiss, and B is serious love-making. "If the girls understand my point, many misunderstandings can be avoided," Dobert remarked. "It doesn't do the male students any harm to see my chart, either," he added. One may smile at the illustration; yet the absence of this kind of information can cause serious difficulties and misunderstandings between basically compatible people.

Thus we have seen that the pitfalls along the road to achieving the maximum benefits of foreign study are many. No student will be able to avoid them all. But he should not be discouraged by this. His understanding of the dangers, his time devoted to planning before he sets out, his determination to make the most of an opportunity, will insure for nearly any student an enjoyable and profitable experience.

PART II

The College and Graduate
Student Abroad

Higher Education Outside the United States

An introduction to different national systems of education . . .
the leading schools . . . requirements and degrees . . . costs . . .
where to write

Anyone considering enrolling as a regular student in a foreign university must of course be familiar with the educational system of which that university is a part. The following brief descriptions are designed to provide a quick survey of the system in countries to which Americans commonly go. It will quickly become apparent to the reader that few undergraduate students and few students who are not planning to study abroad for a considerable time are likely to attempt independent study in such universities. However, even the student who is planning no more than a two-week art course on the Costa Brava or a short stay in Scandinavia can profit from a little knowledge about the local system of higher education. This knowledge absorbed, he is ready to move on to a study of the special programs for foreign students discussed in the following sections.

When you write abroad requesting that information or catalogue material be sent to you, be sure to include international reply coupons, obtainable at any post office. These will be used by your addressee to purchase the postage stamps of his own country needed when he mails the requested material to you. Enclosing United States stamps is, of course, useless.

Europe

AUSTRIA

Since all Austrian institutions of higher learning are centrally controlled by the Federal Ministry of Education, academic requirements, degrees, and instructional methods are highly standardized. Like their European counterparts, Austrian universities are more akin to American graduate schools than to our undergraduate liberal arts colleges. Their curriculum consists of highly specialized professional courses, and the student is expected to be qualified for advanced and independent study, with little guidance from his professors. The average American, therefore, should have finished his undergraduate studies (or, at the very least, two years of college) before planning to enroll at an Austrian university.

Austria has four universities: the University of Graz, located in the picturesque state of Styria; the University of Innsbruck, surrounded by the medieval charm of Tyrol and the majesty of the Alps; the University of Salzburg, the newest Austrian university, founded in 1962; and the University of Vienna, located in the cosmopolitan capital of what was once the Holy Roman Empire. Each of the universities has the following faculties (departments): Catholic theology; law and political science; medicine; and philosophy. The University of Vienna has, in addition, a faculty of protestant theology. The natural sciences are taught in the faculty of philosophy.

Like Germany, Austria also has institutes of technology (*Technische Hochschulen*) which offer specialized curricula in the scientific and technical fields, with only limited work in the humanities. Both Graz and Innsbruck have a *Technische Hochschule* consisting of departments of building engineering and architecture, mechanical engineering and electrotechnics, and the sciences. The Montainistische Hochschule at Leoben offers courses in all aspects of mining and mining engineering.

Other university-level institutes, specializing in a particular field, include the following: Institute for Social and Economic Sciences at Linz (Hochschule für Social-und Wirtschaftwissenschaft); Institute of Agriculture and Forestry at Vienna (Hochschule für Bodenkultur); Institute of International Economics and Commerce at Vienna (Hochschule für Welthandel); Institute of Veterinary Medicine at Vienna (Tierärzliche Hochschule); and the Vienna Academy of Medicine (Wiener Medizinische Akademie für Ärztliche Fortbildung), a postgraduate school for medical specialists.

Finally, there are art and music academies offering courses not taught at the universities or the *Hochschulen*. The Akademie der Bildende Künste (Vienna) specializes in fine arts and architecture; the Akademie für Angewandte Kunst (Vienna) in applied and industrial arts; the Staatsakademie für Musik und Darstellende Kunst (Vienna, Graz) in music, voice, drama, dance, and film production and the Mozarteum (Salzburg), located in the music capital of Europe (the birthplace of Mozart), offers courses in all aspects of music, voice, and drama.

Austrian universities grant only one degree, the doctorate, which requires from three and a half to six years of study, depending on the faculty concerned. Candidates must submit a doctoral dissertation and pass a number of qualifying examinations. Students at the *Technische Hochschulen* receive a diploma at the end of their studies and, if they present a thesis, a doctorate as well. Americans planning to work either for a university or *Hochschule* degree may be granted advanced standing depending on their previous academic record.

Except for summer schools, Austrian universities do not have special courses for foreigners. During the regular academic year, courses are given by the semester, and students may enroll in either the fall or the spring. The fall semester (*Wintersemester*) extends from October through January and the spring semester (*Sommersemester*) from February through June. Lectures (which begin about two weeks after the opening of the semester) are given in German, and the foreign student is expected to have adequate command of that language.

To be admitted, a student should write to the dean of the faculty in question, giving an outline of his educational background, specifying the program in which he is interested, and indicating whether he intends to work for an Austrian degree. Academic transcripts, copies of degrees already obtained, a birth certificate, and, of course, international reply coupons should accompany the letter. The dean will then inform the student if he can be admitted and just how much advanced standing he will be granted in his work toward a degree. Formal enrollment takes place after the student's arrival at the university and just prior to the beginning of the term. The art and music academies have special entrance examinations, the dates and requirements for which should be requested in the student's first letter of inquiry.

By American standards, the cost of study in Austria is quite moderate. Matriculation and tuition fees vary with the faculty and laboratory work involved, ranging from $25 to $170 per semester. Living accommodations are available in small hotels, boarding-houses, or with families. The universities do not maintain dormitories, but the Austrian Foreign Student Service (Oesterreichischer Auslandsstudentendienst, Fuehrichgasse 10, Vienna I) and its branches in other cities, as well as the Austro-American Institute of Education (Operngasse 4, Vienna), will assist students in finding suitable lodgings. A monthly budget of $100–$150 should be sufficient to cover room, board, and incidentals.

Further information on study in Austria is obtainable from the Cultural Section of the Austrian Consulate-General, Hotel Sheraton, 527 Lexington Avenue, New York, N.Y. 10017; Austrian State Tourist Department, 444 Madison Avenue, New York, N.Y. 10022; and Austro-American Society, 2 Stallburg Gasse 2, Vienna.

BELGIUM

Higher education in Belgium follows the traditional European pattern. The main objective is to prepare students for such professional fields as medicine, law, and the civil service. In the universities, it is assumed that students have received their general education in high school, that they are ready for intensive specialization, and that they are capable of independent study with a minimum of professorial supervision. Attendance at lectures is optional, and the comprehensive examinations at year's end are virtually the only check on the student's performance. The average American, therefore, is well advised not to enroll at a Belgian university prior to completion of his undergraduate work.

Belgium has four universities, supported either wholly or partly by the state: Brussels, Liège, Ghent, and Louvain. All have the same faculties (departments)—medicine, law, science, engineering, philosophy, and letters—and, since their degree programs are rigidly prescribed by law, offer roughly the same curricula. Perhaps the only significant difference between the universities is the collection of schools and institutes affiliated with each.

The University of Brussels, partly supported by the state, has the following affiliated institutes: political and social sciences, commerce, Oriental and Slavic philology and history, education, Hispanic studies, maritime law, criminology, aeronautics, telecommunications and acoustics, town planning, physical education, and statistics. The official language is French.

The University of Liège, wholly supported by the state, includes the following affiliated schools: art and archaeology, astrophysics, botany, colonial studies, commerce and economics, criminology, education, geology and physical geography, mechanics, morphology, Oriental history and literature, and physical education. The official language is French.

The University of Ghent, wholly supported by the state, has these affiliated schools: art and archaeology, civil engineering, commerce and economics, criminology, and physical education. The official language is Flemish.

The Catholic University of Louvain, partially supported by the state, has, in addition to the customary faculties, a faculty of canonic law and one of Catholic theology. It also has the following affiliated schools: actuarial science, agriculture, applied economics, applied psychology and education, archaeology and art history, criminology, Oriental studies, philosophy, physical education, religious sciences, and engineering. The university has two sections— one French and one Flemish—and the student must elect to study in one or the other.

There are also State University Colleges at Antwerp (commerce and applied economics, interpretation, and science), and at Mons (commerce and applied economics, education, interpretation, and science).

Other institutions of higher learning offer specialized training in particular fields.

In agriculture, there is an Institut Agronomique at Ghent and another at Gembloux.

In art and architecture, an Académie Royale des Beaux-Arts at Brussels, Liège, Antwerp, and Ghent; the Ecole Nationale Supérieure d'Architecture et des Arts Décoratifs at Brussels; the Institut National Supérieur et Ecole d' Architecture et d'Urbanisme at Antwerp; and the Ecole des Arts et Métiers at Brussels.

In commerce, the Institut Supérieur de Commerce St. Ignace at Antwerp; the Institut Supérieur de Commerce at Etterbeek; the Institut Supérieur Commercial et Consulaire at Mons; and the Ecole des Hautes Etudes Commerciales et Consulaires at Liège.

In international relations, the Collège d'Europe emphasizes specialist training in European cultural, social, economic, diplomatic, and legal history—with particular reference to European integration and unification. This institution has a truly exciting international atmosphere.

In medicine, the Institut de Médicine Tropicale Prince Léopold at Antwerp.

In music, a Conservatoire Royale de Musique at Brussels, Liège, Antwerp, Ghent, and Mons; and the Ecole Inter-Diocésaine de Musique Réligieuse at Malines.

In philosophy and letters, the Institut St. Louis at Brussels and the Collège de Notre Dame de la Paix at Namur.

In technology, the Institut Polytechnique at Mons.

In textiles, the Ecole Supérieure des Textiles at Verviers.

The most common degree granted in Belgian universities is the *licence,* which requires four years of study. Degrees in law or civil engineering take five years; M.D. degrees, seven; and doctorates in philosophy, science, or letters anywhere from six to seven years. Americans who have completed their B.A. or B.S. are admitted with advanced standing and usually given credit for two years of study.

Admission to a degree program is based on individual merit. Since Belgian universities do not supply special application forms, the prospective student should send an initial letter of inquiry to the university he wants to attend. He will then be advised what credentials to submit for consideration.

The regular academic year is divided into semesters, the first beginning on October 1 and the second on February 1 or thereabouts. The registration period extends from October 1 through November 15, which affords the American student an excellent opportunity to sample various lectures before committing himself to a particular schedule of courses. Formal instruction ends during the first week in June, and examinations then run to the beginning of July. There are two weeks of vacation both at Christmas and Easter, as well as a short break between semesters.

Tuition, including matriculation and course fees, usually costs anywhere from $25 to $90, depending on the university and the course load. Fees at Ghent and Liège, which are both wholly supported by the state, are nominal, while those at Brussels and Louvain are slightly higher. The cost of living in Belgium is roughly comparable to that in the United States. Single rooms may be rented for about $55 a month, and full board in a pension may be obtained for about $130 a month. At the University of Brussels, foreign students may find a limited number of rooms at the Cité Universitaire; at Louvain, women students may live at the Sedes Sapientiae, 28 Rue de Bériot; and at the College of Europe in Bruges, students may live at the Maison des Etudiants, where full board and lodging are covered by scholarship grants. A list of available student quarters may be obtained for the various cities: Brussels—from the Office des Renseignements Universitaires, 50 Avenue Franklin Roosevelt; Liège—from the Service Social Universitaire, Place du 20 Août; Ghent—from the Rector's Office of the University, Voldensstraat 9; and Louvain—from the Service de Logement, 69 Rue des Alliés.

One word of warning: As in most European countries, there are laws limiting the employment of foreigners in order to protect local labor. In making his financial plans, therefore, the American student should not count on outside employment. If such employment is a financial necessity, the student is advised to apply to an international organization or to an American firm with operations in Belgium *prior to leaving the United States*. The student may also explore the possibility of a fellowship with the Belgian-American Educational Foundation, which supports advanced research, or the College of Europe, whose grants are handled through the American Committee on United Europe (537 Fifth Avenue, New York, N.Y. 10017).

Sources of information on study in Belgium include the Belgian Government Information Center, 630 Fifth Avenue, New York, N.Y. 10020, and the Belgian-American Educational Foundation, 420 Lexington Avenue, New York, N.Y. 10017.

DENMARK

Higher education in Denmark is under the general supervision of the Ministry of Education. However, the universities exercise considerable autonomy in teaching and administration. Professors, for example, elect their own president (*Rektor*), deans, and the university's governing body; and the several faculties have complete jurisdiction over examinations and the conferral of degrees. The student, as in most European universities, is expected to work independently, to prepare for the degree examinations at his own speed, and to expect only a minimum of supervision from the faculty. Having acquired his general education in high school, he attends the university to prepare for a specific career.

Denmark has three universities. The University of Copenhagen, founded in 1479, has a student body of more than 13,000; and the University of Aarhus, founded in 1928, has a student body of about 4,000. These universities are divided into five faculties (departments): theology, law and economics, medicine, arts, and science. The third and newest university, at Odense, has faculties of medicine, natural sciences, and humanities.

In addition, Denmark maintains a number of *Højskolen* which specialize in technical subjects not taught at the universities. These institutions correspond to the German and Austrian *Hochschulen* and enjoy the same rank and prestige as the universities. They include the Technical University of Denmark (Danmarks Tekniske Højskole) at Copenhagen, which specializes in chemical, electrical, mechanical, and civil engineering; the Copenhagen School of Economics and Business Administration (Handelshøjskole i København), which prepares students for positions in trade and industry; the Royal Danish School of Pharmacy at Copenhagen (Danmarks Farmaceutiske Højskole); the Royal Dental College at Copenhagen (Danmarks Tandlægehøjskole); the Royal Veterinary and Agricultural College at Copenhagen (Den Kongelige Veterinær-og Landbohøjskole), which specializes in veterinary medicine, agriculture, forestry, dairying, horticulture, and land surveying; and the Royal Conservatory of Music at Copenhagen (Det kongelige Danske Musikkonservatorium).

Other institutions of interest to Americans include the Academy for Fine and Commercial Art, Copenhagen; School of Arts and Crafts, Copenhagen; Technical Society Schools, Copenhagen; Technological Institute, Copenhagen; Alfred Jorgensen Institute of Fermentology, Copenhagen; Svend Holtze College of Physical Training, Fredensborg; School of Social Work, Copenhagen; and Carlsberg Laboratories for advanced pure research.

Americans who have not mastered the Danish language, but nevertheless want to study in Denmark, have two alternatives:

1. The Danish Graduate School for Foreign Students offers general background courses in the country's language, politics, economics, social welfare, and education, as well as specialized training in some professional fields. Instruction is in English and is given by specialists drawn from the universities and technical schools. Further information and application forms may be obtained from the Danish Information Office, 588 Fifth Avenue, New York, N.Y. 10036.

2. The Scandinavian Seminar offers American students the opportunity to live for a time in Danish homes and then to attend the Danish Folk Schools (which are resident adult-education colleges). Inquiries concerning this program should be addressed directly to 140 West 57th Street, New York, N.Y. 10019. In neither of these programs does the student receive a university degree.

Students in the regular university or *højskole* curricula are eligible for two degrees: the "candidate's degree" and the doctorate. In the arts and sciences, the "candidate's degree" is usually granted after from five to eight years of study; in theology after six years; in medicine, after seven or eight years; in law or economics, after five to six years; in engineering, after four and one-half to five and one-half years; in agriculture, after three or more years, depending on the curriculum in which the student is enrolled; in veterinary medicine, after six years; in pharmacy, after two years; in dentistry, after four years; in business administration, after three years; and in architecture, after five or six years. The "candidate's degree" will specify the branch of specialization—*cand. jur.* (law), *cand. med.* (medicine), *cand. econ.* (economics), and so on.

Doctorates are granted by both the universities and the *højskoler,* but are relatively rare. Though no minimum period of study beyond the "candidate's degree" is prescribed, the standards for the doctorate are extremely rigorous. Doctoral candidates not only must publish a thesis embodying original research but must defend it publicly before recognized authorities in the field.

The academic year is divided into semesters, the fall semester lasting from September 1 to Christmas and the spring semester from February 1 to the beginning of June.

To be admitted, American students should write a letter of application to the registrar of the university or *højskole,* setting forth in some detail their reasons for wishing to study there and enclosing their college transcripts and a copy of earned degrees. Applications are judged on individual merit, and some applicants may be admitted with advanced standing.

The cost of higher education in Denmark is subsidized by the government and hence quite moderate. The universities charge no tuition and impose only nominal matriculation, examination, and class fees. The technical colleges, however, charge both matriculation and tuition fees, the amount varying with the institution concerned. Room and board are generally available only in boarding houses and with private families, the cost averaging about $100 a month. Aarhus is an exception, because the university maintains seven dormitories open to both Danish and foreign students. (Dormitory space is allocated by the student council, and requests should be addressed to Studenterrædet, Aarhus Universitet, Aarhus). In Copenhagen, as in most European university towns, there are no dormitories. However, the Danish Students Information Bureau (Studiestræde 6, Copenhagen), or the Danish International Student Committee (Sct. Pederstræde 19, Copenhagen) will assist foreign students in locating suitable quarters.

In Denmark, as elsewhere in Europe, American students should not count on outside employment, since the usual restrictions against alien labor are in force.

For further information on study in Denmark, consult the American-Scandinavian Foundation, 127 East 73rd Street, New York, N.Y. 10021, or the Danish Information Office, 588 Fifth Avenue, New York, N.Y. 10036. Students already in Denmark will find the Danish Students Information Bureau in Copenhagen most helpful.

FRANCE

The educational system of France, like the other branches of the French government, is highly centralized. At the heart of the system is the Ministry of National Education, headed by the Minister of Education, a member of the French cabinet. The nation is divided into twenty-three districts called *Académies*, each headed by a *Recteur*, who is a subordinate of the Minister of Education and a sort of superintendent of education for his area. All public education—from the *jardins des enfants* to the university—is under the control of the local *Recteur*.

It follows that there are twenty-three French universities and that so far as degrees, standards, methods, and general philosophy are concerned, all are very much alike. (Three of the universities— at Amiens, Limoges, and Reims—are not yet in full operation.) The University of Paris has the highest prestige among them and is the heaven to which good French professors aspire. But it is very little superior to the provincial universities in quality of faculty or student body. Indeed, in certain fields of knowledge, various provincial centers are judged superior to Paris by many experts. However, Paris does have vast library and archival resources that give it a marked advantage over the other universities as a center for research.

French students enter the universities after completing the course of study at a *lycée* which leads to the degree *baccalauréat*. This places them considerably above the level of graduates of American high schools academically. While no exact method of comparison exists, it is generally conceded that the entering university student in France is at about the level of the junior year at a good American college. French universities are actually more like American graduate schools than undergraduate colleges; they therefore do not admit students from the United States to their regular programs who have not achieved at least junior standing at home.

French universities bear the names of the cities in which they are located. Listed alphabetically, these are Aix-Marseille, Amiens, Besançon, Bordeaux, Caen, Clermont-Ferrand, Dijon, Grenoble, Lille, Limoges, Lyon, Montpellier, Nancy, Nantes, Nice, Orléans, Paris (including the new branch at Nanterre), Poitiers, Reims, Rennes, Rouen, Strasbourg, and Toulouse. Each is divided into faculties (*facultés*) or divisions. With the exception of the "new" universities, all have faculties (departments) of science, letters, and (except for Besançon) law, and most have medical schools as well. Attached to these faculties are a number of institutes which deal with such special subjects as business administration, Oriental studies, and marine biology. These come in bewildering variety. In Paris, for example, there are about forty institutes directly related to the *Faculté des lettres* alone.

The academic year runs from November to June. The program of studies is under the over-all control of the Ministry of Education, which decides what subjects will be taught and prepares the year-end examinations in each subject. Within this framework, however, each professor is free to develop his course of lectures (*cours*) in accordance with his own interests. Typically he deals with some narrow aspect of the general subject, it being his students' responsibility to prepare themselves on their own for the national examination.

There are two major French university degrees, the *Licence* and the *Doctorat d'Etat*. The former is required of all French schoolteachers and calls for about three years of university study. Candidates for it must pass stiff oral and written examinations. The *Doctorat d'Etat*, required for teaching at the universities, is a research degree granted after an indefinite period of study and only on completion of a major piece of original research. Few foreigners ever attempt either of these degrees, essentially teachers' licenses. Instead they aim at what is known as a *Doctorat d'Université*. This is the rough equivalent of an American Ph.D., and a student with an M.A. from the United States can qualify for it in about two years. He must write a thesis in French and pass an oral examination.

Foreign students who do not wish to work for the *Doctorat* may earn a *Certificat d'Etudes Supérieures* or a *Diplôme d'Etudes Universitaires*, both of which are degrees accumulated by regular French students on the way to the *Licence*. In addition there are a number of special certificates available exclusively to foreign students for work in French language and literature. The most important of these is the *Certificat d'Aptitude à l'Enseignement du Français à l'Etranger*, which, as the name indicates, is awarded (after the completion of a rigorous course) to persons planning to teach French in foreign countries. This *certificat* is offered at the universities of Paris, Aix-Marseille, Grenoble, Lille, Montpellier, and Poitiers and normally can be won in a year.

No tuition is required of students enrolling in regular courses in the French universities, but the procedure that an American must follow to obtain a letter of admission is extremely complicated. The necessary documents and steps are outlined below:

A. Birth certificate.

1. The certificate must be "legalized" by the French Consulate having jurisdiction over the state which issued it.

2. The legalized certificate must be translated into French.

3. The translation must be notarized.

4. The notarized translation must be certified by the French Consulate having jurisdiction over the state for which the notary public was licensed.

B. Photostat of one's college degree,* bearing the seal of the college clearly in relief.

1. The photostat must be translated into French.

2. The translation must be notarized.

3. The translation must be certified by the French Consulate having jurisdiction over the state for which the notary public was licensed.

C. A letter written by the student to the *Secrétariat* of the *faculté* in which he wishes to enroll. The French Embassy suggests the following form:

Monsieur le Recteur:
*Le soussigné*_____, *né à*_____ *de nationalité*
_____ *demeurant à* _____,
ai l'honneur de vous demander de bien vouloir m'accorder ___
l'équivalence du Baccalauréat pour me permettre de m'inscrire
à la Faculté de _____, *de l'Université de* _____
et d'y preparer _____. [Indicate degree.]
Je joins à ma demande la copie de mon diplôme de _____
_____ [indicate degree and college from which obtained]
et la copie et la traduction de mon acte de naissance.
Veuillez agréer, Monsieur, l'expression de mes sentiments les
plus respectueux.

D. Three international reply coupons must be enclosed in a single envelope with all the documents above, notarized and translated, and dispatched to the appropriate Secretariat.

After he is admitted to a university, the student must obtain a student visa, since he will be studying more than three months in France. To do this he must send to the Cultural Services of the French Embassy, 972 Fifth Avenue, New York, N.Y. 10021, his letter of admission to the university with evidence of financial solvency (such as a letter from a bank, or proof of a scholarship, or a notarized letter from his parents promising to keep him in funds). The Embassy will then issue a letter of approval.

The student must take this to the nearest French Consulate and

* Actually good students with junior standing are usually allowed to enter.

fill out in quintuplicate a visa application. This application, together with five passport-size photographs, the letter of approval, and a valid United States passport not due to expire until at least sixty days after the expiration of the visa, will normally induce the French authorities to issue the visa. The charge for this is about $10. *Vive la France éternelle!*

GERMANY

The West German system of higher education is decentralized, with over-all supervision of the nation's eighteen universities in the hands of the separate states (*Länder*) of the Federal Republic. Furthermore, each university is largely autonomous and is entirely free of governmental interference in academic matters. Nevertheless, a remarkable degree of uniformity exists. As one German authority stated, "The statutes of the individual universities and academies may differ here and there in small details, but are fundamentally the same." Standards, quality of faculty and student body, degrees offered, and the variety of subjects taught are not appreciably different from one university to another, although in any particular field, one university may naturally be considered superior to others because of specialized library facilities, tradition, or the presence on the faculty of an outstanding authority.

The eighteen "older" German universities are located in Berlin ("Free University"); Bonn; Cologne; Erlangen; Nuremburg; Frankfurt am Main; Frieburg; Giessen; Göttingen; Hamburg; Heidelberg; Kiel; Mainz; Marburg; Munich; Münster; Saarbrücken; Tübingen and Würzburg. In addition, five new universities have recently been established at Bochum, Bremen, Dortmund, Konstanz, and Regensburg. Each is divided into various faculties (departments). Although there are slight variations in the names of these faculties and in their organization, every university has faculties of law, medicine, science, and philosophy (humanities). Particular departments of study will not always be found within the same faculty. Economics, for example, is part of the law faculty at Bonn, but under the faculty of philosophy at Erlangen; at Kiel all the sciences are part of the philosophy faculty. On the other hand, many of the universities in Germany have separate faculties of theology, agriculture, political science, and so on.

There are also nine university-level technical schools (*Technische Hochschulen*) in Germany. These are located at Aachen; Berlin; Braunschweig; Clausthal; Darmstadt; Hanover; Karlsruhe; Munich; and Stuttgart. They are organized along lines very similar to the universities and even offer courses commonly included in the philosophy faculty; nonetheless, they are essentially engineering schools. There are also specialized university-level schools in veterinary medicine, physical education, mining, agriculture, and other subjects.

The German university year usually runs from about the first of November to the end of July, with a long break between semesters in March and April. Actually, the basic academic unit is the semester. Teaching takes the form of lectures (*Vorlesungen*) and seminars or exercises (*Übungen*). Ordinarily there are no examinations for the separate courses. Students seeking degrees attend the university for from three to six years, and a great part of the preparation for degrees is accomplished in private study outside the framework of formal courses. Proficiency is determined by the State Examination (*Staatsexamen*) and is required for admission into the professions. The *Staatsexamen* in law, for example, serves the same function as the state bar examinations in the United States; at the same time it is also the equivalent of a law degree from an American university.

For obvious reasons, foreign students are seldom interested in taking a *Staatsexamen*. Instead they prepare for a diploma examination (*Diplomaprüfung*) in their particular field. Most universities now also award the *Magisterartum* (M.A.) in the humanities. The universities also award doctorates, which are research degrees roughly equivalent to the American Ph.D.

To seek a doctorate, a student must have completed his diploma examination. Foreign students may submit evidence of equivalent work at other universities in lieu of this, but at least two semesters of work at the university where the degree is to be earned are required. The candidate (*Doktorand*) must prepare a dissertation or thesis in German under the guidance of a professor, and it must be approved by the appropriate faculty and printed. An oral examination must also be passed before the degree is awarded. Normally it takes from two to four years beyond the diploma to win a German doctorate.

Tuition, fees, insurance, and other charges vary somewhat according to the university and the faculty, but average between $150 and $300 per year. The cost of living, depending on the region, ranges from $100 to $140 per month. Students must be eighteen years of age and possessed of a "School-Leaving Certificate" equivalent to the *Abitur* awarded to graduates of German secondary schools (*gymnasia*). For Americans this generally means junior standing in a recognized college, but each university in Germany has control over its own admissions procedures, and they are not entirely uniform. The prospective student should write to the Rector of the university at which he wishes to do his work, requesting admission. This letter (in German) should contain an account of the applicant's academic background. In addition he should include a photostat of his college record and an "officially attested" translation of the same; whatever evidence of proficiency in German he can muster; evidence of good health and of good conduct; two passport photographs; and the usual international reply coupons. If accepted, the applicant may present himself at the beginning of the next semester. At that time he must submit, besides his letter of acceptance, the original copy of his School-Leaving Certificate or its equivalent, a passport, and three more passport photographs. He may also be required to take an examination in German.

Great Britain

Universities in the United Kingdom, unlike most of their European counterparts, are private, self-governing institutions. Although they are not subject to the centralized control of the Ministry of Education, they receive most of their financial support from the state through the so-called University Grants Committee. This body is appointed by the Treasury, but a majority of the committee members come from the universities. They determine how government grants to higher education are to be allocated among the various universities, which, in turn, decide for themselves exactly how the funds are to be spent. Normally, the universities are the final arbiters of policy in the academic domain.

At present there are in the United Kingdom some thirty universities, either in full operation or soon to begin operating. The oldest and most famous, of course, are Oxford and Cambridge, which date back to the twelfth century. Both are federations of several residential colleges, each of which is separately incorporated and endowed and independent in its administration and instruction. Only the universities, however, have the power to grant degrees.

Until the nineteenth century, Oxford and Cambridge were the only universities in England and Wales and were the repositories of the nation's intellectual leadership. With the founding of London University in 1836 began the great era of university expansion. London became the catalyst for the founding of other universities because, in addition to providing instruction for its regular undergraduates, it alone allowed nonresident students (that is, people who had never studied at London University) to sit for "external" degree examinations. Because of this system of external degrees, other educational institutions which did not have degree-granting powers could enter their students in the examinations for a London University degree until such time as the quality of their instruction improved and expanded sufficiently for them to apply for a university charter themselves and grant degrees in their own right.

As a result there are today—in addition to Oxford, Cambridge, and London—the following degree-granting universities in England: Aston at Birmingham, Bath, Birmingham, Bradford, Bristol, Brunel, City University of London, Durham, East Anglia at Norwich, Essex at Colchester, Exeter, Hull, Keele, Kent at Canterbury, Lancaster, Leeds, Leicester, Liverpool, Manchester, Newcastle upon Tyne, Nottingham, Reading, Salford, Sheffield, Southampton, Surrey at London, Sussex at Brighton, Warwick at Coventry, and York—plus the Manchester University of Science and Technology, and the Longhborough University of Technology.

Scotland has the following universities: Aberdeen, Edinburgh, Glasgow, Heriot-Watt at Edinburgh, St. Andrews, Strathclyde, and Stirling.

The University of Wales consists of the following constituent colleges: Wales at Aberystwyth, North Wales at Bangor, South Wales and Monmouthshire at Cardiff, Swansea, Institute of Science and Technology at Cardiff, and Welsh National School of Medicine at Cardiff.

Northern Ireland has the Queen's University of Belfast, and New University of Ulster at Coleraine.

There are other institutions of higher learning in specialized fields, such as the Architectural Association School of Architecture, the Central School of Speech and Drama, the Royal Academy of Dramatic Art, and the Royal College of Art.

The traditional method of instruction at most British universities is the formal lecture, supplemented usually by tutorial classes, seminars, laboratory work, and private reading. At Oxford and Cambridge, tutorials form an integral part of the undergraduate's work; almost every week the student prepares an essay or exercise on a topic connected with his course, presents it to his tutor, and then discusses it with him. In the newer universities, this tutorial system also exists to a considerable (and often increasing) extent, but the tutorial classes are generally larger and meet less frequently. The emphasis is on molding the student's qualities of initiative and independence, so that he can master a subject with only minimum reliance on formal classroom work.

Although there is considerable diversity in the usage of degree titles, the universities usually offer a bachelor's or "first degree" in the arts, science, economics, commerce, divinity, engineering, law, medicine and surgery. These degrees normally require three or four years of work (six in medicine and surgery). In Scotland the first degree is the master of arts (M.A.).

Higher degrees, which normally require from two to three years of postgraduate work, include the bachelor of letters, bachelor of philosophy, master of arts, master of science, master of science in economics, master of commerce, master of engineering, doctor of medicine, and doctor of philosophy. Other degrees, such as doctor of letters, doctor of laws, doctor of science, or doctor of engineering, are essentially honorary degrees awarded only for outstanding contributions to the advancement of knowledge in that particular field.

The academic year runs from October to June and is generally divided into three terms of from eight to ten weeks each.

Admission to British universities is based on a process of competitive selection. This means that the possession of suitable qualification does not automatically guarantee admission, as it does in most European countries. American students seeking admission to a *first-degree* program in any British university (other than Oxford, Cambridge, Belfast, or London Medical School) may apply through the Universities Central Council on Admissions. They should write the Secretary, U.C.C.A., 29 Tavistock Square, London, W.C.1. Students applying for a *higher* degree must apply directly to the university of their choice, writing to The Registrar (England and Wales) or The Secretary (Scotland), with the exception of Oxford, Cambridge, and London, where application must be made to a particular college within the university. For further information, graduate students may write to the Adviser to Overseas Candidates for Admission, 17 Silver Street, Cambridge; Academic Registrar, University of London, Senate House, London, W.C.1; or Head Clerk, University Registry, Oxford.

The total cost of study and residence varies according to the university and the course of study. At Oxford and Cambridge, the cost ranges between $2,100 and $2,500; at London, from $1,700 to $2,200; and at most other universities, it is about $2,000. Expenses are higher for those studying medicine, engineering, agriculture, or the natural sciences.

Lodging is a special problem. Only about 33 per cent of the students can be housed in college and university residence halls. The foreign student should contact the appropriate university lodgings officer for a list of living quarters suitable for students.

GREECE

After Greece achieved its independence from the Ottoman Empire in 1830, its first king, Prince Otto of Bavaria, introduced the German system of education to the country. The first university, established in 1837, was also patterned after the German model and eventually became the National and Capodistrian University of Athens. Today, as in most European countries, Greek universities are subject to the centralized control of the Ministry of Education. Though they enjoy a great deal of autonomy and jealously guard their prerogatives, both public and private institutions operate under laws and regulations promulgated by the government. They provide specialized training to prepare students for professional careers.

Greece has four universities. The National and Capodistrian University of Athens and the Aristotle University of Thessaloniki have faculties (departments) of theology, philosophy, law, medicine, and mathematics and physics; Thessaloniki also has faculties of agriculture and forestry, veterinary science, engineering, and dentistry. The University of Patras has faculties of electrical and mechanical engineering, and physics and mathematics. The University at Yammina has faculties of law, mathematics, and philosophy.

In addition, the National Mestovion Institute of Technology at Athens offers curricula in civil, mechanical, electrical, chemical, rural, and topographical engineering and courses in architecture. University-level institutes in agriculture, economics and commercial studies, fine arts, music, and drama are also found in Athens. Finally, there is an American (postgraduate) School of Classical Studies (controlled by a committee representing seventy American universities and open only to United States and Canadian citizens), a British School of Archaeology, and a French School of Archaeology—all in Athens.

The Greek universities offer two degrees: a diploma after from four to six years of study, and a doctorate upon presentation of a research thesis.

The academic year lasts from September to May or from November to June, depending on the institute or university.

Tuition costs about $70 for the academic year. Students must make their own arrangements for housing, but they benefit from a 25 per cent reduction in rates available to foreign students at all Greek hotels. On the average, the cost of living amounts to about $85 per month.

IRELAND

Ireland has two self-governing, independent universities. The University of Dublin (Trinity College) was founded in 1591 and offers curricula in medicine, science, arts, economics, divinity, law, music, education, engineering, and veterinary medicine. The National University of Ireland, founded under the Irish Universities Act of 1908, consists of three university colleges (Dublin, Cork, and Galway) and St. Patrick's College, Maynooth (Kildare). With the exception of St. Patrick's, these colleges are all coeducational.

In addition to the two universities, there are the following institutions of higher learning in Ireland: Dublin Institute for Advanced Studies, specializing in Celtic studies and theoretical physics; Royal Irish Academy at Dublin, specializing in Celtic studies and science; Royal College of Physicians and Surgeons at Dublin; Veterinary College of Ireland at Dublin; Agricultural Institute at Dublin; and the Institute for Industrial Research and Standards at Dublin.

The major degrees offered by Irish universities are the bachelor's degree, requiring about three years of study; the master's degree, requiring one additional year; and the doctorate, requiring about three years beyond the bachelor's degree. The academic year runs from late September to late June, and the language of instruction, except for some courses which are taught in Irish, is English.

To be admitted, the student should write directly to the President of the college of his choice and ask for an exemption from the matriculation examination. (At Dublin this application should be made to the Senior Tutor of the College.) Exemption will be granted only to students who can prove that they have passed equivalent examinations in the required subjects, which in many faculties include Latin. Entrance standards are rigorous, and American students are well advised to apply only after attainment of their B.A.

Tuition fees vary, depending on the curriculum, but the approximate cost of an arts-degree program is $150 per year. Except for the University of Dublin (Trinity College), which maintains student residence facilities, there are no dormitories. A goodly number of the students live at residential hostels. The cost of living is roughly $130 per month.

ITALY

The universities of Italy are among the oldest in the world. Begun as independent schools offering *studium generale* (a place of study open to all), they gradually gained enough power to obtain official recognition from the state. Thus, the University of Bologna, founded as a law school in 1088, was recognized by Frederick Barbarossa in 1155, and specialized schools at Padua, Naples, Rome, Perugia, Pisa, and Florence had obtained similar recognition by the middle of the fourteenth century.

Today there are thirty universities in Italy, twenty-four of which are state universities (Bari, Bologna, Cagliari, Camerino, Catania, Ferrara, Florence, Genoa, Macerata, Messina, Milan, Modena, Naples, Padua, Palermo, Parma, Pavia, Perugia, Pisa, Rome, Sessari, Siena, Trieste, and Turin) and six private or "free" universities (Chiete, L'Aquila, Lecce, Urbino, Catholic University of the Sacred Heart at Milan, and Universita Commerciale "Luigi Bocconi" at Milan). Though not supported by the government, the "free" universities can grant degrees having the same legal standing as those granted by the state universities. In any event, the degree program offered by any university is rigidly prescribed by law, and the Ministry of Public Instruction at Rome exercises centralized control over all Italian education.

In addition to the universities, there are a number of fine arts academies offering a four-year program, organized in separate sections for painting, sculpture, decorative art, and scenic design. All the subjects within each section are prescribed, and students must follow the complete program with no electives. Bologna, Carrara, Florence, Milan, Naples, Palermo, Perugia, Rome, Turin, and Venice each has an Academia de Belle Arti. The one at Carrara specializes in marble work.

As distinct from the art academies, there are art institutes which prepare students to become master craftsmen in such fields as ceramics, woodwork, silver work, and the like. These *instituti d'arte* are located in Rome, Florence, Faenza, Urbino, and Venice, and each specializes in a different field.

Finally, there are music conservatories offering courses for periods of varying duration and leading to different diplomas. There is a Conservatorio di Musica in each of the following cities: Bologna, Bolzano, Cagliari, Florence, Milan, Naples, Palermo, Parma, Pesaro, Rome, Turin, and Venice. Highly specialized courses are available at La Scala Opera School in Milan and Il Pontifico Instituto di Musica Sacra in Rome.

Among the specialized institutes in the social sciences that may be of interest to Americans are the Institute of Economic Development (Istituto de Studi per lo Sviluppo Economico), Naples; Institute of European Studies (Istituto de Studi Europei "Alcide de Gasperi"), Rome; Institute of European Studies (Istituto de Studi Europei), Turin; Institute for the Study of International Politics (Istituto per gli Studi di Politica Internazionale), Milan; and the

University College of Federalist Studies (Collegio Universitario di Studi Federalisti), Val d'Aosta.

The academic year is not divided into semesters, and classes are held from the beginning of November through early June.

Italian universities grant only one degree, the *laurea*—which carries with it the title of *dottore*. In most faculties the degree can be earned in four years except in engineering, architecture, and chemistry (five years), and medicine (six years). Further studies (*corsi di perfezionamento*) leading to a special diploma may be pursued in such fields as law and medicine.

To be admitted to an Italian university, American students must have completed at least two years of college and must have an adequate command of Italian. Applications, accompanied by academic transcripts, copies of earned degrees, and birth certificate and proof of citizenship, should be submitted to the nearest Italian Consulate in the United States for translation and authentication. The consulate, rather than the student, submits these documents to the institution in question and arranges for the student's admission. Applicants already in Italy should contact the Ministero degli Affari Esteri, Direzione Generale delle Relazioni Culturali con l'Estero, Rome, Italy.

Tuition for students enrolled in regular degree programs comes to about $85 per year, plus an additional $20–$80 for those taking laboratory courses. Enrollment fees in the *corsi di perfezionamento* may run as high as $200. Art academies and music conservatories charge no tuition to foreign students.

Although there are special student residences in some of the larger Italian cities, the universities themselves generally do not maintain dormitories. Foreign students may apply for admission to the Villa Fabricotti, 64 Via Vittorio Emanuele, Florence, or the Casa Internazionale, Palazzo Salviati, Piazza della Rovere 83, Rome, but only a handful are accepted. Most students, Italian and foreign, live in *pensioni*, furnished rooms, or hotels. Depending on the city, the cost of living ranges from $180 to $200 per month.

THE NETHERLANDS

Four of the six universities in the Netherlands are wholly or partly state-supported institutions. Admissions, degree programs, and examinations are specified by law and are also subject to regulation by the Ministry of Instruction, Arts, and Sciences. However, the internal affairs of universities are administered by the professors and the rectors, who are elected by their colleagues.

Leyden, the oldest university in the Netherlands, received its university charter in 1575 as a reward for the town's role in the struggle for Dutch independence. Groningen, Utrecht, and Amsterdam were founded in the seventeenth century; the Free University of Amsterdam in the nineteenth; and the Catholic University of Nijmegen in 1923. Leyden, Utrecht, and Groningen are state universities; Amsterdam, a municipal university; and the Free University of Amsterdam (Dutch Reform) and the Catholic University of Nijmegen, independent institutions. Most of these have the following faculties (departments): theology, law, arts, science, philosophy, and medicine.

Certain technical subjects like engineering, architecture, and agriculture are not included in the regular university curriculum and must be studied at special *hogescholen*, which are roughly equivalent to the German *Technische Hochschulen*. There are three *Technische Hogescholen*, at Delft, Eindhoven, and Enschede. These, together with the two institutes of economics, located at Rotterdam and Tilburg, the School of Medicine at Rotterdam, and the Agricultural Institute at Wageningen have the same rank and prestige as the universities.

In addition, there is a State Academy of Fine Arts at Amsterdam and a Catholic Academy of Fine Arts at Maastricht; conservatories of music at The Hague, Amsterdam, Rotterdam, and Utrecht; and an Architectural Academy at Amsterdam.

As in most European countries, attendance at lectures at Dutch universities is entirely voluntary. There are no semester or year-end examinations and no system of credits. University training is considered specialized work in preparation for a specific career, and the student is expected to be capable of independent work when he enrolls. The academic year begins about September 20 and ends about July 10, with vacations at Christmas and Easter. Courses are not divided into semesters.

The university program leading to the final degree of *Doktor* takes from five to eight years, depending on the faculty in which the student is enrolled. Along the way, the student takes several intermediate examinations: the *propaedeutic* (usually after one year), the *candidaats* (usually after three years), and the *doctoraal* (usually after five years). The *doctoraal* examination confers the title of *doctorandus* and permits the student to present a thesis for the award of the doctorate. By American standards, the *propaedeutic* is roughly comparable to the bachelor's and the *candidaats* to the master's degree. At the institutes of technology, the final degree is that of engineer, architect, agricultural engineer, and so on.

In Holland, application for admission to a university should be made by letter to the Rector Magnificus of the institution concerned. Transcripts of the student's record and copies of whatever degrees he has earned must accompany the letter. Each application is judged as a special case, and advanced standing may be granted if the student's previous training merits it. Those who plan to study medicine should apply through the Ministry of Education, Department of Higher Education, Nieuwe Uitleg 1, The Hague, Netherlands.

Tuition costs, uniform throughout Holland, are about $60 per academic year. In scientific and medical courses, there may be extra laboratory fees. Since Dutch universities do not maintain dormitories, students must live in furnished rooms or boarding-houses—searching for the small signs, "cubicola locanda," which dot university towns in September. The housing bureaus at the various universities and the Foreign Student Service, 5 Oranje Nassaulaan, Amsterdam, Netherlands, may be of help in locating quarters. Generally, the student should expect expenses of not less than $120 per month for maintenance and lodging.

NORWAY

Although Norwegian universities are under the general supervision of the Ministry of Education, they are largely independent and self-governing institutions, more akin to American graduate schools than to the undergraduate liberal arts colleges. Students are supposed to have acquired a general education in high school, to enroll in the university only for specialized professional training, and to be capable of independent study. They receive little supervision, proceeding at their own pace toward completion of their degrees. Americans planning to study in Norway not only should have completed two years of undergraduate work but must also have a good working knowledge of Norwegian.

There are two universities in Norway, one at Oslo (founded in 1811) and the other at Bergen (founded in 1948). At the older university, there are faculties (departments) of theology, law (including economics), medicine, liberal arts (including history, philosophy, and social science), mathematics, dentistry, and natural science (including pharmacy). At Bergen there are only three faculties: science, medicine, and liberal arts.

Other institutions of university rank offer specialized curricula not found at the universities. These institutions include the following technical schools (*høgskole*), academies (*akademi*), and conservatoria (*konservatoriet*): The Agricultural College of Norway (Norges Landbrukshøgskole), located twenty-three miles from Oslo; the State Academy of Fine Arts (Statens Kunstakademi), Oslo; State College of Crafts and Applied Arts (Statens Handverks og Kunstindustriskole), Oslo; The Norwegian School of Economics and Business Administration (Norges Handelshøgskole), Bergen; The Norwegian State Dental School (Norges Tannlegehøgskole), Oslo; Norwegian Institute of Technology (Norges Tekniske Høgskole), Trondheim; State Teachers' College of Home Economics (Statens Laererinneskole i husstell), at Stabekk near Oslo; Conservatory of Music (Musikkonservatoriet), Oslo; State School of Physical Education (Statens Gymnastikkskole), Oslo; Norwegian Teachers' Institute (Norges Laererhøgskole), Trondheim; and Veterinary College of Norway (Norges Veterinaerhøgskole), Oslo.

Norwegian universities grant four degrees: the *adjunkt*, the *lektor*, the master's, and the doctorate. To obtain the *adjunkt* degree in the arts and sciences, students must pass full-day examinations in each of three minor subjects as well as an oral examination. The program usually requires from five to seven years of preparation, and successful candidates receive the title *cand. mag.* (Americans working for the *adjunkt* may be admitted with advanced standing if they have completed two or more years of college.) To obtain the *lektor*, students must both pass an oral and written examination and write a thesis in *one* of the fields offered for the previous degree. This usually requires two years of study beyond the *adjunkt*, and successful candidates receive the title of *cand.*

philol. (humanities) or *cand. real* (science). The next degree, the *magister artium* or *magister scientarium*, involves an expansion of the *lektor* thesis; and the highest degree—the doctorate—is awarded only for independent and original scholarship, presented in the form of a major dissertation and defended in a public lecture before leading authorities in the field. Doctorates are not common in Norway.

Outside the arts and sciences, degree requirements—except for the doctorate—are usually less rigorous. The *cand. med.* takes about eight years; the *cand. vet.med.* about six years; the *cand. jur., cand. econ.,* and *cand. theol.* about five years; the *architekt* or *ingenior* degrees about four and one-half years; the *cand. dent.* about four years; the *cand. agric.* about three years; and the *cand. commerce* about two to three years. In all these fields there is also a doctor's degree which, like the doctorate in arts and sciences, is difficult to obtain and hence quite rare.

The academic year consists of semesters, the first lasting from the beginning of September to mid-December, the second from mid-January to mid-June. To be admitted, the American student should submit to the Rector of the university or *høgskole* a formal letter of application, accompanied by his academic transcripts and copies of whatever degrees he has already obtained. In medicine, pharmacy, engineering, commerce, agriculture, veterinary medicine, and dentistry, admission is restricted by the amount of laboratory space available.

Except for nominal matriculation, laboratory, and examination fees, higher education in Norway is free. Single students should find a monthly budget of $120 adequate, especially if they live in the new dormitories at Sogn Student Town in Oslo or similar facilities available at Bergen, Trondheim, and Vollebekk. Married students, especially those with children, should be aware of the fact that suitable apartments at reasonable rentals are in short supply.

Graduate-study fellowships are administered by the American-Scandinavian Foundation, 127 East 73rd Street, New York, N.Y. 10021, and applications should be addressed to the Foundation. For further information on study and life in Norway, contact the Norwegian Information Office or the Norwegian Travel Office, both of which are located at 290 Madison Avenue, New York, N.Y. 10017.

PORTUGAL

Portuguese universities, organized substantially along the Spanish pattern, offer specialized courses to prepare students for professional careers. It is assumed that students have completed their general education in high school and that they are now capable of advanced and independent study.

Portugal has four universities. The University of Coimbra, where many of Portugal's most celebrated authors and statesmen were educated, was founded in 1290. Coimbra, like the Classical University of Lisbon, has faculties (departments) of letters, law, medicine, pharmacy, and science. The University of Oporto has faculties of science, medicine, pharmacy, engineering, and economics. Finally, the Technical University of Lisbon, which consists of a group of schools and institutes each specializing in a different field, offers work in veterinary science, agriculture, economics and finance, and engineering.

In addition, there are a College of Music and Art at Lisbon, a National Conservatory of Music at Lisbon, a Conservatory of Music at Oporto, a School of Fine Arts at Lisbon, a National School of Fine Arts at Oporto, and Institutes of Tropical Studies and Medicine at Lisbon. There is also a faculty of theology at Braga.

Like their Spanish counterparts, Portuguese universities offer two major degrees, the *licenciado* and the *dotour*. The former is awarded after from four to six years of study, while the latter requires the preparation and successful defense of a thesis in addition to the examinations.

To be admitted, the student should write directly to the institution of his choice. A thorough knowledge of Portuguese is a requirement for admission.

Tuition fees for the academic year average about $50. Ordinarily, students make their own arrangements for room and board in private homes, pensions, or university centers. The cost of living ranges from a bare minimum of $60 per month upward.

SPAIN

Higher education in Spain dates back to the period of Moorish domination, between the eighth and twelfth centuries, when the royal courts served as the gathering places of eminent scholars and repositories of great libraries. Salamanca, the first modern Spanish university, was founded by Alfonso I in the thirteenth century, and others were later established by royal decree or through municipal efforts.

Today, all higher education in Spain is centrally directed and controlled by the Ministry of National Education. The country is divided into twelve educational districts, each of which contains a national university. Students enroll in a specific faculty (department) to pursue specialized studies leading to a professional degree. It is assumed that all students have completed their general education *before* coming to the university.

The twelve state universities are: Barcelona, Granada, La Laguna (Canary Islands), Madrid, Murcia, Oviedo, Salamanca, Santiago de Compostela, Seville, Valencia, Valladolid, and Zaragoza. Each of these has a faculty of philosophy and letters, law, and science. Some of the larger universities (like Barcelona and Madrid) also have faculties of medicine, pharmacy, political science, and economics. In addition, there is affiliated with each university a separate school, the Escuela de Estudios Sociales, which offers instruction in contemporary problems, politics, economics, social legislation, and labor problems.

There are four private universities: The University of Deusto at Bilbao has faculties of economics, law, medicine, philosophy and letters, and science. The Catholic University of Navarre at Pamplona, the Pontificial University of Comillas at Santander, and the Pontifical University of Salamanca, each have faculties of canon law, philosophy, and theology. Comillas also has faculties of sociology and science, while Salamanca has a faculty of classical philology and institutes for pastoral theology, Oriental studies, and biblical and spiritual studies. Navarre offers as broad a curriculum as an American state university.

Finally, there are university-level fine arts academies at Madrid, Barcelona, Valencia, and Seville; the music conservatories at Madrid, Córdoba, Málaga, Murcia, Seville, Valencia, Bilbao, Zaragoza, Tenerife, La Coruña, Cádiz, San Sebastián, and Barcelona; and architectural schools at Madrid and Barcelona.

The two major degrees awarded by Spanish universities are the *licenciatura* and the *doctorado,* the former requiring about five or six years of study, and the latter several additional years. Certificates and diplomas are granted in only certain branches of medicine, pharmacy, and the sciences.

To be admitted to a regular degree program, an American student must submit the following documents for "revalidation" or certification by the Spanish Embassy in Washington, which will then forward them to the student's choice of university: (1) a photostat of his high-school or college diploma plus official transcripts, bearing the school seal and the signature of the registrar; (2) catalogues of the schools attended; (3) a birth certificate; (4) a statement of the source and amount of his income while in Spain. Proper presentation of these documents at least four months before the registration period will assure the student's admission. In Spain, as elsewhere, Americans may be admitted with advanced standing if they have attained their B.A. or M.A. degrees. Those with master's degrees are generally permitted to proceed directly toward the *doctorado*.

Students electing to work for a special diploma in Hispanic studies rather than for a regular degree need not submit proof of previous studies. Such students should submit their applications, before August 31, to the Spanish Embassy, Office of Cultural Relations, 1477 Girard Street, N.W., Washington, D.C. 20009. Others may elect to work in the Graduate School of Humanities in Madrid, which offers special courses for foreigners in Spanish language, literature, and culture. Inquiries concerning this nondegree program should be addressed to Graduate School of Humanities, Facultad de Filosofía y Lettras, Ciudad Universitaria de Madrid, Madrid, Spain.

The academic year is divided into semesters, one from early October to mid-February, the other from mid-February to the end of June. Registration for the entire year is accepted only in the fall and must be accomplished in person prior to September 20.

Tuition fees in Spanish universities are nominal (about $50 per year), and the cost of living is approximately $115 per month. Some universities (Madrid, Barcelona, Granada, Salamanca, Santiago de Compostela, Seville, Valencia, Valladolid, Zaragoza) maintain student residences—*Collegios Mayores*—but these are extremely crowded, and the student is well advised to make his reservation early. Other accommodations are available in *pensiones* (boarding houses) and private families. Noteworthy is Madrid's University City, an American-style campus with modern classroom buildings, student residences, and athletic facilities.

For further information, the student should contact the Spanish Embassy in Washington or the Spanish consulates located in major American cities. Another important organization is the Instituto de Cultura Hispánica, Avenida de los Reyes Catolicos, Ciudad Universitaria, Madrid, Spain, which arranges home hospitality, assists students in locating housing, provides introductions to professional societies, and organizes holiday trips.

SWEDEN

University education in Sweden, as in all European countries, consists of professional training for a specific career and is roughly comparable to graduate study in the United States. Academic supervision and guidance are kept to a minimum, and students have great freedom in planning their schedules. While the programs in the technical, medical, and dental schools are rigidly prescribed, students are free to present themselves for their degree examinations whenever they feel adequately prepared.

Sweden has five universities. The University of Lund, founded in 1668, and the University of Uppsala, founded in 1477, are state universities and include the traditional faculties (departments) of law, medicine, philosophy, and theology. The University of Stockholm, founded in 1877, has faculties of law, mathematics and humanities, and natural science. The University of Gothenburg, founded in 1889, offers only two faculties: humanities and medicine. Both Stockholm and Gothenburg are "private" universities, depending only in part on state support. Sweden's newest university, the University of Umeå, was founded in 1963 and includes faculties of medicine, dentistry, natural science, and arts and social science.

Subjects like engineering, architecture, music, and art are not included in the regular university curriculum, but are taught at *högskolan* (roughly comparable to the German and Austrian *Technische Hochschulen*). These institutes enjoy the same status and prestige as the universities: The Royal Institute of Technology at Stockholm (Kungl. Tekniska Högskolan); The Chalmers Institute of Technology at Gothenburg (Chalmers Tekniska Högskolan); The Stockholm School of Economics and Commerce (Handelshögskolan i Stockholm); The Gothenburg School of Economics and Commerce (Handelshögskolan i Göteborg); The Caroline Medico-Surgical Institute at Stockholm (Kungl. Karolinska Mediko-Kirurgiska Institutet); The Institute of Dentistry at Stockholm (Tandläkarhögskolan); The Institute of Dentistry at Malmö (Tandläkarhögskolan); The Institute of Pharmacy at Stockholm (Kungl. Farmaceutiska Institutet); The Institute of Veterinary Science at Stockholm (Kungl. Veterinärhögskolan); The Institute of Agriculture at Uppsala (Kungl. Lantbrukshögskolan); The Institute of Forestry at Stockholm (Kungl. Skogshögskolan); The Royal School of Music at Stockholm (Kungl. Musikhögskolan); and The Royal Academy of Art at Stockholm (Kungl. Konsthögskolan).

Other schools of interest include the Graphic Institute at Stockholm (Grafiska Institutet), which offers courses in printing, typography, and other graphics; The Swedish State School of Arts, Crafts, and Design at Stockholm (Konstfackskolan); The School of Arts and Crafts at Gothenburg (Sjöldföreningens Skola); The Royal Central Gymnastics Institute at Stockholm (Kungl. Gymnastiska Centralinstitutet); and The South Swedish Institute of Physical Therapy at Lund (Sydsvenska Gymnastik-institutet).

Finally, there are two study programs of special interest to Americans:

1. The International Graduate School for English-speaking Students offers, under the auspices of the University of Stockholm, courses in the social and political sciences as well as in Swedish language and literature. For well-qualified graduate students, research facilities are also available in other fields. Students in the social sciences may enroll for a one-year diploma course, and those who remain an additional year are eligible for the Master of Social Science (M.S.Sc.) degree. The school also confers a Master of Arts (M.A.) and a Master of Science (M.Sc.) degree. For further information and application forms, contact the American-Scandinavian Foundation, 140 West 57th Street, New York, N.Y. 10019.

2. As in the case of Denmark, the Scandinavian Seminar sends American groups to Sweden each year for the study of Scandinavian culture. The students selected for this program live for a while in

Swedish homes and then attend one of the Swedish Folk Schools (residential adult-education colleges). Direct all inquiries to the Seminar, % The American-Scandinavian Foundation, 140 West 57th Street, New York, N.Y. 10019.

Swedish universities award three major degrees: the *kandidat* or *magister* degree, granted after from two and one-half to six years of study, depending on the field of specialization; the *licentiat*, which generally requires another three years and the preparation of a thesis; and the doctorate, which demands extensive work beyond the *licentiat* and the preparation of a thesis.

To be admitted, students should apply by letter to the institution of their choice, submitting at the same time such credentials as transcripts, a photostat of their birth certificate, and copies of any degrees earned. As a rule, American students who have completed two years of accredited college work can count on being admitted.

The academic year is divided into semesters, the first lasting from the end of September to late December, the second from January to the end of May.

Tuition at Swedish universities is free, except for special courses, but there are nominal registration fees, student union dues, and examination fees. Students generally make their own housing arrangements, either with families or in boardinghouses. Cut-rate meals are obtainable in student restaurants connected with the universities. In all, the American student should count on a minimum monthly budget of about $175.

For further information, write to The Swedish Institute for Cultural Relations with Foreign Countries, Kungsgatan 42, Stockholm 3, Sweden; the Sverige-Amerika Stiftelsen, Grevturegatan 14, Stockholm, Sweden; or the Sveriges Förenande Studentkärer (Swedish National Union of Students), Aluddsvägen 7, Stockholm K, Sweden.

SWITZERLAND

Switzerland is a confederation of twenty-five member states (cantons) which differ in culture, language, and religion. Within its territory, each canton is sovereign in education on the primary, secondary, and university levels. In fact, the Federal Institute of Technology in Zürich is the only institution of university rank maintained by the federal government.

Though Swiss universities are free from centralized government control, they all have the following characteristics in common. First, they are graduate schools, offering specialized professional courses rather than a curriculum in general education. Second, they offer little or no "campus life"; a Swiss university is a collection of professors, lecture halls, laboratories, libraries, and clinics. Third, the student at a Swiss university lives where he pleases and provides for his own entertainment and social life. His class attendance is optional, and in most courses he is not even given a regular assignment schedule. The student, in other words, is treated as an adult: it is up to him to decide what courses he ought to attend and how much work he needs to do.

Swiss universities seem to hold a particular fascination for foreigners. In fact, some 4,700 of the 16,000 regular full-time students are from abroad, representing more than forty different nationalities. The explanation may be the excellent facilities of a free country that has been spared the ravages of war; the lovely, picturesque, and hospitable surroundings; the relatively low student-teacher ratio, which makes the professor more accessible than at most European universities; and finally, the possibility of writing a thesis not only in German, French, or Italian but also in English and Spanish.

Switzerland has ten institutions of higher learning. In the German-speaking part of the country are the universities of Basel, Bern, and Zürich, the Federal Institute of Technology at Zürich, and the School of Economics and Public Administration at St. Gallen. In French-speaking Switzerland are the universities of Geneva, Lausanne, and Neuchâtel, the Institute of Technology at Lausanne, and the bilingual University of Fribourg. There is no university in the Italian-speaking part of Switzerland.

Though different in many respects, these universities have basically the same structure. They are divided into faculties (departments): theology (Roman Catholic at Fribourg and Protestant in the other universities); law (jurisprudence, political economy, and sociology); arts (philosophy, history, and linguistics); science (mathematics, natural science, and physical science); and medicine. The universities of Fribourg and Neuchâtel have no faculty of medicine, while the universities of Bern and Zürich have a faculty of veterinary science as well as a faculty of medicine. Some of the universities have specialized institutes (dentistry, pharmacy, and so on) attached to their faculties.

The two institutes of technology, like the German and Austrian *Technische Hochschulen,* give courses in all branches of technology and engineering. The school at St. Gallen prepares students for responsible positions in industry, commerce, and government service.

Swiss universities award two degrees: the doctorate and the licentiate. These are granted after seven or eight semesters of study (thirteen for medicine), but the student admitted with advanced standing may complete the requirements in less time. Generally, the universities in German Switzerland grant only the doctorate, while the universities in French Switzerland grant both degrees. The institutes of technology at Lausanne and Zürich award a diploma in engineering (civil, mechanical, electrical, and others) as well as a doctorate in technology. The School of Economics at St. Gallen awards both a licentiate and a doctorate in economic or administrative science.

The academic year is divided into semesters: the winter semester from mid-October to the beginning of March, the summer semester from mid-April to mid-July. There are many summer sessions for foreigners.

To be admitted to a regular degree program at a Swiss university, the applicant must be at least eighteen years old, with a Swiss high-school diploma (maturity degree) or its foreign equivalent. An American applicant is sure to be admitted if he has a B.A. or B.S. degree and may be admitted (at the University of Geneva, for example) if he has finished his sophomore year at an accredited college. Applications for admission should be submitted to the registrar of the university before September 15 for the winter semester and before March 1 for the summer semester. They should be accompanied by a curriculum vitae, a certified copy (or photostat) of the student's college transcripts and/or degrees, and his birth certificate. At registration, the student must also present a "certificate of good character" and a passport (or other proof of identity). Finally, he must register with the local Aliens' Police and, if he expects to stay in the country more than three months, apply for a "Permit of Residence."

Study in Switzerland is more expensive than in most European countries, but less than at most American state universities. Matriculation, tuition, and incidental fees (including health insurance) amount to approximately $200 per academic year, depending on the university and the course of study selected. The cost of room and board, either in a pension or with a private family, comes to about $150 per month. (At Fribourg, Geneva, and Zürich, the student may live in a hostel; and at Basel, Bern, Geneva, Neuchâtel, and Zürich he can eat in special student restaurants.) The single student should plan on a minimum of $2,000 a year—and the married student on $3,200—to cover tuition, maintenance, and incidentals. "Working one's way through college" is out of the question for foreign students, since they cannot count on outside jobs to supplement their financial resources.

The Central Office of Swiss Universities (Beckenhofstrasse 31, 8035 Zürich) provides information on admission requirements and course offerings at different institutions of higher learning and also arranges for student and teacher exchanges. Editions Leemann A. G. (Postfach Zürich 34) publishes the *Almanach Universitaire Suisse,* which contains a synopsis of all courses and curricula in Swiss universities. The Swiss National Tourist Office (608 Fifth Avenue, New York, N.Y. 10020) regularly issues, and makes available upon request, a list of housing accommodations for students. Finally, the secretariat of each institution stands ready to answer specialized inquiries concerning academic or personal matters.

Latin America

Latin America consists of twenty countries, each with its unique history, characteristics, and traditions. While it is therefore difficult to generalize, it is still possible to speak of the Latin American countries as a group and to point out salient differences between their educational system and our own. And here the striking fact is that the two systems are almost completely different—in organization, administration, financial support, equipment, instruction, examinations, aims, and traditions.

First, with the exception of some church, municipal, and private institutions, most Latin American universities are established by the state. Their courses and curricula are so rigidly prescribed by law that until recently many universities have not even bothered to issue catalogues listing their courses. Like European universities, Latin American institutions have also been disinclined to introduce major modifications in curriculum in response to changing economic and social conditions.

Also, like their European counterparts, Latin American universities usually do not offer the kind of general survey courses found in North American liberal arts colleges. (However, some have recently inaugurated a "common basic year" of introductory core courses in cultural subjects—the University of Costa Rica and the University of San Marcos in Peru, for example.) Most Latin American institutions assume that their students have received an adequate cultural background during their secondary-school studies and therefore most generally enroll the entering student immediately in a program of strictly prescribed, required, and specialized courses leading to a professional degree. There are few, if any, electives and few nonprofessional courses. In this sense, the Latin American university is much more akin to a United States law school or medical school than to one of our undergraduate colleges.

Another noteworthy difference is the fact that the academic year in Latin American countries rarely coincides with that in the United States. In the countries south of the equator—Argentina, Bolivia, Brazil, Chile, Paraguay, Peru, and Uruguay—the seasons are the reverse of those in the United States, and the academic year therefore runs from March (or April) to November (or December). In countries north of the equator, the academic calendars are adjusted not only to seasonal but to climatic differences as well, often within the same country. Thus, most Ecuadorian institutions operate from October to June, but the university in the port city of Guayaquil opens in May and closes in December. In Colombia, most universities operate from February to November, but the two universities in the southeast (Cauca and Nariño) open in October and close in June. In Mexico, the institutions in the central and southern highlands run from March to December, while those in the northern and coastal areas run from September to June. In Venezuela and the Caribbean island republics (Cuba, Haiti, and the Dominican Republic), the academic calendar corresponds roughly to that in the United States.

In most Latin American universities, instruction is largely entrusted to practitioners in the various professions and arts who serve as adjunct professors or lecturers. The number of full-time professors is relatively small. Moreover, classes are usually held in the evening, so that both students and teachers may be gainfully employed by day. Finally, for both traditional and economic reasons, instruction is largely by lecture and demonstration, even in the sciences and engineering. Compared to most United States institutions, Latin American universities are severely circumscribed in their operations by a shortage of textbooks, laboratories, library facilities, and permanent full-time staff.

With respect to university class attendance, examinations, and degrees, Latin America resembles Europe much more than the United States. Class attendance is optional, and the student's grades typically depend on year-end examinations in each of the subjects for which he has enrolled. In addition, after passing all the courses required by the curriculum and submitting an appropriate thesis, the student must take a comprehensive examination for his degree administered by a specially appointed board of examiners or "jury." The degree examination may be written, oral, or practical and covers not only the candidate's professional competence but the content and conclusions of his thesis. Noteworthy in this connection is the fact that the thesis requirement in Latin American universities is practically universal for all university-level degrees and is not confined to postgraduate degrees alone.

The degree most commonly granted by Latin American universities is the *licenciado*. (In Brazil, this degree is known as the *bacharel*, and in Peru as the *bachiller*.)* On the average, it takes five years to complete this degree. In most countries, the holders of the *licenciado* may obtain a doctorate upon presentation of a thesis and examination. In a few instances, one or two years of postgraduate study are required for the doctorate, and at least one institution (National University of Mexico) has introduced an intermediate degree of *maestro* between the *licenciado* and the doctorate.

Needless to say, there are exceptions to these generalizations. In

---

* In most Latin American countries, the *bachiller* is a secondary-school diploma roughly analogous to the French *baccalauréat* and the German *Abitur*. The two exceptions are Brazil and Peru, where it is a university-level degree. In these countries the secondary-school diplomas are known as the *certificado de curso secundario* and the *certificado oficial de educación secundaria*, respectively.

a few countries and a few fields (particularly law), the only degree conferred is the doctorate, in which case it is equivalent to the *licenciado*. In many countries, the degree of *maestro* is an undergraduate degree in education equivalent to the *licenciado*. Some institutions, instead of conferring the *licenciado* or doctorate, award a professional title, such as engineer, agronomist, or architect. Finally, many Latin Ameican universities also operate schools which are below university rank and grant the degree of *bachiller*. The *bachiller* granted by these schools is no more than a high-school diploma, even though it bears the imprint of a university, and is not to be confused with the *licenciado* or the United States bachelor's degree.

To be admitted as a regular degree candidate to a Latin American university, the student from the United States must meet the same requirements as the high-school graduates of the country concerned. And this is not always easy, because Latin American high schools generally have more stringent curricula—including, for example, at least three (and more often five) years each of natural science, social science, mathematics, and foreign languages, as well as elements of astronomy, geology, and mineralogy, philosophy, ancient and medieval history, and national and world history. This means that before being admitted to degree candidacy, the United States applicant is frequently required to complete special courses or examinations, or both, in subjects included in the national secondary curriculum but not even given in United States high schools.

The United States student who wants to transfer to a Latin American university after two or three years of college encounters similar complications. Since most of the courses he has taken as an undergraduate are "cultural" or "liberal arts" background courses, rather than the specialized professional courses offered in Latin American universities, he is not likely to receive many credits for past work or to be accorded very advanced standing.

The United States student may, therefore, be well advised to take one of the following alternatives. He may enroll as a special student and attend selected courses in the hope of transferring the credits so earned to his home university, thus continuing normal progress toward his United States degree. (This may be especially advantageous to the undergraduate specializing in Latin

American area studies.) Or, the student may wait until he has completed his undergraduate degree and then enroll in a Latin American university for graduate work. In this case, he will find that Latin American universities will usually accept the United States bachelor's degree as a prerequisite for admission to their own graduate program.

In any event, the importance of having a firm command of the national language cannot be overemphasized—Portuguese in Brazil, French in Haiti, and Spanish in the remainder of Latin America. In many universities, knowledge of the national language has been formally established as a prerequisite to the admission of foreign students, who are required to pass a proficiency examination in the language before being admitted.

Fees charged by Latin American universities, though they vary among countries and among institutions, are in the main nominal. (The University of the Republic, Montevideo, Uruguay, not atypical, charges no tuition at all.) Occasionally foreign students are required to pay higher tuition, somewhat like the out-of-state fees charged by our own state universities. Rarely are dormitory facilities maintained by the university, and where they exist at all, they are generally reserved for out-of-town students who are citizens of the country in question. Typically, Latin American university students live in private homes or boardinghouses and must find such accommodations with little or no help from the university. Living costs, with the exception of a few countries, are noticeably lower than in the United States. For more precise information on costs in particular Latin American countries, consult the pamphlets in the American Republics Series, available from the Office of Publications Services, Pan American Union, Washington, D.C. 20006.

Specific information on university education in Latin America can be obtained from the Documentation and Information Service, Division of Education, Pan American Union, Washington, D.C. 20006, which maintains an exhaustive documentation file and serves as a clearinghouse for detailed information on Latin American universities. This office will answer specific inquiries concerning particular countries, universities, courses of study, admission requirements, degrees offered, and so forth. Inquiries should specify the field of study in which the student is interested, his academic level, and the country in which he plans to study.

Information on financial aid may be obtained from the Exchange of Persons Service, Department of Technical Cooperation, Pan American Union, Washington, D.C. 20006, which publishes two bulletins on the subject. The first, *Fellowships and Loans of the Organization of American States for Study Abroad,* issued yearly and available free of charge, lists and describes all financial assistance available from the Organization of American States. The second, *Exchange of Persons,* issued twice a year and available at nominal cost, contains news notes and descriptions of scholarships offered by public and private organizations.

Canada

Although university education in Canada dates back to the founding of the University of King's College, Nova Scotia, in 1789, most Canadian universities were established during the nineteenth century. In western Canada, university development has taken place almost entirely during the twentieth century.

In Canada, as in the United States, the term "university" is used rather loosely. It may be applied to small undergraduate colleges with fewer than three hundred students or to large and complex organizations like Toronto (which includes both federated universities and affiliated colleges) and Laval (which includes more than fifty affiliated institutions). In general, however, Canadian universities fall into three categories. First, there are institutions legally controlled by or connected with a religious group, such as Laval and Montreal (Roman Catholic), King's and Bishop's (Church of England), and Mount Allison (United Church of Canada). Second, there are essentially provincial universities with varying degrees of state control, such as New Brunswick, Toronto, and Alberta; these are roughly analogous to our state universities. Third, there are independent institutions supported by endowments and gifts, usually with some additional government aid, such as McGill, Queen's, and Sir George Williams.

While higher education in Canada has developed a pattern and character of its own, it has nevertheless been influenced strongly by the French, British, and United States systems. In the French-speaking provinces, university education is a replica of the French model; the universities offer the typical French degrees of *licence* and *doctorat*. The British influence can be seen in the collection of "colleges" within the same university and the provision for specialized undergraduate study leading to the "honors" degree (in most cases requiring superior grades and an extra year of study). The United States influence explains the existence of private, semiprivate, and state universities and the development of graduate schools. In Canada, as in the United States, education is not the federal government's responsibility, and there is no centralized Ministry of Education exercising control over Canadian higher education.

The names and locations of Canadian universities are as follows:
Acadia (Wolfville, Nova Scotia)
Alberta (Edmonton, Alberta)
Bishop's (Lennoxville, Quebec)
British Columbia (Vancouver, British Columbia)
Brock (St. Catherines, Ontario)
Calgary (Calgary, Alberta)
Carleton (Ottawa, Ontario)
Dalhousie (Halifax, Nova Scotia)
Guelph (Guelph, Ontario)
University of King's College (Halifax, Nova Scotia)
Lakehead (Port Arthur, Ontario)
Laurentian (Sudbury, Ontario)
Laval (Quebec, Quebec)
McGill (Montreal, Quebec)
McMaster (Hamilton, Ontario)
Manitoba (Winnipeg, Manitoba)
Moncton (Moncton, New Brunswick)
Memorial University of Newfoundland (St. John's, Newfoundland)
Montreal (Montreal, Quebec)
Mount Allison (Sackville, New Brunswick)
Mount St. Vincent College (Halifax, Nova Scotia)
Notre Dame (Nelson, British Columbia)
New Brunswick (Fredericton, New Brunswick)
Nova Scotia Technological College (Halifax, Nova Scotia)
Nova Scotia Technical College (Halifax, Nova Scotia)

Osgoode Hall Law School (Toronto, Ontario)
Ottawa (Ottawa, Ontario)
Prince of Wales College (Charlottetown, Prince Edward Island)
Queen's (Kingston, Ontario)
Royal Military College (Kingston, Ontario)
Collège Ste. Anne (Church Point, Nova Scotia)
St. Dunstan's College (Charlottetown, Prince Edward Island)
St. Francis Xavier (Antigonish, Nova Scotia)
St. Mary's (Halifax, Nova Scotia)
Saskatchewan (Saskatoon, Saskatchewan)
Sherbrooke (Sherbrooke, Quebec)
Simon Fraser (Burnaby, British Columbia)
Sir George Williams College (Montreal, Quebec)
Toronto (Toronto, Ontario)
Trent (Peterborough, Ontario)
Victoria (Victoria, British Columbia)
Waterloo (Waterloo, Ontario)
Waterloo Lutheran (Waterloo, Ontario)
Western Ontario (London, Ontario)
Windsor (Windsor, Ontario)
York (Toronto, Ontario)

In addition, the following institutions are federated with the University of Toronto: St. Michael's College, University of Trinity College, and Victoria University.

The major degrees granted in the English-speaking universities generally follow the British pattern (see United Kingdom). In the French-speaking universities, the major degrees are the *licence* and the *doctorat* (see France).

The academic year runs from September to May, and students are admitted only in the fall.

The language of instruction varies from university to university. In most the official language is English; but at Laval, Sherbrooke, and Montreal, it is French, and at Ottawa, Collège Ste. Anne, and St. Joseph's, both English and French.

To be admitted, the student should write directly to the registrar of the university of his choice. The admissions procedure is roughly the same as in the United States. Tuition fees vary from about $300 to $750 per year, depending on the university and the course of study. (In law and medicine, tuition is higher.) Housing at many universities is provided in residence halls. The cost of living is approximately the same as in the United States.

Iceland

Higher education in Iceland is, for the most part, patterned after the Danish system. The University of Iceland, located in Reykjavik and founded in 1911, includes the usual faculties (departments): theology, medicine, law and economics, philosophy, and engineering. The university also maintains research laboratories in veterinary medicine, in bacteriology and pathology, and in subjects related to Icelandic industries. Each of the faculties grants a "candidate's degree" (see Denmark) which requires from five to eight years of study, depending on the field.

Tuition at the university is free, and only nominal registration and examination fees are imposed. Students may enroll for either the fall semester (mid-September to the end of January) or the spring semester (early February to mid-June). Academic and personal questions about study in Iceland should be directed to Islenzk-Ameriska Felagid, Hafnarstraeti 19, Reykjavik. A word of caution: all instruction is in Icelandic.

Israel

Higher education in Israel is a mixture of the British and American systems. For the most part, the universities are private establishments deriving their income from tuition, endowments, and contributions (both local and foreign). In recent years, however, the central government has supported the construction of university buildings with substantial grants from the Ministry of Education and Culture, and the city of Tel Aviv has founded a municipal university, with faculties of humanities, law, medical education, sciences, and social sciences. In spite of this aid from the state, the universities are autonomous—being governed by boards of trustees composed of laymen (many of whom are leaders in the Jewish community abroad) and by academic councils composed of members elected by the faculty. There is no centralized authority controlling higher education.

The Hebrew University of Jerusalem opened in 1925. Located

on Mount Scopus (where, eighteen centuries before, Titus commanded the Roman hordes sacking the Holy City), it offers undergraduate and graduate work in science, social sciences, humanities, medicine, dentistry, law, and agriculture. After the partition of Jerusalem in 1948, the university had to be moved from Mount Scopus and was re-established on a new central campus at Givat Ram. Following the Arab-Israeli war of 1967, the Mount Scopus Campus returned to Israeli hands, and some sections of the university are now operating there. The university offers a special one-year course for American students at both the graduate and undergraduate level. The University Institute of Haifa is under the supervision of the Hebrew University.

The Technion, located on the slopes of Mount Carmel near Haifa and overlooking the Mediterranean, is an institute of technology patterned after the German *Technishche Hochschulen*. It specializes in all branches of engineering, but also has faculties of science, architecture, and humanities.

Bar-Ilan University, founded in 1955 and located at Ramat Gan, is patterned after American universities. However, it has a religious orientation, seeking to achieve a synthesis between general and social knowledge, science and faith. The university has four departments: Jewish studies, humanities and social sciences, languages and literature, and natural sciences and mathematics. Every student is required, regardless of his field of specialization, to take courses in the Jewish studies division. Since the university has as a special aim the promotion of closer ties between Jewish youth abroad and the state of Israel, many scholarships are offered, including some for students at the Teachers Institute of Yeshiva University in New York. The university is supported by the American Committee for Bar-Ilan University and is governed by its board of trustees in New York.

The Weizmann Institute of Science at Rehovot is primarily devoted to postgraduate and postdoctoral research in applied mathematics, nuclear physics, electronics, X-ray crystallography, isotopes, polymers, biophysics, organic chemistry, and experimental biology. The Institute also offers courses leading to the doctorate in these fields.

The academic year runs from late October to July and the language of instruction is Hebrew.

The major university degrees in Israel are the bachelor's, the master's, and the doctorate. The bachelor's degree requires at least three years of work (four at the Technion), the master's an additional one or two years, and the doctorate at least two years beyond the master's. The medical degree takes six years, and the degree of *Ingenieur* (engineer) a year of professional experience and the completion of a project after the bachelor's degree.

To be admitted, the student should contact the registrar of the university in question. (The Technion and Bar-Ilan University require candidates to pass an entrance examination.) Applications for the special one-year course for American students at the Hebrew University should be sent to American Friends of the Hebrew University, 11 East 69th Street, New York, N.Y. 10021.

Tuition at most Israeli universities is about $225 per year, and the cost of living approximately $150 per month. The Hebrew University, Bar-Ilan, and the Technion can accommodate some students in dormitories; but most students must make their own arrangements for housing off campus.

CHAPTER 7

Approaches to Foreign Study

The tutorial system . . . foreigners are commonly offered special (and easier) programs . . . there are even some English-only courses . . . annual fellowship and scholarship programs . . . interuniversity exchanges . . . junior-year-abroad programs (including a detailed look at Sweet Briar's Junior Year in France) . . . overseas branches of American universities

John Smith enters the hall and slips shyly into an aisle seat. He opens his new notebook, uncaps his pen, and looks about. The rows of banked seats are rapidly filling. There is a hum of conversation in the air, a scraping of chairs, a shuffling of papers. All the sounds are familiar enough, but John is tense with expectation. His first class at a foreign university is about to begin. He is here on his own, for an entire year.

Suddenly the door opens, and the professor enters. Instantly the students leap to their feet. The professor strides to the podium, opens his brief case, and extracts a sheaf of papers. The students sit again and are silent. Then the professor clears his throat and begins to read his lecture.

John listens intently, pen poised. The hour passes. The professor gathers his papers, stuffs them back into his brief case, and marches from the room. Gradually the students collect their belongings and drift out. John remains in his seat, pen in hand. The page before him is blank.

John is no dolt, and his knowledge of the language and the subject is good. But he has gained little or nothing from the lecture. The professor spoke more rapidly than John had expected he would and sometimes not as clearly as John would have liked. Furthermore, the subject of his discourse was anything but simple. Time and again John noticed the young local student on his left frowning intently in a concentrated effort to grasp the full meaning of what was being said. After fifteen minutes John had a violent headache. When he did understand a few sentences and tried to note them on his pad, he was dismayed to discover that he could not do so. The moment he attempted to translate the thought into English, he lost the thread of the professor's lecture; and when he picked it up again, he couldn't remember just what he'd wanted to record. It was, all in all, a harrowing experience. As he left the hall, John wished he had never decided to study abroad.

John Smith is an imaginary character. You can think of him as a teacher in his fifties, seeking a master's degree, or as a twenty-year-old undergraduate. You can consider him an American in Paris or in Bonn. No matter; thousands of students and scholars abroad go through experiences somewhat like his. Those who are persistent enough, intelligent enough, and proficient enough in the second language may sooner or later reach the point where they can understand and profit from regular university classes. John Smith's ear will very likely become accustomed to the speed, accent, and inflection of native speech; he will probably master the special vocabularies of various subjects in a few weeks. He may quickly find the knack of taking notes in a foreign language.

Then again, he may not. And therefore, for reasons both good and bad, to be applauded or deplored, there are a fairly wide variety of special arrangements whereby an American like John Smith can study abroad.

A Tutor Makes Things Easier

One way—indeed, the very best way—to deal with the problem of language and context is to work with a native tutor who knows the subject and has already attended the course in question. If the student can meet with such a person each week, discuss the lecture, ask questions, and consult about readings in the field, many handicaps can be overcome. Even a native student would profit from such help, of course, and but for the cost this approach would probably be widely used in all universities of the "European" type.

For Americans, however, the tutorial system has still other important advantages. The tutor can provide background information missing in the usually narrow lectures. He can also test the student periodically, thus establishing a concrete record which the student can show to a university at home in order to get academic credits for his overseas work. For these reasons, American colleges that operate programs in foreign universities nearly always employ such tutors. Usually the tutor meets with a group rather than with an individual, and then the discussions provide excellent language training as well as a better understanding of the subject matter.

A second arrangement that can be adopted if one wants to study in a foreign university, but is somewhat shaky in the language of the country, is to take part in one of the special programs offered to foreigners by the universities themselves. Usually (not always) these deal only with the local language and culture and are frequently given at many levels. Some language courses are intended for what the French call *débutants* (beginners); others are designed for high-school language teachers and other specialists who are trying to improve their accents or study the fine points of grammar and phonetics. The instructors, aware that they are working with foreigners, speak slowly and try to use uncomplicated expressions, or they follow a necessarily complex phrase with a simple, explanatory one. When a difficult technical term must be used, most will repeat it or write it on the blackboard. They tend to assume less knowledge on their students' part and to provide more general information in their lectures. Then, too, the student body in these programs can be extremely interesting and stimulating, since students come to them from all over the world. And since most or all are strangers to the host country, they are more likely to seek friends, respond to social advances, and participate in the organized extracurricular activities sometimes added to the schedules. At the same time, these programs are an integral part of the regular educational system, and the student is truly participating in a foreign educational experience.

The Goals May Be Set Lower

Inevitably, the intellectual level of special university courses for foreigners is seldom as high as that maintained in the regular university offerings. When they deal with students whose understanding of the language is limited, teachers generally tend to lower their sights. In cases where grades are awarded, examiners perhaps too readily make allowances for inaccurate and ineffectively expressed papers. Entrance requirements are frequently low or even non-existent. Foreign universities simply do not consider elementary or intermediate language instruction to be a legitimate branch of *higher* education, and their attitude toward these language courses is occasionally carried over into others dealing with local history and culture.

Fortunately, the trend in most of these institutes for foreign students appears to be in the direction of higher academic standards. When the first edition of our *Guide* was published in 1962 it contained the following imaginary monologue purporting to depict the prevailing attitude of the leaders of French-sponsored programs:

> How delightful it is for students from all over the world to study with us here in France! They meet so many interesting people, and surely they learn something about our language and our magnificent culture. But—is it necessary to take them very seriously? (They speak French, if at all, with *such* atrocious accents!) We'll put them in a special course by themselves, and when it is over, if they have attended conscientiously, and perhaps—why not? . . . even if they do not!—we might arrange a *certificat de présence* or a small diploma.

As a generalization of the current situation, this statement would be unfair; nearly everywhere officials who run these programs take their academic obligations seriously. The quality of the instruction is high, the size of the language classes, especially at the elementary level, is small, and reasonable efforts are made to see that entrance standards are maintained and that the students apply themselves to their work. The *certificat de présence* remains, but more meaningful diplomas exist for those who are willing to earn them.

Nevertheless, it must be emphasized that a course for foreign students at any university is not to be compared intellectually with the regular university program.

In Paris, for example, the Cours de Civilisation Française à la Sorbonne is, as the title suggests, technically part of the Sorbonne, but it is not to be confused with the Faculté des Lettres of the Sorbonne which offers courses in parallel subjects. The Cours was organized after World War II primarily because Paris was crowded with foreign soldiers who "wanted to pick up a little French culture." It proved an admirable vehicle for accomplishing this worthy purpose, but as an institution of higher education it has, as one French official put it, no connection *(rien à faire)* with the Faculté des Lettres, one of the world's great centers of learning. Essentially it is a language school, one that also offers lectures in French culture and civilization, some of them delivered by first-rate scholars; but it is not "the Sorbonne" as that term is normally used by knowledgeable persons. The temptation that leads both American students who have studied at the Cours and some of the French teachers and officials connected with it to blur the distinction is understandable, but unfortunate. The situation is similar elsewhere. When one encounters a young American undergraduate who says that he has just returned from a year's study at the University of Munich, or Madrid, or Florence, keep in mind that he is probably talking about a special program for foreigners at these universities, something basically different from what study at such an institution means for local nationals working for regular degrees.

Foreign nations offer these programs in large measure because they consider the impact of society upon the visiting student more important than the impact of the classroom. Edouard Morot-Sir, of the French Embassy in the United States, in discussing his country's courses for foreigners, points out that students attending them "will return home with new friendships and a broader understanding of the world we live in." He says nothing about the academic achievements such students are expected to make; and this is perfectly justifiable, so long as the student approaches the program in the same spirit and with the same objectives.

Custom-Tailored for Americans

Some American college officials, feeling that locally offered programs are unsuited to the needs of their students, have set up special courses of their own overseas. Suppose, for example, that a college wants to send a group of its junior-year Spanish majors to Spain. What an opportunity, the American college authorities reason, to speed the development of aural comprehension and oral facility! And how wonderful for their undergraduates to be able to study Spanish history on the soil where it was made, to learn to appreciate Spanish art by working in the Prado, repository of the greatest collection of Spanish masterpieces in the world! But the regular students at the University of Madrid naturally need no junior-year courses in their own language, and they mastered the fundamentals of their own history and culture back in secondary school; consequently the University of Madrid quite logically does not offer language courses or "survey" courses in Spanish history, literature, or art in its regular program. Americans, therefore, rent classroom space in the city and seek out qualified Spanish instructors willing to teach the courses they feel are needed. These special classes are taught in Spanish, but in the American manner. There is usually some discussion; the students write reports and term papers; and regular examinations are given.

There are many important advantages to this type of instruction for American students abroad. The teacher is native to the country and is very likely able to impart the subtle quality of his particular culture even when teaching by "American" methods. He speaks clearly and slowly, always on the lookout for the frowns that indicate a lack of understanding, and yet his accent is authentic and his language idiomatic. Ideally, the student gets a type of instruction that combines the magisterial approach of the foreign professor with the intimacy and informality of the American. The home college has general control over subject matter (which need not be confined to language) and academic standards. It can state with some confidence that a student completing a course has earned a certain number of credits with a particular grade. The student gains the benefits of living and working in a foreign land, of being taught by native instructors, with a minimum of disruption to his established study habits.

But this type of arrangement has certain weaknesses, too. The situation, to begin with, is artificial. Most students who go abroad want to study under actual foreign conditions, not in a special "hothouse" environment. Often foreign educators and students either look down on these programs or are insulted by the idea that their own institutions are not considered suitable for visitors. (Imagine how Americans would feel if a group of Swedish students suddenly arrived in Cambridge, Massachusetts, and tried to hire a Harvard professor to give them a course—according to their own specifications —in American history!) And so it is sometimes difficult to get qualified people to teach these courses in the "proper" manner; and further, because they themselves never experienced the kind of instruction expected, many foreign teachers simply deliver their regular lectures to the group. Others have great difficulty in fixing on the level at which the courses should be pitched.

Finally, these special classes tend to isolate the American students from local university life, herding them together, whereas to achieve maximum benefits from their foreign experience they ought to be kept apart from each other, thrown on their own, encouraged to make contacts with local people. Fortunately the sponsors of these programs are aware of this danger, and they try, often with a considerable degree of success, to compensate for it.

All You Need to Know Is Your Own Language

All the aforementioned educational plans employ native instructors teaching in the language of the country, but of late there has been an increasing movement to develop classes in foreign countries in which the instruction is in English. At present such classes are offered in France, Germany, Italy, Spain, Mexico, Holland, Denmark, Norway, Sweden, Japan, and perhaps several other nations.

Much can be said in behalf of this idea. After all, thousands of American college students have not studied a modern foreign language, while others have had only a smattering of training. Some know how to *read* a second language, but have difficulty in speaking it or comprehending it outside the classroom. Yet all may want the experience of living and studying in a foreign environment, and certainly they can profit from doing so, although generally not as much as those who understand the local tongue.

In a few cases, chiefly in the Low Countries and Scandinavia (where most educated people know English), the academic authorities regularly offer foreigners programs delivered in the English language. These usually deal with national history and culture and are combined with intensive work in the local language. The method of instruction is that of the host country, which usually means large lectures except in language classes.

Other programs have been constructed on what we might call the "American plan," where a foreign, English-speaking faculty, aided by an occasional visiting American, provides a series of courses complete with discussion groups, examinations, and credits to be taken back home at the end of the year. A few American colleges have even established branches abroad, sending members of their own faculties over to teach courses taken directly from the home-college catalogue.

The sponsors of most such programs argue that a student abroad can "absorb" a foreign culture without knowing the language and that the nonacademic benefits of study abroad are in themselves sufficient to justify sending students away from the home campus for extended periods. They also declare persuasively that education is difficult enough when the instructor and pupil understand each other perfectly. How foolish then, they say, to make it still more difficult by placing the barrier of an unfamiliar or imperfectly mastered language between them. The difficulty, of course, is that these programs are quite far removed from the local educational system. "This really isn't the University of Oslo," an American studying in the University of Oslo International Summer School points out—despite the fact that she lives in a university dormitory, eats in the university restaurant, and attends lectures in university buildings.

The Whole Spectrum—Take Your Choice

To choose from among the many different plans available, the prospective student must consider both his needs and his abilities. The closer his foreign educational experience approximates that of regular university students in the country he is visiting, the nearer he will come to knowing that country, its people, and its educational philosophy. The closer his training approximates that provided in America, the easier the transition and the greater the assurance that his progress toward an American degree will be maintained. Phrased negatively, the foreign university is hard to adjust to, but the American-type program is potentially less rewarding. For most American students, the best solution can only be determined after a careful weighing of alternatives and by reconciling contradictory aims. There is, in other words, no one best way for all who wish to study abroad.

Educators, recognizing this truth, have established many kinds of special programs employing these various arrangements in different combinations. Let us look at the most common types—other than enrollment as a regular student at a foreign university—that are currently available to Americans.

1. *Annual Fellowship and Scholarship Programs.* These, of which the Fulbright and Rhodes scholarships may be considered typical, are usually for graduate students and will be dealt with only briefly in these pages. Participants either enroll in foreign universities or study abroad independently. The students are invited (or at least expected), and can therefore be sure that some organized effort is being made to ease their adjustment to the foreign environment. As we shall see, there are organizations everywhere eager to provide aid and comfort to Americans studying abroad independently. The independent student must seek this help out for himself; scholarship and fellowship winners have it thrust upon them. This, however, is the only special advantage for such students.

2. *Interuniversity Exchanges.* A large number of American colleges and universities maintain ties with "sister" institutions overseas. Students from American university X go to foreign university Y; and in turn, students from Y come to X, in each case usually for one academic year. Without exception these programs operate on a very small scale, generally with only one American and one foreign student a year exchanged. Seldom are more than five or six students involved at one time.

Although they are expected to attend the regular university lectures, American students in these exchanges benefit from a certain amount of special attention. Often, highly prized space is found for them in student dormitories, thus providing clean and economical quarters and the chance to get to know other students easily and naturally. At least one local professor or administrator will be cognizant of their existence and perhaps offer friendship and guidance. And usually the home university assures the student in advance that his work abroad will be counted toward his American degree, although, as one American administrator admits, this is frequently done "pretty much on faith."

If a student knows the language well enough to follow the lectures, this is a magnificent way to study abroad. But although the number is growing, there are not enough of these exchange arrangements to take care of more than a tiny fraction of our students who are interested in participating.

3. *"Junior Year Abroad."* This is the best-known of the overseas

programs for undergraduates. It is rather difficult to generalize because there are so many varieties, but all such programs have most of the following characteristics: In September a group, commonly composed of third-year students from one or more institutions, is sent overseas to study in some university city. After an intensive period of language drill, usually lasting about six weeks, academic work is divided between attendance at the regular university lectures and at special classes organized by the sponsor, but taught in the local language by native scholars. For each university course attended, the student ordinarily takes an additional hour a week with a native tutor. The special classes are small and are conducted in the American manner. While abroad the students live either with private families (this is considered the most desirable arrangement), in student dormitories, or in rooming houses or hotels if no better facilities can be found. Invariably the sponsoring institution assumes responsibility for finding and supervising these housing arrangements, and general direction of the overseas program is in the hands of an American professor, who sometimes has a local assistant.

At the end of the academic year, the student returns home with thirty credits in specific subjects and with grades that are recognized by the sponsoring college and therefore can be transferred to other American institutions without difficulty. Some academic-year programs, however, are managed by organizations other than American institutions of higher learning, and some even have classes conducted in English only. Students who wish to participate in these programs should make sure before doing so that their home institutions will accept the credits thus earned.

For the benefit of students interested in participating in a junior-year group, Professor R. John Matthew, Director of the important Sweet Briar Junior Year in France Program, has prepared for this book the following description of a typical student's experiences in his program:

Upon request for information concerning the Sweet Briar Junior Year in France, the student (who must be enrolled in an accredited four-year college or university) receives a bulletin explaining the program and an application blank. He must execute the application in accordance with instructions as stated therein and must be recommended by the chairman of the French or language department, the chairman of his major department if he is not a French major, and the Dean of his college. A statement that he is in good health and able to carry on an academic program abroad must be submitted by his college or family doctor. The application, accompanied by a transcript of the student's college record through the first semester of his sophomore year, is forwarded to the Virginia office of the Junior Year in France for processing, with a deadline of March 15.

If his application is approved, the student receives notification of his admission into the program as soon as possible thereafter. Upon payment of the initial fee he is sent, in due course throughout the spring and summer, up to sailing date (approximately September 1), a number of information sheets telling about the group of which he is a member, the preparations he should make before sailing, and giving advice and information on the year abroad. Among these are questions he must answer concerning living arrangements with French families for the year, advice as to securing his passport and visa. A visa is needed in France for all persons who are to remain more than three months.

A few days before sailing, temporary headquarters are set up in New York, where participants and their families may come for last-minute details and information needed for embarking. The day before sailing there is a reception in the headquarters hotel, where participants and parents may meet and become acquainted. The Assistant to the Professor-in-charge meets the students during this period and sails with them. During the crossing she has conferences with every student concerning living arrangements with French families in the provincial city of Tours, to which the students go for the six-weeks preliminary session. Also there are daily orientation meetings for the group on board. The orientation lectures concern all aspects of life in France, and opportunity is given for questions and answers.

Upon arrival in Fance, students are met by buses which take them to Tours, after a night in Caen and lunch the following day in Le Mans. In Tours each student is met by some member of his French family who takes him for his first night to what will be his home for the next six weeks. The next day a placement test is given to all students in the group and, based on the results of the test, students are placed in more or less homogeneous sections so far as linguistic ability is concerned. Classes begin the following day on an intensive basis and continue for six weeks, involving as many phases of language learning as possible, to enable the student to enter more efficiently the French university system. In Tours, the instructors are all native Frenchmen under the academic jurisdiction of either Tours or Poitiers. During the preliminary session, numerous lectures are given concerning contemporary institutions in France. A few excursions are arranged for the group as a whole to visit the château country but, much more important, the students travel about the countryside in small groups of two or three on bicycles, which can be obtained locally.

During this period, the Assistant again meets with every student to work out living arrangements with French families for the academic year in Paris. Also, the Professor-in-charge, who has met the students on their arrival in France, has a conference in Tours with every student concerning his academic program in Paris. In supervising the preliminary session he has learned a great deal about the students, not only by meeting and talking with them, but by learning about them from their instructors. A fairly complete program of courses is established for each student before he arrives in Paris. Toward the end of the six-weeks period, the students organize a "Fête d'Adieu" for their French families and the local government officials who have had receptions for them during their stay, especially the Mayor of Tours and the provincial governor.

When the six weeks are over, the students leave for Paris, stopping this time at Chartres for lunch, which gives them an opportunity to visit the cathedral. At the Paris headquarters, some member of each French family with which the students will live for the rest of the academic year comes to take them to their Paris homes. The students arrive in Paris in time for the beginning of classes at the University and its many institutes, and for most of them this means the following Monday or Tuesday after arrival, though a few courses may not begin until early in November. Each student's program, tentatively established in Tours, is checked to make sure there are no conflicts as to hours and places of class meetings. Some minor changes may be made at this time in individual student programs due to unforeseen conditions, such as a professor's illness or a change in the scheduling of classes at the university or its affiliated institutes.

At the Paris headquarters, the Professor-in-charge and the Assistant maintain office hours throughout the week for any consultations which may be necessary, both academic and social. The students pursue their courses for the school year, having final examinations, prepared by their professors, at the end of each semester. Since most courses are year courses, the grades at the end of the first semester are temporary, but they do give the student some idea of his standing at the time. The grades received at the end of the year are final and are the grades reported to the student's home college.

Again toward the end of the year, a "Fête d'Adieu" is organized by the students for the Paris families and their friends. During the year the students publish a newspaper, *Transition,* to which various members of the group contribute. This paper serves as a memento of their year in France and allows for expressions by all on their experiences, opinions, criticisms and appreciations. A few students travel extensively in the summer before the school year begins, but many more remain for extensive travel for the summer after they have finished their studies. Nearly all students travel widely both at Christmas and Easter vacation time. Though the academic year confines them primarily to Tours and Paris in France, the places to which they travel as individual Americans are far-flung and varied. They travel as far north as Sweden and the British Isles, as far south as Italy and Spain, occasionally into North Africa, and as far east as Greece.

Students' majors may range from art to zoology. The following is a sample program, with some brief comments made by the student, who chose courses on the French theatre, French poetry, French philosophy and political science:

(*a*) *International Relations Since 1945.* "Perhaps the most interesting course at 'Science Po.' The professor is brilliant but difficult to follow; however, he is good, and it is worth all the difficulty involved. A dissertation was required and a final examination each semester."

(*b*) *Historical Evolution of the Colonial Policy.* "A stimulating course for those who are interested in problems of decolonization. The subject is treated by metropolitan centers and by periods. Two oral dissertations and a final examination each semester."

(*c*) *Modern Theatre.* "A discussion on the European theatre in general, with special emphasis on the modern French theatre; follows a general plan and involves regular visits to the plays available in Paris. Two or three written dissertations per semester and final examinations. One must read the plays of the authors studied. This course was extremely stimulating and I was never bored."

(*d*) *Diderot and Problems of the Theatre.* "This course has an interest for those who are concerned with the relationship of theory and practice, a study of three works of Diderot which deal with the problem and a 'rapprochement' of these ideas with the theatre in general. A knowledge of the works of Diderot is required, as well as the movements of the century. A dissertation and a final exam each semester."

(e) *Voltaire.* "A rather profound study of *Micromégas, Candide,* and *l'Ingénu,* more a study of the key-ideas of the author. Two-thirds of the lectures were explanations of the text, style, etc., but one-third covered the philosophical content. The professor was most exacting."

(f) *Paul Claudel* (The Five Great Odes). "The odes were examined especially from the point of view of the author as a man; a course outside the ordinary and very well done. One must know the main works of Claudel to follow the course. A dissertation and final examination each semester."

Though this program, chosen by a student from the Middle West, is a heavy one and probably involves credits which the student may not need, it does show the possibilities that are open to a student if he is willing to meet the challenge offered him in a junior-year-abroad program. To sum up the experience of the year spent in study abroad, there is no better conclusion than that written for *Transition* by a former participant: "Our junior year in France is not simply a transition. It is a symphony of transitions. It is the conscious evolution from the status of the college student to the role of the adult, constantly aware of his responsibilities to himself and to the society in which he lives. It is the bridge which will forever cross the gap between our thinking in terms of the American people and our thinking of humanity as a whole. It is a panorama of unforgettable impressions which will henceforth be our frame of reference for seeing ourselves and the world. It is our debut into international understanding and appreciation. It is our coming of age."

4. *Overseas Branches.* This is a relatively new and still uncommon development in overseas education. Students at the sophomore or junior level are sent to a foreign country with one or more instructors from the sponsoring college. Language requirements are minimal or nonexistent, although an intensive course in the language of the country (given by native teachers) is generally a required part of the curriculum. Students remain abroad for one semester (sometimes longer) and return with a semester's credit in regular American courses easily transferable to other institutions. While abroad the students live either in a group by themselves or in the homes of local families, such arrangements being made by the sponsoring authorities. Because of the expense of transporting and maintaining American professors abroad, the curricula of such branches offer relatively little choice.

The "branch" concept has also led to the development of a few educational institutions abroad (such as the Institute for American Universities at Aix-en-Provence) that provide "American type" college classes, but are not connected with any institution of higher learning in the United States. Generally, most of the classes in these schools are taught in English, but the opportunity to attend regular university classes is available to those who have the necessary mastery of the native tongue. Since the standards of such institutions are more difficult to evaluate than those of regular college overseas branches, the student ought to make sure before enrolling that credits here earned will be honored on his home campus.

The line between the overseas branch and the academic-year or junior-year program is becoming increasingly blurred. There are junior-year programs without language requirements and branch programs that use foreign teachers lecturing in English. But as a rule the junior year is oriented toward language proficiency and analysis of the culture of the region, while the branch stresses general education.

A final word about the different kinds of programs of foreign study seems now in order. The prospective student should view both himself and the programs realistically. He should not set for himself a task beyond his powers. For example, unless an undergraduate is thoroughly grounded in the necessary foreign language, has at least a B-plus general average, and knows exactly what he wants to study, he should not attempt to work unaided in most foreign universities. On the other hand, no student will achieve maximum benefit from his time abroad if he does not pursue a program that challenges his best abilities. Even a fair-to-middling scholar who has taken the equivalent of two years of a foreign language at the college level would be foolish to enroll in *any* English-language program if a comparable foreign-language program existed. The foreign-study field covers such a broad canvas that it is up to each student, with the help of whatever assistance he can get from this book, from his academic advisers, and from other sources, to decide for himself where he best fits into the picture.

CHAPTER 8

Programs Sponsored by Foreign Universities: Regular Academic Year

74 year-programs for undergraduates and graduate students . . . Innsbruck to Guadalajara and Nice to Jerusalem . . . plus offerings at 33 British universities

The following listing of programs organized by universities abroad especially for foreign students is far from complete. We have not attempted to include those in the countries of Communist East Europe, although many exist and occasional American students attend a number of them. Furthermore, the field of overseas education is growing so rapidly that we have undoubtedly missed a number of programs even in the countries we have covered. As these are called to our attention, and as new programs are created, we shall collect information about them for future editions of this book. We would very much appreciate hearing from participants in any of these programs about their experiences, especially if they note any inaccuracies in our program descriptions. Please write *The New Guide to Study Abroad*, 49 East 33rd Street, Sixth Floor, New York, N.Y. 10016.

Students hoping to earn credits toward an American degree by participating in any of the programs should obtain the approval of the authorities of their own college *before* formally enrolling.

Austria*

Graz

• **Anderl-Rogge Institute**

This is a one- or (for beginners) two-semester program at all levels of German, including lectures in German culture. Classes run 15 hours per week. Minimum age is seventeen. Cost: winter semester, about $145; spring semester, about $140. For information, write the Institute at Bürgergasse 4 u. 14, 8010 Graz.

• **University of Graz Language Courses**

This is a one-semester program in beginning and intermediate German with classes 4 hours per week. Minimum age: eighteen. Cost for tuition, $6. For information, write University of Graz, Faculty of Philosophy, Universitätsplatz 3, 8010 Graz.

Innsbruck

• **Lerch's International Language School**

This program offers courses in the German language at all levels. Classes are held for 17 hours per week, and students may enter at any time during the school year. Minimum age: fourteen. Cost: $12 registration fee plus $26 per week for room, board, and tuition. For information, write Schule Tirol, Kapuzinergasse 10, 6020 Innsbruck, Tirol.

• **University of Innsbruck Language Courses**

A one-semester program (October to February or April to July) in beginning and advanced German. There are 6 hours of classes per week. Students must be at least eighteen years old. Cost: about

* For additional information about Austrian programs, see *German Language Courses for Foreign Applicants and Students in Austria,* copies of which can be obtained from Austrian Foreign Students Service, University of Vienna, 1010 Vienna I, Dr. Karl Lueger-Ring 7, Austria. For other information, write the Austrian Institute, 11 East 52nd Street, New York, N.Y. 10022, or the Austrian State Tourist Department, 444 Madison Avenue, New York, N.Y. 10022.

Students in Vienna should consult the valuable *Weiner Studentenführer,* copies of which may be obtained by writing the Austrian Institute, 11 East 52nd Street, New York, N.Y. 10022.

$12–$16 per semester. For information, write the University at the Faculty of Philosophy, Innrain 52, 6020 Innsbruck.

Vienna

• Sprachschule Kautezky German Language Courses for Foreigners

Courses in beginning and advanced German held from October to late June for 4 hours per week. Cost for tuition, $8–$12 per month. For information write the school at Schubertring 6, 1010 Vienna.

• University of Vienna

A one-semester program (October to January or March to June) offering German at all levels. Cost: about $25. Applicants must be at least eighteen years of age and be high-school graduates. For information, write Faculty of Philosophy, Dr. Karl Lueger-Ring 7, 1010 Vienna.

• Vienna International Courses

Students in this program take courses for at least two months for 6 or 10 hours per week. Instruction is offered at all levels of German, and the courses are held between mid-October and mid-June. Minimum age is sixteen. Cost for registration (10 hours per week), about $30. For information, write Universität, 1010 Vienna 1.

• Vienna Language Institute

Courses at all levels of German run for five months, with 4 hours of classes per week. Cost: about $6 per month. For information, write Sprachinstitut Vienna, Universitätsstrasse 11, 1010 Vienna 1.

BELGIUM *

Various Cities

• Language Courses for Foreigners

Four Belgian universities offer special language courses (French and Dutch) for foreign students. Students should write to the uni-

---

* For additional information, see *A Guide to Higher Education in Belgium*, copies of which can be obtained from the Belgian Information Service, 50 Rockefeller Plaza, New York, N.Y. 10020. See also the more detailed *Etudier en Belgique*, obtainable at the same address.

versity concerned. The universities are: the University of Brussels, in Brussels (French); the State University of Liège, in Liège (French); the Catholic University of Louvain, in Louvain (French, Dutch); and the University of Ghent, in Ghent (Dutch).

DENMARK*

The University of Aarhus, in Aarhus, and the University of Copenhagen, in Copenhagen, offer instruction in the Danish language. Interested students should write to the universities.

Elsinore

• International People's College

This college offers courses in languages, social sciences, and other topics throughout the year. Several languages are used, including Danish and English. Minimum age: eighteen. Cost, about $260 per semester. For information, write the college at Elsinore.

FRANCE†

Aix-en-Provence

• Aix-Marseille Institute of French Studies for Foreign Students

This program of lectures and practical exercises in French language and civilization is open to American juniors with a good knowledge of French. A two-semester program running from October to June and leading to a diploma in French Language and Letters is awarded after an examination. Cost, for tuition (1 year), about $60 plus maintenance. For information, write Institut d'Etudes Françaises pour Etudiants Etrangers, 23 Rue Gaston-de-Saporta,

---

* For additional information, see *Educational Facilities for Students and Visitors in Denmark*, copies of which can be obtained from the Danish Information Office, 280 Park Avenue, New York, N.Y. 10017.

† For further information on French programs, see the annual issues of *Courses for Foreigners in France, Study of Art in France*, and *Study of Music*. Copies of these publications can be obtained by writing the French Cultural Services, 972 Fifth Avenue, New York, N.Y. 10021.

Aix-en-Provence, France. For housing, write Comité d'Accueil pour Etudiants Etrangers, Rue les Gazelles, Aix-en-Provence.

Besançon

• **Besancon Institute of French Language and Civilization**

A program of lectures, seminars, and practical exercises in French language and civilization, political science and economics. Certificates and diplomas are awarded after examination. A good knowledge of French is required. This is a two-semester program running from November until late June. There is also a one-semester course in French pronunciation at various levels of difficulty, which makes extensive use of the Besançon language laboratory. Cost, about $45 per semester. For information, write M. le Secrétaire, Institut de Langue et Civilisation Françaises, 30 Rue Mégevand, Besançon. For housing, write: Service d'Accueil pour Etudiants Etrangers, same address.

Bordeaux

• **Bordeaux Center of French Studies for Foreign Students**

This program of intensive language study is open to students, seventeen years of age or older, with a very good knowledge of French. In addition to special language classes, students may attend regular lectures at the university. Cost, about $17 per semester. There are two semesters running from mid-October to the end of May. For information, write Directeur du Centre d'Etudes Françaises pour Etudiants Etrangers, 20 Cours Pasteur, Bordeaux. For housing, write Centre Régional des Oeuvres Universitaires, 89 Cours Aristide Briand, Bordeaux.

Caen

• **Caen Course of French Language and Civilization
for Foreign Students**

This program offers an elementary language program open to juniors with a basic knowledge of French and an advanced program in language and civilization for juniors with a good knowledge of

French. Diplomas and certificates are granted after examination. There are two semesters, running from October to June. Cost for tuition (1 year), $45. For information, write Secrétaire des Cours pour Etrangers, Université de Caen, Rue du Gaillon, Caen.

Clermont-Ferrand

• **Clermont-Ferrand Special Course for Foreign Students**

This program in French language and civilization is open to students with a very good knowledge of French. A diploma of French university studies is awarded after a year's residence. Cost, about $30. The program runs from October to the end of May. For information, write Cours pour Etudiants Etrangers, Faculté des Lettres, 29, Boulevard Gregovia, 63, Clermont-Ferrand. For housing, write Mme. la Secrétaire du Centre Régional des Oeuvres Sociales Universitaires, 25, Rue Etienne-Dolet, Clermont-Ferrand.

Dijon

• **Dijon French Course for Foreign Students**

Language study plus courses in French theater, philosophy, literature, and civilization. Students may also attend regular university courses. There are no entrance requirements. A diploma in French studies may be won by examination after two semesters (November to late June). Cost, $16 per semester or $25 for the academic year. For information, write Cours Permanents pour Etudiants Etrangers, 2 Boulevard Gabriel, 21, Dijon.

Grenoble

• **Grenoble Course of French Language and Civilization
for Foreign Students**

Language instruction and courses in French civilization leading to various certificates and diplomas, including a diploma for teachers of French, awarded after two years of study. The academic year runs from mid-October to mid-June. Cost, about $140 per semester, $45 per month. For information, write M. le Secrétaire Général du Comité du Patronage des Etudiants Etrangers, Cours

Permanents, Faculté des Lettres, Place Verdun, 38, Grenoble. For housing, write Office Universitaire du Logement, Place Pasteur, 38, Grenoble.

Lille

• Lille Catholic Faculty

Courses in this program, which runs from late October to late May, include French literature, religion, education, theater, and philosophy. Each student must take at least 15 hours of courses per week and must have a thorough knowledge of French, as all courses are taught in that language. Cost, about $175 per year. For information, write M. le Chanoine, 60 Boulevard Vauban, 59 Lille. For information on housing, write M. le Vice-Recteur des Facultés Catholiques, same address.

• Lille Institute of University Expansion

This program in French language and civilization at elementary and advanced levels is open to juniors. Qualified students may also attend regular university lectures. Cost, about $40 a year, plus maintenance (about $140 a month). The academic year runs from November to June. For information, write Institut d'Expansion Universitaire, Office des Etudiants, 9 Rue Auguste-Angellier, Lille. For housing, write: Service du Logemont, Centre Régional Oeuvres, 74 Rue de Cambrai, 59, Lille.

Lyon

• Lyon Catholic Faculty Course for Foreign Students

This program in French language and civilization leads to various certificates and diplomas. The academic year runs from October to June. Cost, about $50 per year. For information, write Secrétariat des Facultés Catholiques, 25 Rue du Plat, Lyon.

• University of Lyon—French Course for Foreigners

This is a program in French language at various levels of difficulty, together with lectures on French contemporary civilization.

The course runs from November to late June. Cost, about $10 per month. For information, write Secrétariat du Cours aux Etudiants Etrangers, 18 Quai Claude Bernard, Lyon. For housing, write Comité d'Accueil, same address.

Montpellier

• **Institute of Foreign Students Montpellier**

Courses in French language, history, and literature, including one for beginners. There are about 30 hours of classes per week, and the program, unlike most French vacation courses, takes place from early September to mid-October, primarily because Montpellier is extremely hot in the summer months. There is a language laboratory available. Cost, $40 (5 weeks). For information, write Secrétaire de l'Institut des Etudiants Etrangers, Facultés des Lettres, Route de Monde, Montpellier. *Useful for students who intend to study independently at a French university during the regular academic year, since it ends shortly before the regular sessions. It has the disadvantage, however, of being located in a region where the people speak a very poor quality of French.*

• **University of Montpellier French Course for Foreigners**

This program offers courses in French language and civilization at various levels of difficulty. Diplomas are offered, including a diploma for teachers of French, granted upon examination after two years' residence. The academic year runs from November to July. Cost, $30 per semester. For information, write Secrétaire, Institut des Etudiants Etrangers, Université de Montpellier, Route de Monde 34, Montpellier, France. For housing, write, Service du Logement, 11 Rue Boudin, 34, Montpellier.

Nancy

• **Nancy French Course for Foreigners**

This program offers courses in French language at various levels of difficulty and an advanced course in French civilization. The academic year runs from November to June. Cost, about $30 per semester. For information, write Secrétaire des Cours pour Etrangers, Faculté des Lettres, Université de Nancy, Nancy. For housing, write Comité des Oeuvres, 16 Cours Leopold, Nancy.

Nantes

• **University of Nantes**

This university offers a program running from late October to June. Cost, about $20 per semester. For information, write Secrétariat de la Faculté des Lettres et Sciences Humaines, 38 Boulevard Michelet, 44, Nantes. For housing information, write Centre Régional des Oeuvres Universitaires et Scolaires, Logement des Etudiants Etrangers, 1 Place Alexis Ricordeau, 44, Nantes.

Nice

• **University of Nice—Course for Teachers**

This series of French-language courses is offered at various levels, open to anyone sixteen years of age or older. Advanced courses in French language and civilization and in various other modern languages are open to juniors. Cost, $30–$40 per semester. Program runs from early November to the end of May. For information, write Secrétaire Général, Cours Permanents, 65, Promenade des Anglais, Nice. For housing, write Comité d'Accueil pour Etudiants Etrangers, Centre Local des Oeuvres Universitaires, 18 Avenue des Fleurs, Nice.

Paris

• **L'Alliance Francaise**

This is a school for foreigners wishing to learn French. A wide variety of courses is available the year round, including advanced classes for interpreters. Cost, $11–$15 per month. For information, write Ecole Pratique de l'Alliance Française, 101 Boulevard Raspail, Paris 6. *This is a large cosmopolitan institution with an annual enrollment of more than 30,000 students, which specializes in elementary language instruction. The teaching, by and large, is excellent, though rather conservative. The stress is on grammar; most "conversation" classes are too large to afford much opportunity for individual practice and guidance. While lacking in the spirit of an institution of higher learning, the school brings students into contact with their colleagues from many other countries.*

• **Catholic Institute in French Civilization**

This is a program in French language, offered at various levels of difficulty, and of French civilization. The academic year runs from early October to the end of June. Cost, about $35 per course for the year and subject to the number of hours carried. For information, write Directrice, Institut de Langue et de Culture Française, 21 Rue d'Assas, Paris 6. For housing, write Service Social de l'Institut Catholique, same address. *This program is open to students of all faiths. The teaching is serious, and students are required to work very hard, but the approach to language study is very conservative, with heavy stress on grammar and the memorization of rules. There is relatively little opportunity for individual expression, but for students interested in obtaining a solid foundation in French, this is an excellent program.*

• **Foreign French Teachers' Institute, University of Paris**

This program is limited to students of at least junior standing who have taken three years of French. There are courses in French grammar, French culture, contemporary French literature, and, for teachers, in French language, literature, and education. In addition, three years of graduate study lead to the Diplôme de Professeur de Français a l'Étranger. Cost, $33–$53 per semester, depending on the course. For information, write Secrétaire Générale, Institut des Professeurs de Français a l'Etranger, 46 Rue Saint-Jacques, Paris 5. *A worth-while program, especially useful for American teachers of French. Both the conversation classes and the lectures on French culture are distinctly above the average. The program is for advanced students. Especially valuable if taken in conjunction with the program of the Institute of Phonetics.*

• **Institute for Phonetics**

This program in French pronunciation, both practical and theoretical, is for advanced students only. The academic year runs from early November to mid-June. Cost, about $25 per semester. For information, write Institut de Phonétique, 19, Rue des Bernardins, Paris 5. For housing, write Service d'Accueil aux Etudiants Etrangers, 96 Boulevard Raspail, Paris 6. *A program for students already able to understand French who wish to improve their pronunciation. Classes are limited to twelve students each, and effective use is made of a language laboratory. The teaching is first-rate. Clearly a superior program.*

• **Sorbonne Course in French Civilization**

Running from mid-October to mid-June, this program has courses in French language at all levels and in various aspects of French civilization. A regular university program is open to foreign students with a good knowledge of French. Cost, about $240 per semester for beginners; about $55–$75 per semester for intermediates; about $40 per semester for the course in French civilization; and about $160 per semester for the university program. For information, write Directeur des Cours de Civilisation, Bureau de Renseignements Universitaires à la Sorbonne, 47, Rue des Ecoles, Paris 5. *The work at this institution is difficult to evaluate because of the size and complexity of its programs, but the general academic level is greatly improved over what it was when the first edition of this guide was published. The intensive (25-hour-a-week) course is highly recommended for beginners.*

Rennes

• **Rennes French Course for Foreigners**

This program of French language and civilization courses leads to diplomas, awarded after examination. The academic year runs from late October to late May. Cost, about $35 per year. For information, write Secrétariat des Cours pour les Etrangers, Faculté des Lettres et Sciences Humaines, 7 Place Hoche, Rennes. For housing, write Centre Régional des Oeuvres Universitaires, Services Logement, 14, Rue Saint Yves, Rennes.

Rouen

• **University of Rouen**

This program, with courses in French language at all levels and in French civilization, runs from early November to late May and offers diplomas for one, two, and four semesters of study. Cost, $50 per year, or $30 per semester. For information, write M. le Directeur, Cours pour Etrangers, Université de Rouen, Faculté des Lettres et Sciences Humaines, Rue Lavoisier, 76, Rouen.

Strasbourg

• **Strasbourg French Course for Foreigners**

An elementary program in French language and civilization and a more advanced course open only to those with junior standing are offered in this program. A certificate is available after examination on the completion of two semesters and a diploma after four semesters' work, an examination, and a term paper. The academic year runs from mid-October to the end of June. Cost, about $50 for two semesters. For information, write Directeur, Institut d'Etudes Françaises Modernes, Cours pour Etrangers, Université de Strasbourg, Strasbourg. For housing, write Centre Régional des Oeuvres Universitaires, 1 Quai Dietrich, Strasbourg.

Toulouse

• **Toulouse Center of French Study for Foreigners**

This center offers a program in French language and civilization during the regular academic year. For information, including costs, write Secrétaire, Institut Normal d'Etudes Françaises, Faculté des Lettres, 56 Rue du Taur, Toulouse.

Tours

• **Touraine Institute**

This program offers courses in French language at various levels of difficulty and in French civilization. The academic year runs from early October to the end of June. Cost, about $145 per year. For information, write Secrétaire, l'Institut de Touraine, 1 Rue de la Grandière, Tours. For housing, write the same address.

GERMANY*

Various Cities

• Goethe-Institute German Program

This is a program of introductory and advanced courses in German. The institute has branches in a number of German cities, and courses last eight weeks. Cost, about $315 for tuition, room, and partial board. For information, write Goethe Institute, Lenbachplatz 3/I, Munchen. (For details see Summer Programs.)

• Language Courses for Foreigners

Most German universities and institutes of technology offer courses in the German language for foreigners during the winter. The academic year runs from November to late July. For information, write Akademisches Auslandsamt of the appropriate university.

In addition, the following universities offer special programs in German and German civilization:

Interpreter's Institute, University of Heidelberg.

Foreign and Interpreters' School of Germersheim, University of Mainz.

German Language Courses for Foreigners, University of Munich.

Bonn

• University of Bonn Spring Program for Foreigners

This program offers courses in German language and literature running from late March to mid-April. Cost, about $55. For infor-

---

* For additional information on German programs, see *Academic Studies in the Federal Republic of Germany,* copies of which may be obtained by writing the Deutsche Akademischer Austauschdienst, Kennedyallee 50, 532 Bad Fodesberg, Frankengrahen 50.

mation, write Akademisches Auslandsamt der Universität Bonn, Koblenzer Strasse, 24–26, Bonn.

GREAT BRITAIN*

A large number of British colleges and universities accept American college students who wish to take a one- or two-year course in Britain. These students are known as occasional students. These colleges and universities are listed below with their addresses and their course offerings.

ENGLAND

UNIVERSITY OF ASTON IN BIRMINGHAM
Gosta Green, Birmingham 4
(c/o Academic Registrar)
Engineering, Science, Social Sciences.

UNIVERSITY OF BIRMINGHAM
P.O. 363 Birmingham 15
Arts, Commerce, Social Science, Law, Science, Engineering.

UNIVERSITY OF BRADFORD
Bradford, 7
All subjects.

UNIVERSITY OF BRISTOL
Senate House, Bristol 2
Normally only in arts.

UNIVERSITY OF DURHAM
Old Shire Hall, Durham
All subjects.

---

* For more information about British programs, see *Some Notes for the Guidance of Overseas Students Who Wish to Study at British Universities* and the more detailed *Higher Education in the United Kingdom* (London, 1966), copies of which can be obtained from the British Information Services Reference and Library Division, 845 Third Avenue, New York, N.Y. 10022.

UNIVERSITY OF EAST ANGLIA
Earlham Hall, Norwich
Arts, Sciences, Social Studies.

UNIVERSITY OF EXETER
Exeter
(c/o Academic Registrar)
Arts, Sciences, Social Sciences, Law.

UNIVERSITY OF HULL
Hull, Yorkshire
Arts (including Music and Theology), Pure and Applied Sciences,
Social Sciences, Law.

UNIVERSITY OF KEELE
Staffordshire
Arts, Social Sciences, Law.

UNIVERSITY OF KENT AT CANTERBURY
Canterbury, York
Humanities, Natural Science, Social Sciences.

UNIVERSITY OF LANCASTER
University House, Bailrigg, Lancaster
(c/o The University Secretary)
Arts, Social Science, Pure Science.

UNIVERSITY OF LEEDS
Leeds 2 (c/o Registrar and Secretary)

UNIVERSITY OF LEICESTER
Leicester
Arts, Science, Law, Social Sciences.

UNIVERSITY OF LIVERPOOL
Liverpool 3
Arts, Science, Law, Engineering Science.

UNIVERSITY OF LONDON
Senate House, London, W.C. 1

In certain colleges only. For a list of colleges, write Academic Department.

UNIVERSITY OF MANCHESTER
Manchester 13
Arts, Science, Technology, Economic and Social Studies, Theology.

UNIVERSITY OF NOTTINGHAM
University Park, Nottingham
Arts, Law, Social Science (including Economics and Politics).

UNIVERSITY OF READING
Reading
Letters, Science, Agriculture (one academic year minimum).

UNIVERSITY OF SHEFFIELD
Sheffield 10
Arts, Pure Science, Law, Economic and Social Studies.

UNIVERSITY OF SOUTHAMPTON
Highfield, Southampton
(c/o Academic Registrar)
Arts, Engineering, Applied Science, Social Science, Law, Science.

UNIVERSITY OF SUSSEX
Falmer, Brighton
(c/o Assistant Registrar for Admissions)
Arts and Science (one academic year minimum).

UNIVERSITY OF WARWICK
Coventry, Warwick
Arts, Social Sciences, Engineering, Science.

UNIVERSITY OF YORK
Heslington, York
Arts, Social Sciences, Natural Sciences.

Wales

UNIVERSITY COLLEGE OF NORTH WALES
Bangor (c/o the Registrar)
Arts, Science, Rural Science, Music, Divinity.

UNIVERSITY COLLEGE OF SOUTH WALES AND MONMOUTHSHIRE
Cardiff (c/o the Registrar)
Arts, Economics and Social Studies, Science (including Applied Science), Music, Divinity.

UNIVERSITY COLLEGE OF SWANSEA
Swansea (c/o the Registrar)
Arts, Economic and Social Studies, Science (including Applied Science).

UNIVERSITY COLLEGE OF WALES
Aberystwyth (c/o the Registrar)
Arts, Economic and Social Studies, Science, Music, Law, Rural Science.

WELSH COLLEGE OF ADVANCED TECHNOLOGY
Cathays Park, Cardiff (c/o the Registrar)
Applied Physics, Chemistry and Biology, Engineering (Civil, Electrical, and Mechanical), Mathematics, Pharmacy, English and Liberal Studies for postgraduates only.

Scotland

UNIVERSITY OF ABERDEEN
Aberdeen
(c/o the Secretary)
Arts, Divinity, Music, Social Sciences, Law.

UNIVERSITY OF EDINBURGH
Edinburgh
(c/o Secretary)
Arts, Divinity, Music, Social Sciences, Science.

UNIVERSITY OF GLASGOW
Glasgow W. 2
(c/o Secretary and Registrar)
Arts, Divinity, Music, Social Sciences, Science, Law.

UNIVERSITY OF ST. ANDREWS
College Gate, St. Andrews
(c/o Secretary)
Arts, Science, Divinity, Engineering and Applied Science, Law, Social Science.

UNIVERSITY OF STIRLING
Stirling
(c/o Secretary)
Arts, Science, Social Science.

Northern Ireland

THE QUEEN'S UNIVERSITY OF BELFAST
Belfast 7
(c/o the Clerk of Admissions)
Arts (including Music and Education), Economics, Law.

ISRAEL

Jerusalem

• **Hayim Greenberg Teachers Institute**

This program includes courses in Jewish studies and teaching techniques. It runs from September to June, although students are encouraged to spend the summer in Israel before classes begin. All students are granted scholarships, but they must pay their travel expenses. For information, including costs, write Department of Education and Culture, the Jewish Agency, 515 Park Avenue, New York, N.Y. 10022.

• **Hebrew University—Program for Foreigners**

This program runs for one year, beginning in July with a four-month intensive program in Hebrew. All students are required to take special courses in Jewish studies and may also take regular university courses. Cost for tuition, room, board, and round-trip transportation from New York to Israel, $2,300–$2,500. For information, write One Year Study Program Committee, American

Friends of the Hebrew University, 11 East 69th Street, New York, N.Y. 10021.

ITALY*

Rome

• Dante Alighieri Society

This society offers a program of courses in Italian language at various levels of difficulty and in literature and art. Courses are given in two-month sessions, running from October to June. For information, including costs, write Secretary, Società Dante Alighieri, Piazza Firenze 27, Rome. *The teaching methods in this school are conservative, with heavy emphasis on grammar and reading and little on the development of speaking ability or the mastering of the vocabulary of everyday speech. The level of work, however, is high, and American students comment favorably on the opportunities offered to meet other foreign students in the program.*

Perugia

• The Italian University for Foreigners

This school offers an extensive program in Italian language and culture, running in three 3-month semesters from April through December. The language courses are given at all levels, with the beginning and intermediate courses being given each semester. The advanced course is given in three sections over the entire school year. Courses in Italian art and music are offered (in Italian) throughout the year. Cost for partial tuition, $16 per month. A detailed catalogue describing the program may be obtained from the Italian Information Center, 686 Park Avenue, New York, N.Y. 10021.

---

* For additional information on Italian programs, write to Istituto Italiano di Cultura, 686 Park Avenue, New York, N.Y. 10021.

Florence

• **University of Florence Course for Foreigners**

This program provides practical instruction in Italian at various levels of difficulty. The academic year runs from November to June, with the usual two semesters. Cost for tuition, $40 (winter) and $30 (summer). For information, write Secretary, Centro di Cultura per Stranieri, Via S. Gallo, 25/A, Florence.

JAPAN

Tokyo

• **International Christian University**

Courses are given in both Japanese and English at this university. Students wishing to study for one year only are not required to have a knowledge of Japanese. Courses are given in the humanities, social sciences, and natural sciences, and there are graduate programs in education and public administration. The academic year runs from September to June. Cost for tuition, about $20–$260 per term, depending on student status. For information, write the Japan International Christian University Foundation, Room 1220, 475 Riverside Drive, New York, N.Y. 10027.

• **Other Institutions**

Three institutions offer special programs in the Japanese language for foreigners. Interested students should contact the relevant institution: International Students Institute, Kashiwagi, Shinjuku-ku, Tokyo; Tokyo Japanese Language Center, 21 Shiba Park, Minato-ku, Tokyo; Tokyo School of Japanese Language, 38 Nampeidai, Shibuya-ku, Tokyo.

• **Sophia University**

The international division of this university offers courses in English, both for special students and for students working for a degree. For further information, including costs, write Sophia University Associates of America, Inc., 211 East 87th Street, New York, N.Y. 10028.

• Waseda University

The international division of this university offers a full-year program for American students. Cost for tuition, about $90–$180, depending on student status. For further information, write the International Division, Waseda University, 647 1-chome, Totsuka-machi, Shinjuku-ku, Tokyo.

MEXICO

Guadalajara

• Mexican North American Cultural Institute

This institute offers courses in Spanish on all levels of instruction throughout the year in six-week sessions. Classes meet for 6 hours per week. Cost for tuition, $100. For information, write Instituto Cultural Mexicano-Norteamericano de Jalisco, A.C. Guadalajara, Jalisco.

Guanajuato

• Allende Institute

Offers courses throughout the year, except from late November to early January, in Spanish language and art. A master's degree in language, art, and creative writing is available. Housing is in local hotels. Cost for tuition, about $50 a month. For information, write Instituto Allende, San Miguel de Allende, Guanajuato, G.T.O.

• Spanish American Academy

This is a year-round program in Spanish language, Mexican culture, and Latin American literature. For information, including costs, write Academia Hispano-Americano, Insurgentes 7, San Miguel de Allende, Guanajuato, G.T.O.

Mexico City

• **Iberian American University**

A Jesuit university offering a special one-year program for American students at the junior-year level. Emphasis is on Spanish language and Mexican and Latin American culture. Courses are conducted in Spanish. For further information, including costs, write Director, Junior Year, Universidad Iberoamericana, Cerro de las Torres 395, Mexico 21, D.F.

• **Institute of Interpreters and Translators**

This program is for students wishing to be professional interpreters or translators. Certificates are offered for completion of four-semester program, which includes courses in Spanish language and in rapid translation from Spanish to other languages. For information, including costs, write Instituto de Interpretes y Traductores, Tiber 113, Mexico 5, D.F.

• **Institute of Modern Languages**

This institute offers four-week sessions in Spanish language throughout the year. The program is intended mainly for businessmen and others who need a short intensive course in spoken Spanish. For information, including costs, write Instituto de Lenguas Modernas, S. A., Reforma 509, Mexico, D.F.

• **Mexican North American Institute of Cultural Relations**

This institution offers two programs: a trimester program with three 12-week sessions running from mid-January to early December with 3 hours of classes a week; and an intensive program of 15 hours of classes per week for three weeks, in 13 sessions running from early January to late December. Courses in both programs are limited to Spanish language at all levels. Cost for tuition, about $20 and $45. For information, write Instituto Mexicano Norteamericano de Relaciones Culturales, Hamburgo 115, Mexico 6, D.F.

• **Mexico for Foreigners, The University of the Americas**

This American-sponsored and accredited institution, formerly called Mexico City College, offers a four-year undergraduate program conducted in English leading to a B.A. or B.S. degree. A master's degree is also offered in several subjects. This college employs United States methods and standards. Students live with local families. Cost for tuition, $250 per quarter. For further information, write Dean of Admissions, University of the Americas, Kilómetro 16, Carretera, México-Toluca, Mexico 10, D.F. *This institution offers a wide variety of courses and admits students for as short a time as one quarter. Although some Mexicans are enrolled, a large majority of the students are Americans, and the campus is somewhat isolated from Mexican life.*

• **Special Courses for Foreigners, National University of Mexico**

The National University offers a year-round series of courses, divided into four sessions of approximately 10 weeks' duration, emphasizing Spanish language and Mexican culture and history. Prerequisite: at least two years of college. For information, including costs, write Registrar, Special Courses for Foreigners, Universidad Nacional Autónoma de Mexico, Edificio de Filosofía y Letras, Ciudad Universitaria, Mexico 20, D.F. *This program offers good language instruction and an opportunity to see Mexican university life firsthand. Recommended for mature students, especially for those with some previous knowledge of Spanish.*

NETHERLANDS

Leyden

• **University of Leyden Language Courses for Foreigners**

Leyden offers a Dutch-language course for foreigners in the first three months of the academic year (mid-September to mid-December). For information, including costs, write the University. Information about other Dutch-language courses can be obtained from S.B.B.S., F. C. Dondersstraat 16, Utrecht.

NORWAY

Bergen

• **University of Bergen**

Bergen offers courses in the Norwegian language. For further information, including costs, write the Nordisk Institute, University of Bergen, Allegaten 33, Bergen.

Oslo

• **University of Oslo**

A limited number of American college juniors are accepted each year on an individual basis. They are expected to take courses in the Norwegian language throughout the year and to attend the University's International Summer School. The University also offers intensive courses in Norwegian language for foreign students in the autumn and spring semesters. These are intended primarily for regular students at the University, but when space permits, others may be admitted. There is also a series of weekly lectures in English on Norwegian life and institutions. For information on both kinds of programs, including costs, write Foreign Student Advisor, University of Oslo, Karl Johansgate 47, Oslo.

SPAIN*

Barcelona

• **The University of Barcelona**

The University of Barcelona offers courses in Spanish language, literature, art, history, and culture from October to May. No previous degree or diploma is required. Cost for tuition, about $20–$85, depending on student status. For information, write Secretario del

* For additional information on the Spanish programs, see the annual *Courses for Foreigners in Spain,* copies of which can be obtained from the Office of Cultural Relations, Spanish Embassy, 1629 Columbia Road, N.W., Washington, D.C. 20009. Although prepared primarily for Latin American students, the Instituto de Cultura Hispánica publication, *Estudios en España* (7th edition, Madrid, 1967) contains a wealth of information useful to all foreign students in Spain.

Curso de Estudios Hispánicos, Facultad de Filosofía y Letras, Universidad de Barcelona, Barcelona 7.

Canary Islands

• **Course for Foreigners**

This is a two-month program in Spanish language, literature, history, and art and in the geography, economics, and culture of the Canary Islands. It runs from mid-January to mid-March. For information, including costs, write Instituto de Estudios Hispánicos de la Universidad de La Laguna, Puerto de la Cruz, Santa Cruz de Tenerife, Canary Islands.

• **Courses for Foreigners**

Organized by the International University of the Canary Islands, this one-month program (mid-March to mid-April) offers courses in Spanish language, literature, history, art, and culture. There is a similar program offered from mid-November to mid-December. Cost, about $20. For information, write Universidad Internacional de Canarias, Bravo Murillo, 21, Las Palmas de Gran Canarias.

Granada

• **University of Granada**

The University of Granada offers a course in Hispanic studies, running from mid-October to June. Subjects include Spanish language, history, and culture and Hispanic-Moslem culture. Cost for tuition, $20–$100 per course, depending on student status. For information, write Facultad de Filosofía y Letras de la Universidad de Granada, Calle de Puentezuelas, Granada.

Madrid

• **Central Language School Course for Foreigners**

The Central Language School sponsors a program in elementary, intermediate, and advanced Spanish, from mid-October to June.

Classes are held in the evening. For information, including costs, write Secretaría de la Escuela Central de Idiomas, Calle de Jesús Maestro, Madrid 3.

• **University of Madrid Autumn Course for Foreigners**

This program offers courses in Spanish language, literature, history, and art. It runs from early October to the third week in December. Cost, about $50. For information, write Facultad de Filosofía y Letras, Cursos para Extranjeros, Ciudad Universitaria, Madrid 3.

• **University of Madrid Course of Hispanic Studies**

This program in Spanish language, literature, history, art, and geography runs from October to June. Cost for diploma course, about $85. For information, write Facultad de Filosofía y Letras, Ciudad Universitaria, Madrid 3.

• **University of Madrid Hispanic Studies Course for Foreigners**

This program in Spanish language, literature, art, and history leads to various certificates and diplomas. The academic year runs from early October to the end of May. For information, write Cultural Office of the Spanish Embassy, 1629 Columbia Road, N.W., Washington, D.C. 20009. (All twelve Spanish universities offer programs essentially like that of Madrid. No prior registration is necessary. Cost about $85 for diploma course. For special information and dormitory reservations, write Sr. Secretario del Curso de Estudios Hispánicos at the appropriate university.)

• **University of Madrid Single Subject Course for Foreigners**

This is one of the few courses for foreigners in Spain in which a limited topic is studied. The program is held from early January to the end of February and focuses on the art, history, and literature of Spain's Golden Age. Students may study all three aspects of the Golden Age culture if they wish, or they may limit themselves to courses in just one or two. Cost, about $35. For information, write

Secretaría del Curso Monográfico de Invierno para Extranjeros, Facultad de Filosofía y Letras, Ciudad Universitaria, Madrid 3.

• **University of Madrid Spring Course for Foreigners**

This is a program in Spanish language, history, art, music, and literature, running from early March to June. Cost, about $50. For information, write Secretaría del Curso para Extranjeros, Facultad de Filosofía y Letras, Ciudad Universitaria, Madrid 3.

Málaga, Granada

• **Malaga-Granada Winter Course**

This program is similar in content to the University of Granada's autumn course. It runs from mid-January to late February and is held partly in Málaga and partly in Granada. Unlike the autumn course, it offers credits for American students. Cost about $40. For information, write Curso para Extranjeros, Universidad de Granada, Granada.

Salamanca

• **University of Salamanca Course in Hispanic Philology**

This program in Spanish language, history, and civilization, especially for teachers of Spanish, leads to various certificates and diplomas. The program runs from early April to early June. For information, including costs, write Secretario, Curso de Filologia Hispánica, Universidad de Salamanca, Salamanca.

Zaragoza

• **University of Zaragoza**

This university offers winter courses leading toward the diploma of Hispanic studies. The program begins in early November and ends in late April and includes courses in Spanish language, literature, history, and culture. For information, including costs, write Secretaría de Facultad, Zaragoza.

SWEDEN*

Stockholm

• **Stockholm University Institute for English-Speaking Students**

The Institute offers two programs, a Junior Year and an International Graduate School. The Junior Year program is in Scandinavian area studies only, while the International Graduate School offers a one-year program leading to a diploma in the social sciences and a two-year program leading to a master's degree. Courses are given in English, but students are expected to study Swedish. Cost for tuition, $700 (year); $70 for diploma course. For further information, write the American-Scandinavian Foundation, 127 East 73rd Street, New York, N.Y. 10021, or the Institute for English-Speaking Students, Sveavagen 166, Stockholm Va.

Various Cities

• **Other Special Language Courses**

Several Swedish universities offer courses in the Swedish language for foreigners. Write care of the Extra-Mural Department. These courses are free.

University of Gothenburg, Kaserntorget 7, Gothenburg 2
University of Lund, Skomakaregatan 10, Lund 1
University of Stockholm, Grevturegatan 9, Stockholm 0
University of Uppsala, Drottninggatan 13, Uppsala

* For additional information, see *Studying in Sweden: Hints and Suggestions for Foreign Students,* copies of which can be obtained from the Swedish Institute, Kungsgatan 42, Stockholm 3.

SWITZERLAND*

Various Cities

• **Courses for Foreigners**

Five Swiss universities offer language instruction for foreigners. The following, through their Schools of Modern French, offer programs in French language and literature:
University of Fribourg, Fribourg
University of Geneva, Geneva
University of Lausanne, Lausanne
University of Neuchâtel, Neuchâtel
The University of Berne, Berne, offers a program in German language for foreign students.

TAIWAN

Taipei

• **Courses for Foreigners**

Three national universities are open to foreign students: National Chengchi University, National Taiwan University, and National Normal University. All are in Taipei. Only the National Normal University, through its Chinese Language Training Center, offers intensive instruction in the Chinese language for foreign students.

A good knowledge of Chinese is prerequisite for acceptance. For further information, including costs, write Office of the Cultural Counselor, Embassy of the Republic of China, 2311 Massachusetts Avenue, N.W. Washington, D.C. 20008.

---

* For additional information, consult *Swiss Universities: A Short Guide*, copies of which can be obtained from the Swiss National Tourist Office, 10 West 49th Street, New York, N.Y. 10020.

Programs Sponsored by Foreign Universities: Summer

Many summer programs to choose from . . . take a long, hard look before you decide, because quality varies greatly . . . 217 programs around the world for college students

Perplexing in their variety are the great numbers of summer programs offered to students and teachers by foreign universities and special institutes. Some purport to grant credit; others do not. Academic standards vary from stiff to practically nonexistent, although it is probably safe to say that standards are generally lower than in courses offered during the academic year. "They are on holiday, after all," the Director of one European summer course reminded us. "If they can't pronounce maybe they'll become good translators." Subject matter runs the gamut from "paleolithic art" to "contemporary economic problems" and "comparative government." Certainly the prospective student should examine any program he is interested in carefully before committing himself, so that he is sure of getting what he wants.

The Typical Summer Course

By far the most common of the summer courses for foreigners is the "language and civilization" type. These programs are essentially the same in all the major centers toward which American students gravitate, from Paris to Rome and from Vienna to Madrid. Formal language study (usually about three or four hours per day) is offered at several levels, typically elementary, intermediate, and advanced. To this are added general lectures (commonly one each day) on various aspects of the history, literature, arts, and customs of the country. These make up the "civilization" part of the program.

The language instruction in these courses is most often provided by teachers in the local elementary and secondary schools or by advanced students in the universities. The general lectures, however, are given by university professors and other specialists, many of them distinguished scholars. In the prospectuses and catalogues circulated by the summer schools, much is naturally made of these bright lights, although, in reality, they seldom have very much to do with the students, as should be obvious to anyone who considers the nature of the work being carried on.

The quality of the language instruction varies from institution to institution and even within institutions, according to the talents of the individual teachers. With some notable exceptions teaching methods are "old-fashioned" in that they stress grammar and translation—in short, the formal study of language—at the expense of casual conversation or the use of electronic equipment that has become so important in recent years in American language teaching.* The teachers seldom assign homework or check closely on the progress of their students. Furthermore, the teaching of grammar is usually unsystematic and overly concerned with fine points. Little stress is placed on teaching the student to speak; his ear is trained, but not his tongue. At the very least, however, the student works with a teacher who is a native-born speaker of the language, a boon unfortunately still far from universal in American colleges.

The "civilization" lectures naturally vary greatly in quality, since in any center it is very unusual for more than two or three lectures to be given by any one person. They are nevertheless useful, aside

---

* A number of these schools do have "language laboratories," but the majority opinion is clearly that expressed by M. Boutron, Director of the course for teachers of French at the Alliance Française in Paris. "*Moderation, prudence, sobriété*," he says. "The machine must never be allowed to replace the teacher. We let the students know that these gadgets exist, but basically we rely on traditional methods developed after years of experience." Of course, when the student lives in a community where the language he is studying is spoken, there is much less need for "laboratory" instruction.

from their subject matter, in training the ear of the student by subjecting him to a wide variety of accents, intonations, speeds of delivery, and so on. Thus his vocabulary is bound to grow almost as a concomitant of faithful attendance. In some cases, however, there is little or no pattern to the course of lectures; each speaker addresses himself to a different topic, and there is little to connect the talks in the listener's mind. Furthermore, they are often devoted to subjects for which, however interesting, the average student has little background, such as local archaeology or the minor works of obscure poets. The University of Vienna lecture series in July 1967, for example, provided discourses on subjects ranging from classical German poetry to "History and Social Structure" and "The Relationship of the Viennese Dialect to Literary German." On the other hand, some of these schools provide closely integrated lecture *courses*. Students enrolled in the excellent University of Caen summer program in 1967 could choose between a series on contemporary French authors, one on the Fifth Republic, a third on twentieth-century French art, and so on, and these were even organized to suit the comprehension of students with varying degrees of knowledge of the French tongue.

Almost everywhere, these language programs are formally connected with a foreign university, but the connection is sometimes only nominal. Usually they do not receive much financial help from the parent organization and must depend on student fees. This frequently tends to drive down entrance requirements; and in extreme cases, it can even lead to shockingly unacademic efforts to drum up trade. For example, the following passage appeared as an advertisement in the International Edition of the *New York Times:*

> Would you like to take Courses at the seaside in summer? Choose among those of Alicante, Palma de Mallorca, Barcelona, Peñíscola and Valencia on the MEDITERRANEAN; San Sebastian and Santander on the BAY OF BISCAY; and Cadiz on the ANDALUSIAN ATLANTIC. Or in the hills? Jaca, Segovia, Leon, Granada, offer you their efficient courses and amid incomparable scenery. . . . You will be able to obtain in all of them CERTIFICATES OF PROFICIENCY and/or ATTENDANCE . . . and the highly-prized DIPLOMA OF HISPANIC STUDIES. Furthermore, you should know that the MARKS EARNED CAN COUNT AS "CREDITS" at the students' request.

This advertisement, filled with extremely misleading statements (its blatant bad taste aside), was published over the name of the Spanish Ministry of Education. If other countries do not employ the "hard sell" to the same extent, their summer language institutes are nonetheless sometimes more interested in quantity than quality. Even in highly centralized France, one influential official in the Ministry of Education confessed to us that he was powerless to control the policies of individual summer schools, much as he would like to do so in some cases.

This does not mean that these institutes are uniformly bad. Quite the contrary; many are exceptionally good. And even at the poorest of them, students can learn a great deal if they are willing to work hard at their studies.

Aside from the formal educational programs, nearly all foreign summer schools assume some responsibility for housing their students. The growing number of universities that have erected dormitories are eager to keep their facilities occupied during the vacation period, and in other cases local secondary-school dorms are often used. Some summer schools have taken over villas at lake and seaside resorts to house enrollees. When housing is provided, meals are usually included. Schools that do not have such facilities normally publish lists of approved hotels and rooming houses for their students.

These programs also offer many excursions and visits to local places of interest. Some of these are excellent; others vary from indifferent to chaotic. When local teachers guide these excursions the quality of the commentary is high, but often they are mere commercial tours, the information, parroted by professional guides, inaccurate, out of date, and dull. All the schools leave the student with a great deal of time to do as he pleases. This, of course, is highly desirable. Even the serious student should not eschew recreation and relaxation while studying abroad. One of the purposes of this book is to help the student select the institution best suited to his needs, and another is to show him how to combine study and play in an effective manner. We would very much appreciate hearing from participants in any of these programs about their experiences, especially if they note any inaccuracies in our program descriptions. Please write *The New Guide to Study Abroad*, 49 East 33rd Street, Sixth Floor, New York, N.Y. 10016.

ARGENTINA

Buenos Aires

• University of Buenos Aires Summer Seminars

Intended mainly for Latin American graduate students, but open to highly qualified Americans, this program sponsors seminars in topics of major concern to modern Latin America. For information, including costs, write University of Buenos Aires.

AUSTRIA*

Bergenz

• University of Vienna Theater Institute

This is a week-long program (in early August) on problems of producing the classics in the modern theater. For information, including costs, write Institut für Theaterwissenschaft, Hofburg, Batthyanystiege, Vienna.

Eisenstadt

• Eastern Academy Seminar in East European Languages

This program runs from late July to late August. The languages taught include Serbo-Croatian, Russian, Czech, and Hungarian. Prerequisite: two years of language study. Cost, $150 for tuition, room, and board. For information, write Osterreichisches Ost- und Südosteuropa-Institut, Josefsplatz, Vienna 1.

Graz

• Anderl Rogge Institute Summer Program

This institute provides a series of courses in German language at various levels of difficulty and in German and Austrian literature

* For detailed information about Austrian summer courses, see the annual *Sommerkurse in Osterreich,* published by the Austrian Committee for International Student Exchange (Türkenstrasse 4/III, Vienna, Austria). Copies may be obtained from the Committee, or from the Austrian State Tourist Department, 444 Madison Avenue, New York, N.Y. 10022.

and civilization. The courses are scheduled between early June and mid-October, and a number of excursions are provided. Students must be at least sixteen years of age. Cost, $75–$110 for tuition and excursions. For information, write Institut Anderl Rogge, Bürgergasse 4, Graz.

Innsbruck (Mayrhofen)

• **University of Innsbruck Summer School**

This program offers four 3-week sessions from late June to mid-September dealing with the German language at various levels of difficulty and with Austrian history and culture. A number of excursions are also provided. Students must be sixteen years of age. Cost, $84–$90 for tuition, board, and room. For information, write Internationale Ferienkurses, University of Innsbruck, Innsbruck.

Linz (Unterweissenbach)

• **Society for East and Southeast Studies**

This program, held in Unterweissenbach, specializes in the study of Russian language at all levels and of Soviet culture. It is held in two sessions from early July to early August and from early August to late August. Some knowledge of Russian is prerequisite. Cost, $120–$192 for tuition, room, and board. For information, write Society for East and Southeast Studies, Bismarckstrasse 5, Linz. *An intensive program best suited for advanced students with a professional interest in Russian. Students from many nations attend. The village of Unterweissenbach is very isolated, however, and there are few cultural opportunities or diversions other than strolling in the beautiful countryside.*

Salzburg

• **International Summer Academy of Fine Arts**

Instruction in painting, sculpture, architecture, lithography, and other fine arts, in a picturesque setting at Fortress Hohensalzburg, from mid-July to mid-August. Applicants must be eighteen years of age, but there is no other entrance requirement. Cost, $82 for tuition. For information, write Secretary, International Summer Academy of Fine Arts, P.O. Box 18, Salzburg. *A large and complex program, with students from many countries attending. Salzburg is so crowded with tourists in summer, however, that it is difficult to learn much about "the real" Austria or to get much practice in speaking German in the community.*

• International Summer Course

Classes in German language at various levels of difficulty, including a course for beginners and an advanced program in economics and political science, all running from July to August. Excursions are arranged, and certificates are available after examination. Cost, $32–$40. For information, write Internationale Ferienkurse für Deutsche Sprache, Residenzplatz 1, Salzburg.

• Mozarteum Summer Academy

This academy provides instruction for advanced students in voice and instrumental music, with classes scheduled from mid-July to late August. Cost, $68–$108 for tuition; board and lodging, about $5 per day. For information, write Director, International Academy for Music, Schwarzstrasse 26, Salzburg.

• Salzburg Summer School

Courses in German language at all levels, Austrian culture, and European economics and politics, running from early July to mid-August and conducted in English. Prerequisite: one year of college. Cost, $320 for tuition, room, board, excursions. For information, write Austrian Institute, 11 East 52nd Street, New York, N.Y. 10022.

Strobl

• University of Vienna Summer School

Classes in law, political science, and other subjects held in English, in a program which runs from mid-July to late August. There is also a program in the German language, including an "intensive" course. Students must be juniors at least, and there are prerequisites for various courses. Applicants must present an academic transcript. Grades are awarded in a form suitable for students seeking to obtain academic credits. Cost, $190 for tuition plus $130 for room and board. For information, write Institute of International Education, 809 United Nations Plaza, New York, N.Y. 10017. *Although German is taught, this program is not intended for students primarily interested in language study. The high concentration of Americans, the isolated location of the school on an Austrian lake, and the use of English in lectures all militate against it as a language school. Although there is a tendency to minimize the importance of formal academic work, the program provides an excellent means for Americans who do not know German to sample the point of view of European professors. There is much more contact between professors and students than is usual in European universities.*

Vienna

• Academy of Music Dance Program

This program offers instruction in various aspects of the dance, for both dancers and teachers, for two weeks in early July. Students must be at least seventeen years of age, with appropriate experience and a minimal understanding of German. Cost, $28 for tuition. For information, write Vienna Academy of Music and Dramatic Art, Schloss Schoenbrunn, Vienna 13.

• Austrian College Society International Forum

An advanced seminar on some question of current importance, the topic varying annually. The program consists of a series of lectures by specialists from different countries, simultaneous translations into the major languages being provided. It runs from mid-August to early September. A number of excursions are provided. Cost, $128 for tuition, room, and board. For information, write Secretary, Austrian College Society, Reichstrasse 17, Vienna.

• International Summer Course

This program, held at Kahlenberg in the Vienna Woods, is divided into two 3-week sessions. The first is for beginners in German language and runs from early to late July. The second is for intermediates and begins in late July. For information, including costs, write Director, International Summer Courses, Lindengasse 32, Vienna 7.

• University of Vienna Summer Course

German-language courses at various levels of difficulty and a series of lectures on German civilization. There are three 4-week sessions, running from early July to late September. Students must be at least sixteen years of age. About 25 per cent of the students are American, but many nations are represented. Cost, $36 for tuition. For information, write Secretary, Wiener Internationale Hochschulkurse, Vienna 1. *The students in this large program are of all ages, abilities, and backgrounds, but the classes are small and the general attitude serious and businesslike.*

BELGIUM

Brussels

• Free University of Brussels Summer Program

Courses in French language and literature at various levels of difficulty,in a program that runs from late July to late August. Cost, $25 for tuition and some excursions. For information, write Secrétaire des Cours Vacances, Université Libre de Bruxelles, 50 Avenue F. D. Roosevelt, Bruxelles. *This small program has the advantage of having very few English-speaking students. The language commonly used among the students is French. However, the classes are too large for the effective teaching of conversational French.*

BRAZIL

Rio Grande do Sul

• **Catholic University Program in Intensive Portugese**

This is a four-week intensive program in Portuguese in July. For information, write Secretario Geral da Pontifícia, Universidade Católica do Rio Grande do Sul, Praca D. Sedastião, Pórto Alegré, Rio Grande do Sul.

CANADA

Banff

• **School of Fine Arts Summer School—University of Alberta**

This program, which consists of several courses from mid-June to early September, offers classes in the arts and in modern languages. Class time amounts to about 2 hours per week. Advanced students of French live and study in a special chalet. Tuition cost varies. For information, write Director, Banff School of Fine Arts, Banff, Alberta.

Montreal

• **University of Montreal Summer School**

This program, which lasts from early July to mid-August, offers courses in French language and civilization at various levels of difficulty, including a course for beginners. Those attending must be at least seventeen years of age and must have a good knowledge of French if taking French civilization courses. Cost, $235 for tuition, plus $200 for room and board. For information, write University of Montreal, P.O. Box 6128, Montreal 3.

• McGill University Summer School

This program lasts from late June to mid-August and offers courses in French language and civilization at various levels of difficulty. Students must be eighteen years of age or older, with two years of college French, and able to provide letters of recommendation. Cost, $442 for tuition, room, and board. For information, write Secretary, French Summer School, McGill University, Quebec.

Quebec

• Laval University French Summer School

Courses in French language and civilization, at various levels of difficulty, for beginners through the graduate level, with instruction given in French. The courses are held in two 3-week sessions between early June and mid-August. Cost, $415 for tuition, room, and board. For information, write Secrétariat des Cours d'Eté, Université Laval, Quebec.

Various Cities

• Other Canadian Programs

In addition to offering the programs listed above, which for one reason or another seem to attract most American students, all Canadian universities admit American students to their regular summer programs. These are similar in scope and subject matter to those given at United States colleges and universities. The sessions usually run from early July to mid-August, and tuition varies.

The Canadian Government Travel Bureau (680 Fifth Avenue, New York, N.Y. 10019) publishes an annual booklet, *Summer Courses in Canada,* which describes briefly the offerings of all the universities. For specific information about programs and costs, write directly to the Registrars of the proper institutions. Their addresses follow:

University of Alberta, Calgary, Alberta
University of Alberta, Edmonton, Alberta
Victoria College, Victoria, British Columbia

University of British Columbia, Vancouver 8, British Columbia
University of Manitoba, Winnipeg, Manitoba
Mount Allison University, Sackville, New Brunswick
University of New Brunswick, Fredericton, New Brunswick
Teachers' College Summer School, Fredericton, New Brunswick
Memorial University, St. John's, Newfoundland
Acadia University, Wolfville, Nova Scotia
St. Francis Xavier University, Antigonish, Nova Scotia
Mount Saint Vincent College, Rockingham, Halifax County, Nova
    Scotia
Saint Mary's University, Halifax, Nova Scotia
McMaster University, Hamilton, Ontario
Queen's University, Kingston, Ontario
University of Ottawa, Ottawa 2, Ontario
University of Toronto, 65 St. George St., Toronto 5, Ontario
Ontario College of Education, 371 Bloor St., Toronto 5, Ontario
University of Western Ontario, London, Ontario
Carleton University, Ottawa 1, Ontario
Bishop's University, Lennoxville, Quebec
University of Montreal, P.O. 6128, Montreal 3, Quebec
MacDonald College of McGill University, Ste. Anne de Bellevue,
    Quebec
Université de Sherbrooke, Case Postale, 790 Sherbrooke, Quebec
University of Saskatchewan, Saskatoon, Saskatchewan.

COLOMBIA

Bogotá

• **University of the Andes Summer Program**

Courses in Spanish language, at all levels, from late June to late
July. For information, including costs, write Department of Modern
Languages, Apartado Aereo 4976, Bogotá, D.E.

CZECHOSLOVAKIA

Prague

• **Charles University Slavonic Language Program**

A program in Czech and Slovak language and culture and Russian
language, for teachers and advanced students of Slavonic languages

and literature, from late July to late August. Cost, about $70 for tuition, room, and board. For information, write Letní škola slovanských studii, filosofická fakulta KU,n. Krasnoarmejců 1, Prague.

DENMARK*

Aarhus

• **Medical Summer School**

Limited to thirty preclinical medical students, this three-week program (in August) features lectures on physiology, biochemistry, and anatomy (all in English). Cost, $100 for tuition, room, and board. For information, write IMCC, Aarhus afdeling, Gustav Wiedsvej 31, Aarhus C..

Copenhagen

• **Committee for the Propagation of Knowledge about Denmark Abroad, Summer Course**

This organization offers classes in the Danish language at various levels of difficulty and a series of lectures in English on Danish civilization. The session lasts four weeks, from late July to late August. Cost, $17.35 for tuition. For information, write Danish International Student Committee, Studiestraede 36, 1159 Copenhagen K.

• **Intensive Danish Language Courses**

Held for beginning, intermediate, and advanced students, these intensive courses run for three weeks, beginning in early August. Cost, $7 for tuition. For information, write Folkeuniversitet, Frue Plads, Copenhagen K.

* For more details about the Danish summer programs, write the Danish Information Office, 280 Park Avenue, New York, N.Y. 10017, or American Scandinavian Foundation, 127 East 73rd Street, New York, N.Y. 10021. The Danish Ministry of Education publishes an annual booklet, *Holiday Courses for Students and Visitors from Abroad,* available through these organizations.

• **Teacher's Summer School**

This program, which runs from late June to late July, is for experienced teachers and administrators. Courses are given in comparative education and Scandinavian culture. Limited to twenty-five Americans and twenty-five Scandinavians. Courses are given in English. Cost, $1,000 for tuition, room, board, and study tours. For information, write the Danish Institute for Information About Denmark and Cultural Cooperation with Other Countries, Kultorvet 2, 1175 Copenhagen K. Similar programs are conducted in Sweden and Norway.

Elsinore

• **International People's College Summer Program**

Courses in English on various aspects of Danish life and culture and on international problems, running from early July to early September. For information, including costs, write International People's College, Elsinore. *This program makes no pretension of serious academic goals; the stress is on meeting people from other nations and developing international good will.*

Espergaerde

• **Summer Programs for International Understanding**

Held in July and August, this program includes short courses on international issues and study of the culture of the country. Cost, $6 per day for tuition, room, and board. For information, write Dr. Peter Manniche, Espergaerde. *Similar courses under the same auspices are provided in Norway and Sweden.*

FINLAND

Tampere

• **University of Tampere Summer Program**

Finnish language and culture are taught in this program, which runs from early June to early July. Some knowledge of Finnish is required. Cost, $96 for tuition. For information, write Finnish Ministry of Education, Korkeavuorenkatu 21, Helsinki 13.

FRANCE*

Aix-en-Provence

• **University of Aix-Marseille Summer Program**

The emphasis of this program is on French language, which is taught at all levels. Advanced students, however, take courses in French literature and art. The program runs from mid-July to late August. Cost, $50 for tuition, plus $100 for room and board. For information, write Director des Cours d'Eté, Faculté de Lettres, Les Fenouillettes 13, Aix-en-Provence.

Amiens

• **School of Church Singing and Liturgy**

Courses in music theory, history of music, choral music, flute, and choral direction, held for a week in late July. Cost, $4 per day. For information, write Ecole du Chant et de Liturgie des Frères, 6, Rue du Conge, 80, Amiens.

Angers

• **Institute of Sacred Music**

There are two 1-week sessions in this course: early September, liturgical singing; early- to mid-September, polyphony. Students must be at least eighteen years old and have an elementary knowledge of music. Cost, $12 for tuition. For information, write Secrétariat des Sessions, Université Catholique, BP 858, 49, Angers.

---

* For more details on French summer programs, see the annual *Courses for Foreigners in France Offered by the French Universities: Summer,* copies of which may be obtained by writing to French Cultural Services, 972 Fifth Avenue, New York, N.Y. 10021.

Bagnères-de-Bigorre

• **Universities of Bordeaux and Toulouse Summer Program**

This program is held in three sessions of two, three, and four weeks, in July and August. Minimum age: sixteen. Cost for tuition, room, and board: about $130–$300, depending on length of program. For information, write Administrateur, Centre Universitaire d'Eté de Pau, Villa Formose, Allées de Morlais, 64 Pau.

Besançon

• **University of Besancon Summer Program**

In this program, courses in all levels of French language are held, along with a course of lectures on French civilization. The program runs from late July to late August. Cost, $46 for tuition, plus $74 for room and board. For information, write M. le Sécretaire de la Faculté des Lettres et Sciences Humaines, Cours Annuel, 30 Rue Mégevand, 25 Besançon.

Boulogne

• **University of Lille Summer Course**

A program of courses in French language and civilization at various levels of difficulty. There is a course for beginners. The program lasts from early July to late August in one 4-week session and one 8-week session. Cost, $10 tuition per week; $30 tuition, room, and board per week. For information, write Directeur des Cours de Vacances, Faculté des Lettres, Université de Lille, 9 Rue Auguste-Angelier, Lille. *Although it has the advantage of a very light American enrollment, this program has the disadvantage of being located in a seaside resort heavily patronized by British vacationers. The city is practically bilingual.*

Caen

• **International Vacation Course**

This program, sponsored by the University of Caen, offers a four-week session of classes in July, in French language and civilization at various levels of difficulty, and an advanced course in French civilization. Students must be eighteen years of age. Cost, $165 for tuition, room, board. For information, write Secrétaire du Cours International de Vacances, Esplanade de la Paix, F 14, Caen. *This is an unusually well-organized program. Enrollment is limited to 200, of whom no more than 50 may be from any one nation. There is a student government and considerable contact outside of classes between students and faculty. Classes are moderate in size.*

Cannes

• **Classical Ballet Center**

This is a two-month course in classical ballet, with other classes in modern Spanish, and classical Chinese dancing and in the history of art and in French language. Minimum age: ten. Cost, $7–$8 per day for room, board, and one dance class. For information, write Centre de Danse Rosella Hightower, "Gallia," 06, Cannes.

Corsica (Morosaglia)

• **National Federation for the Expansion of Music, Corsica**

This is a four-week program held in August at Morosaglia, Corsica. Instruction is given in voice, direction, and the teaching of music. There are two sections: one for students in the sixteen to seventeen age group; the other for students eighteen to twenty-two. Cost, $160 for tuition and room. For information, write Président de la Fédération Nationale d'Associations Culturelles d'Expansion Musicale, 23 Rue Asseline, Paris 14.

Dijon

• **University of Dijon Vacation Course for Foreigners**

This program offers two-month courses in French at various levels of difficulty and a series of lectures on different aspects of French civilization, with a special program for teachers. Cost for tuition, $30–$60, depending on length of program. Room ranges from $22 to $44. For information, write, M. le Directeur des Cours de Vacances,

36 Rue Chabot-Charney, Dijon. *This program is notable for the low percentage of Americans generally enrolled. There are relatively few distractions, and the general mood of the institution is business-like and serious.*

Gérardmer

• University of Nancy Summer Course

This one-month program, running from late July to late August, offers classes in French for intermediate- and advanced-level students only. A number of French students participate in the program to encourage the speaking of French at all times. Cost, about $120–$140 for tuition, room, board. For information, write Cours Permanents pour Etudiants Etrangers, 23 Boulevard Albert Ier, Nancy.

Grenoble

• University of Grenoble Summer School

This program, held in the heart of the French Alps, runs from the beginning of July to the middle of September and offers courses in the French language at various levels of difficulty, as well as lectures on French civilization. Students must be at least sixteen years of age, with some prior knowledge of French, and they must enroll for a minimum of three weeks. They live in university dormitories or pensions. About 1,500 students usually attend, and of these approximately 15 to 20 percent are Americans. Cost, $32–$120 for tuition, depending on length of stay. Rooms available from $14–$35 per month. For information, write M. le Secrétaire Général du Comité de Patronage des Etudiants Etrangers, Faculté des Lettres, 38, Grenoble. *This program, consistently one of the most popular in France, is well planned, administered, and staffed. A disadvantage is the large number of English-speaking participants.*

• Summer School of Theoretical Physics, Les Houches
(University of Grenoble)

From early July to late August, a series of lectures on some aspect of physics is given in French and English. Students must have a knowledge of advanced physics and a very good knowledge of French. Cost, $180 for tuition, room, and board. For information, write Omnès, Directeur des Etudes, Ecole de Physique Théorique, 46 Avenue Félix-Viallet, 38 Grenoble.

Guadeloupe (French Antilles)

• **University of Bordeaux Summer Program**

No beginners in French language are admitted into this program, which runs from mid-July to late August. Courses offered include advanced grammar and composition and French civilization. Students live in dormitories. Cost, $96–$145 for tuition, room, and board. For information, write M. le Directeur du Centre International d'Etudes Françaises, B.P. 626, Pointe-à-Pitre, Guadeloupe, French Antilles.

Le Mans

• **St. Gregory School of Sacred Music**

This program is divided in two sections: a week in mid-July, courses in Gregorian chant; two weeks in late July, courses in the Ward method, music culture, harmony, and organ. Cost, $5–$10, depending on course followed. For information, write Schola Saint Grégoire, 26 Rue Paul Ligneul, 72 Le Mans.

Lyon

• **University of Lyon Summer Program**

This five-week program, given in the ancient capital of Gaul, runs from mid-September to mid-October and offers courses in the French language on various levels of difficulty, along with lectures on French civilization. Cost, $28 for tuition (5 weeks). Rooms available on request. For information, write Secrétariat Général des Cours pour Etrangers, 18 Quai Claude-Bernard, Lyon. *A useful program for students planning to enroll in French universities. The low percentage of Americans is an added advantage.*

Montpellier

• **University of Montpellier July Program**

This four-week program has two courses, one in elementary and intermediate French language, which stresses language study, and one in advanced French language, with emphasis on French literature. Prerequisite: two years of college. Cost, $40 for tuition (5 weeks). Rooms available at $20 per month. For information, write Directeur, Cours de Juillet, Faculté des Lettres, Place de la Voie Domitienne, 34 Montpellier.

Nice

• **International Center of French Studies**

Daily lectures on French language, literature, and civilization, in two 1-month sessions, held in July and August. Some knowledge of French is required. Afternoon conversation classes are also offered. Cost, $10–40 for tuition, depending on length of stay. For information, write Lycée de Nice, 18 Avenue des Fleurs, Nice. *Although this program is designed primarily for teachers of French, a majority of the students are not actually teachers. There is little opportunity for contact with French students, since the center is a self-contained unit on the outskirts of Nice.*

• **International Summer Academy**

Training in music, dramatics, dance, painting, and sculpture for advanced students, under the supervision of the French Ministry of Cultural Affairs. Language instruction is also available. The program runs from early July to early fall, there being two sessions. Diplomas are awarded to outstanding students after public auditions at the end of the program. Cost, $30–$70 for tuition. For information, write Académie Internationale d'Eté, 24 Boulevard de Cimiez, Nice, France, or Secrétariat, Académie Internationale de Musique, 89 bis Avenue Sainte-Marie, Sainte-Mandé. *This program would be useful only to professional musicians and advanced students. Knowledge of French is essential.*

Paris

• **Academie Charpentier**

Held in conjunction with the Académie de la Grande Chaumière, this program features courses in painting and design. Held in July, August, and September. Minimum age: fifteen. Cost, $60 for tuition (half a day for four weeks). For information, write Directrice, 73 Rue Notre-Dame des Champs, Paris 6.

• **Académie du Feu Sculpture Program**

In a two-month program (July and August) for students between sixteen and thirty, the Académie du Feu offers courses in wood and stone sculpture and in pottery, painting, and designing. Cost, about $25 for tuition. For information, write M. Szabo, 22 Rue Delambre, Paris 14.

• **Académie Goetz**

This is an all-summer program with courses in figurative and non-figurative art and in metalwork and etching. Cost, about $20 monthly, $10 weekly, $2 daily. For information, write Académie Goetz, 18 Rue d'Odessa, Montparnasse, Paris 14.

• **Academy of Lyric Song**

Running for four weeks from mid-June to mid-July, this program features courses in choral singing, direction, pantomime, and accompaniment. Four private lessons are included. Cost, about $5 per day. For information, write Secrétariat de l'Académie de Chant et d'Art Lyrique, Noemie Perugia-Georges Aajue, 5 Cité Pigalle, Paris 9.

• **L'Alliance Francaise**

This institution offers a two-month program (July and August) providing courses in French language at various levels of difficulty (including a program for beginners). There is also a special course for teachers of French, running from mid-July to the end of August. Cost for tuition, $12–16 per month. For information, write Ecole Pratique de l'Alliance Française, 101 Boulevard Raspail, Paris 6. *For evaluation see above, p. 162.*

• **American Summer Course at the Sorbonne**

The University of Paris offers a special six-week program, beginning about July 1, "designed for American students who want to acquire college credits while vacationing in Europe." The offering includes (1) courses in elementary and intermediate grammar; (2) a general course on French civilization; (3) courses in advanced grammar, composition, and phonetics; and (4) lecture courses in French literature, drama, and art. Tours to monuments and museums, at which attendance is compulsory, are part of the regular education program. In addition, one concert or play per week is scheduled. There are no entrance requirements. Certificates of attendance are awarded, and students may request that a transcript of grades be sent to their home university. Cost for tuition, $100. For information, write American Summer Course at the Sorbonne, La Sorbonne, 47 Rue des Ecoles, Paris 5. *This program is operated along the lines of an American undergraduate college and, being restricted to Americans, provides for no classroom contact with foreign students.*

• **Atelier del Debbio**

Modeling, design, and sculpture taught from July through September. Minimum age: eighteen. Cost, $90 for tuition. For information, write Professor Del Debbio, 11 Impasse Ronsin, Paris 15.

• **Studios of Sacred and Monumental Art**

This program specializes in religious and monumental art. Students must be at least eighteen and must intend to pursue art careers. Other prerequisite: work in previous art courses. Cost, about $20 per month. For information, write M. Raymond Delmarre, Grand Prix de Rome, 8 Place de Furstenberg, Paris 6.

- **Catholic Institute Summer Course, Paris**

This institution, an independent university recognized by the French government, offers courses in French language at various levels of difficulty; in French literature, philosophy, history; and in other subjects. There is a program for teachers of French. It is a very large program, with an attendance of about 1,100 students per summer, of whom about 10 per cent are generally Americans. There is a single four-week session in July, and the program is rather intensive; classes are held six days a week. Cost for tuition, $34, room and board, $110–$150. For information, write Directeur des Cours d'Eté, 99 Rue de Rennes, Paris. *For evaluation see above, p. 163.*

- **Ecole du Louvre**

There are two 2-week sessions in this program, which is held in July. The first half of the month is devoted to courses in the history of French architecture and sculpture; the second half to courses in the history of French painting. A diploma may be earned by passing an examination. Cost, about $10 per session for tuition. For information, write Secrétariat de l'Ecole Louvre, 34 Quai du Louvre, Paris 1. *A first-rate program of high-level, well-integrated lectures, each series given by an authority in the field.*

- **Ecole Paul Colin**

This is a ten-day course in late August with classes in design, painting, and graphic art. Minimum age: sixteen. Cost, tuition per month, about $35 (full day) and $20 (half day). For information, write Ecole Paul Colin, 11 Rue des Martyrs, Paris.

- **European College of Social and Economic Science Summer Course**

This private college offers a four-week course of lectures and discussions on contemporary European society open only to college graduates. Knowledge of French is necessary. There are visits to historic places and important factories in the areas, and the fourth week of the program consists of an extensive optional tour to the sites of various international organizations. Cost for tuition and study trip, $180, separately, $100. For information, write College Européen des Sciences Sociales et Economiques, 184 Boulevard Saint Germain, Paris 6. *This program centers around a fairly close-knit subject, but the system of lectures by a large number of different specialists makes it difficult to maintain unity and continuity. A considerable number of French students participate.*

• **Institute of Phonetics Vacation Course**

Two 3-week sessions dealing with the pronunciation and intonation of the French language, running from mid-June to the end of July, offered by an institute that is part of the University of Paris. Because of the specialized nature of the program, considerable knowledge of French is necessary. Cost, $24 per session for tuition. The work is essentially practical in nature. For information, write Secrétariat, Institute de Phonétique, 19 Rue des Bernardins, Paris 5.

• **Jacques Lecoq Mime Theater**

For qualified professional artists and teachers over twenty-one, this is a four-week course (in July) in the art of mime. Cost, about $100 per month. For information, write Jacques Lecoq, Mime Théâtre, 83 Rue du Bac, Paris 7.

• **Le Stage Mondial de la Danse, Paris**

Classical, neoclassical, modern, French, and Spanish dance for beginners, advanced students, and professionals. The program runs from early to mid-July. Cost, about $60 for tuition. For information, write Directrice du Stage Mondial de la Danse, 19 Rue de Verdun, 11 Carcassonne.

• **Paris Academy of Music**

This six-week program runs from early July to early August in Paris and then for two weeks in August in Nice. Private lessons are given in voice, piano, orchestral instruments, theory, and conducting.

There are also lectures, vocal and instrumental groups, clinics, and tours. Cost, about $600 for tuition, room, partial board. For information, write Paris Academy of Music, 25 Rue Saint-Didier, Paris 16.

• Schola Cantorum Program in Dance and Music

Courses in music are given in this program for four weeks in July. Courses in classical, folk, and modern dance are given for a week in September. Minimum age: fifteen. For information, including costs, write (music) M. R. Richard, 25 Rue Saint-Didier, Paris 16; (dance) Mme. Jacqueline du Bousquet, 130 Avenue de Versailles, Paris 16.

• Serge Rachmaninoff Conservatory

This is a four-week program (July) with instruction in various instruments, in voice, and in classical dance. Only experienced musicians are admitted. Cost, about $25 per month for one-hour lesson. For information, write Conservatoire Serge Rachmaninoff, 26 Avenue de New York, Paris 16.

• Sorbonne Summer Program

There are three sections in this program: late June to late July; late June to mid-August; and mid-July to mid-August. Courses are given in all levels of French language, in French civilization, and in French phonetics. A certificate may be earned. Cost, about $40–$140 for tuition, depending on selection of courses and length of program. For information, write Cours d'Eté, Bureau de Renseignements, 47 Rue des Ecoles, Paris 5.

• Summer School for Foreign Teachers of French

This school, connected with the Sorbonne, offers a five-week summer session (early July to mid-August) for teachers and advanced students of French, with two main courses: (1) language study, including exercises in translation, pronunciation, and conversation on a medium, advanced, and very advanced level; and (2) lectures and seminars in contemporary French literature. Each course runs about 18 hours per week. The entrance requirements are junior standing at least and a good working knowledge of French. Certificates are granted on examination, and a diploma in French language and literature is awarded on successful completion of two summer sessions. Cost, $12 for tuition. For information, write Secrétariat de l'Institue des Professeurs de Français à l'Etranger-Sorbonne, 46 Rue St. Jacques, Paris. *For evaluation, see above, p. 163.*

Pau

• Institute of French Studies for Foreigners

This institute, under the joint control of the overlapping universities of Bordeaux and Toulouse, offers a series of three- and five-week sessions between mid-July and the end of August. Courses in French language are offered at various levels of difficulty along with an advanced program of language and French civilization for teachers of French. A basic knowledge of French is required for beginners' courses, and students must be at least eighteen years of age. Cost, about $130–$160 (three weeks) and $230 (five weeks) for tuition, room, and board. For information, write, Institut à Etudes Françaises pour Etrangers, Villa Formose, Allée de Morlaas, Pau. *This program is apparently more closely supervised by the sponsoring universities than is common among French summer schools. Classes are relatively small, and a modern language laboratory is available. There is an additional advantage: about a hundred French students, participants in a program of British and North American studies held concurrently at the Institute, are in frequent contact with the students in the French-language programs.*

Poitiers

• Center for Advanced Study of Medieval Civilization, Poitiers

Sponsored by the University of Poitiers, this program consists of a course of lectures on medieval France, running from mid-July to mid-August, and is open only to advanced students holding the equivalent of an M.A. at least. Applicants must also be twenty-four years old and able to understand French. Two letters from medievalists and a curriculum vitae must be submitted. Cost, $20 tuition and $90 for room and board. For information, write Directeur, Centre d'Etudes Supérieures de Civilisation Mediévale, 24 Rue de la Cahine, Poitiers. *A program for research specialists only. Poitiers contains a large library of medieval materials, and many European specialists participate, as well as an occasional American.*

Quimper

• **University of Rennes Program**

This program is divided into five levels, including an advanced course for teachers of French. It runs from mid-July to mid-August, and students may participate for two or four weeks. Advanced students take courses in French civilization taught by university professors. Cost, $30 for tuition (four weeks). Room and board, available $3 per day. For information, write Maître de Conférences au C.L.U. de Brest, 15 Rue Paul-Verlaine, 29 Quimper.

La Rochelle

• **Institute of French Studies**

This institute, nominally under the jurisdiction of the University of Poitiers, offers courses in French language at various levels of difficulty and a course in French literature for advanced students. The program runs from mid-July to early September, but students may enroll for as brief a period as two weeks. The minimum age is seventeen. Cost, about $6 per day for tuition, room, and board. For information, write Directeur L'Institut d'Etudes Françaises, 14 Rue du Palais, La Rochelle. *This school would seem to be especially suited for younger students and beginners, since classes are relatively small and there is more supervision of the students than at most French summer schools. In addition, a small number of French students eat with the participants and provide general guidance.*

Royan

• **Audio-Visual Language Center**

A six-week course for beginners in French language and a four-week course for intermediate and advanced students. Cost for tuition, $80 (four weeks), $110 (six weeks). For information, write M. l'Administrateur, C.A.R.E.L., Palais des Congrès, Royan 17.

St. Malo

• **University of Rennes Summer Course**

A program primarily in intermediate and advanced French and a more advanced program in French literature at various levels of difficulty. There is also a program for teachers of French. The program runs from mid-July to late August and is divided into three 3-week sessions. Cost, for tuition, $20–$40. For information, write Cours d'Eté de l'Université, Faculté des Lettres, Place Hoche, Rennes.

Strasbourg

• **University of Strasbourg Summer Course**

Courses in French language at various levels of difficulty, including courses for beginners and for teachers of French. There is a parallel program of instruction in German in this bilingual city. The program runs from early July to late August. Students must be at least sixteen years of age. There are about 500 students in the French program and 100 in the German; of these about 10 per cent are usually Americans. Cost, $10–$15 per week for tuition. Room and board available. For information, write Secrétariat des Cours de Vacances, Palais de l'Université, Strasbourg. *This program is situated in a moderately sized, well-located city, and relatively few Americans attend. Students in the university dormitories report excellent opportunities to meet French students in residence there. The chief drawback is the large size of the classes, especially during the early weeks of the session.*

Tours

- **Institute of French Studies**

Courses in the French language at various levels of difficulty and a program of lectures on French civilization for advanced students offered by an institute nominally under the control of the University of Poitiers. Three 1-month sessions during the summer. There are no entrance requirements. Students range in age from the mid-teens to the sixties. Cost, $20–$80 for tuition. Room and board available. For information, write Secrétariat Administratif de l'Institut de Touraine, 1 Rue de la Grandière, Tours. *This large institution offers good but rather old-fashioned instruction in French and is located in an area where most people speak French with an excellent accent. It is very crowded, however, and represents something of the character of a factory.*

- **Center for Advanced Study of the Renaissance**

A course of lectures on the French Renaissance, running for three weeks in early July. It is open only to advanced students holding the equivalent of an M.A. Applicants must have a good knowledge of French. Cost $40 for three weeks. For information write Secrétariat, C.E.S. Renaissance, 59 Rue Nericault-Destouches, Tours. *This program is for research specialists only. Many European experts participate, as well as an occasional American.*

Ustaritz

- **International University of the Pyrénées**

Sponsored by the Catholic University of Toulouse, this mid-July to mid-August program deals with themes related to contemporary civilization. Cost $15–$25, depending on length of stay. For information, write Secrétariat du Collège International des Pyrénées, 31 Rue de la Fonderie, Toulouse. *This program is for students with a good knowledge of French. It has the advantage of being attended by a considerable number of French students (about 25 per cent), since it is not a language school.*

Vichy

• University of Clermont Cavilam Program

This program consists of four-week sessions held throughout the summer. Courses are given in professional subjects. Costs, $15–$30 a week; room and board, about $5 daily. For information, write Cavilam, B.P. 164, 03 Vichy.

• International Cultural Institute

All levels of French language are taught here, and advanced students take courses in French history, culture, and literature. The program runs from early July to late August and may be taken for any length of time over two weeks. Certificates may be earned. Cost, $15–$40. For information, write Director, International Cultural Institute, Rue de Maréchal Foch, 03 Vichy. *Although Vichy is crowded with tourists in the summer, it maintains an authentic provincial atmosphere. This program is well run and is recommended especially for students with only a minimal background in French.*

GERMANY*

Bonn

• Bonn Music Program

Held in connection with the annual Beethoven Festival, from mid-September to early October, this program features advanced music courses in German, English, and French. Cost for tuition, $50. For information, write Staatsliche Hochschule für Musik, Dagobert-Strasse 38, Cologne.

* For more details on German programs, see the annual *Ferien- und Sprachkurse an den Hochschulen der Bundersrepublik Deutschland,* copies of which may be obtained by writing to Deutscher Akademischer Austauschdienst, Nassestrasse 11, Bonn.

• **University of Bonn International Vacation Course**

This two-week program, starting about the middle of July and intended primarily for foreign students, teachers, scholars, and journalists, consists of lectures and discussions on current German political, economic, and cultural issues. Extensive visits to various educational institutions and governmental offices are designed to acquaint participants with Germany's position in the postwar world. Since lectures and discussions are in German, a working knowledge of the language is an absolute prerequisite for participation. For information, including costs, write Akademisches Auslandsamt der Universität Bonn, Nassestrasse 11, Bonn. *The lectures are delivered by leading parliamentarians, party officials, union leaders, economists, journalists, and university professors. This program is not— nor is it intended to be—an academic undertaking.*

• **University of Bonn Summer Program**

This three-week program in German language and civilization, starting about August 1, is offered in the famous Rhineland city which is now the capital of Germany. Language courses at all levels of difficulty are supplemented by lectures and seminars on literature, linguistics, art, politics, and so on. Classes are small (fifteen to twenty), and each seminar group works on one topic for the duration of the course. A diploma is available on examination. Cost for tuition, $15. For information, write Akademisches Auslandsamt der Universität Bonn, Nassestrasse 11, Bonn. *This is a serious, well-run program especially suitable for beginners and intermediate students of German. For those interested in economics and politics, the proximity to the German seat of government also affords unusual advantages.*

Cologne

• **University of Cologne Language Course**

This is a two-month program in September and October offering courses in the German language at various levels of difficulty. Students must be at least seventeen years old. Cost for tuition, about

$15. For information, write Akademisches Auslandsamt, Universitätsstrasse 16, Cologne.

Darmstadt

• **Kranichsteiner Musikinstitut**

Advanced courses in modern music (including composition, conducting, and theory) held in three languages from early August to early September. Cost for tuition, room, and board, $75. For information, write Magistrat der Stadt, Kranichsteiner Musikinstitut, Nieder-Ranstadter Strasse 190, Darmstadt.

Erlangen

• **University of Erlangen-Nürnberg Summer Program**

Noncredit lectures on the role of Germany in modern Europe, held in the first three weeks of July. German language is taught at all levels, and some knowledge of German is required for the lectures. Cost for tuition, room, and board, about $120. For information, write University of Erlangen-Nürnberg, Schlossplatz 4, Erlangen.

Frankfurt am Main

• **University of Frankfurt Summer Program**

This four-week program in German language and literature, beginning about August 1, offers courses at various levels of difficulty, including a course for teachers and specialists in *Germanistik*. Entrance requirements call for a minimum age of eighteen, university standing, and some knowledge of German (even for the elementary course). A diploma is available on examination, but only to students in the intermediate and advanced sections. Cost for tuition and excursions, about $30. For information, write Akademische Auslandsstelle, University of Frankfurt, Mertonstrasse 17, Frankfurt a.M. *This program places major emphasis on literature, offering a different major theme each year, and is most suitable for students on the intermediate and moderately advanced levels. One advantage of the program is the group of about fifteen German university students who act as tutor-guides for the participants.*

Freiburg

• **University of Freiburg Summer Program, Freiburg**

This one-month program, given in August, offers intensive courses in the German language and lectures on German civilization. To be admitted students must be at least eighteen years of age, with a good knowledge of German. Cost for tuition, about $50. For information, write Akademisches Auslandsamt der Universität Freiburg, Belfortstrasse 11, Freiburg im Breisgau.

Göttingen

• **University of Gottingen**

Courses in German language and culture and a program of lectures on international affairs from early August to late September. Cost for tuition, about $120; for study trip, about $70. For information, write Fritjof Nansen Haus, Merkelstrasse 4, Göttingen.

Hamburg

• **University of Hamburg Summer Program**

This four-week session, starting at the beginning of August, is intended primarily for teachers of German and specialists in Germanic studies. While there are courses in German literature, the main emphasis is on phonetics, intonation, and modern methods of teaching German to foreigners. Lectures are given in fairly large sections (about seventy) but language classes are held to about fifteen and are broken down by nationality groups. A language laboratory is available to participants, and its use as an instructional device receives considerable attention. Cost for tuition, room, and board, about $110. For information, write University of Hamburg, von-Melle-Park 6, Hamburg 13. *This seems to be an excellent pro-*

gram for linguists and teachers of German who want a refresher course in the most modern methods of teaching German to foreigners. The lectures on German literature are only an ancillary part of the program. A major strong point of the program is housing: most of the participants live with the families of teachers in the Hamburg area.

Heidelberg

• University of Heidelberg Summer Program

This four-week course in German language and literature, starting about the beginning of August, is offered in one of Germany's most charming and picturesque university cities. In addition to language courses at various levels of difficulty, there is a course for teachers and specialists in *Germanistik*. Entrance requirements include university standing and a basic knowledge of German. Cost for tuition, room, and board, about $130. For information, write Akademisches Auslandsamt, Universität Heidelberg, Grabengasse 14, Heidelberg. *Though consistently one of the most popular summer schools in Europe, this program suffers from large classes, an above-average number of Americans, and a pervasive holiday atmosphere. Also, the presence of countless tourists and the proximity of the European Headquarters of the U.S. Army make Heidelberg less than an ideal place for contact with German life.*

Kiel

• University of Kiel Summer Program

This four-week program offers courses in German language and civilization. Language courses at various levels of difficulty are supplemented by lectures on "Contemporary Germany." Participants must have a good knowledge of German. Cost for tuition, room, and board, about $110. For information, write Ferienkursburo der Universitä Kiel, Olshausenstrasse 40–60, Kiel.

Mainz

- **University of Mainz Program, Mainz**

This three-week program in German language and civilization, starting about the beginning of August, takes place in the ancient Rhine city of Mainz. Language courses on various levels of difficulty are supplemented by a series of lectures on diverse topics. A minimum age of eighteen and some knowledge of German are among the entrance requirements. Cost for tuition, room, and board, about $130. For information, write Akademisches Auslandsamt der Universität Mainz, Box 606, Mainz. *One advantage of this program is the small percentage of English-speaking participants.*

Marburg

- **University of Marburg Summer Program**

This three-week program, starting in mid-July, offers courses in German language and civilization. The lectures revolve around a central theme of "Germany and Europe" such as "The Goethe Era." Participants must have a good knowledge of German. Cost for tuition, room, and board, about $100. For information, write Internationaler Ferienkurs, Philipps-Universität, Beigenstrasse 10, Marburg (Lahn). *An advantage of this course is the small percentage of English-speaking participants.*

Munich

- **Goethe-Institut Summer Course for Teachers**

The institute offers a series of three-week "refresher" courses for teachers of German, running from early July to mid-September, in major cities like Munich, Nürnberg, Stuttgart, Lübeck, and Bonn. An additional one-week guided study tour to Berlin is an optional part of the course. The primary purpose of this course is not to perfect the participants' command of the language, but rather to afford him general exposure to German life and culture through lectures, discussions, and excursions. A diploma is available on examination. For information, including costs, write Goethe-Institut, Lenbachplatz 3, Munich. *The virtue of this course is that it provides teachers of German with a general and introductory orientation to German life, but it is not sufficiently long, intensive, or systematic to be very effective.*

• **Goethe-Institut Language Course for Foreigners**

This institute, operating through study centers located in small West German towns, offers eight-week courses at various levels of difficulty in the German language. The program extends from June through September, and its primary purpose is to give beginners intensive training in the understanding and use of modern conversational German. Foreigners preparing themselves for study at a German university may choose to register for two 8-week sessions. The program consists of 33 class hours per week. The only entrance requirement is a minimum age of eighteen. Cost, about $320. For information, write Goethe-Institut, Lenbachplatz 3, Munich. *This is an excellent program for teaching German to beginners. The location of the study centers in small towns not only gives the student a pervasive exposure to the language but also brings him into closer contact with German life. An added advantage is the small size of the classes.*

• **International Summer Course**

This three-week course, starting about August 1 and sponsored by Munich's institutions of higher learning, consists of lectures on Germany's role in the postwar world as well as informal excursions and guided visits to places of historic interest. The course is open to students with a good working knowledge of German. Cost for tuition, room, and board, $100. For information, write Akademische Auslandsstelle Munchen, E. V. Leopoldstrasse 15, Munich. *This program provides a journalistic orientation session on postwar Germany. The lectures, though presented by leading personalities, do not add up to an integrated course. The emphasis throughout is non-academic.*

• **University of Munich Summer Program**

This one-month course, starting about August 1, offers intermediate and advanced courses in the German language, seminars in German literature, and lectures on German history and civilization. Since there is no course for beginners, a fair knowledge of German is a prerequisite. Diplomas are available on examination, but only to those registered in the advanced sessions. Cost for tuition, $20. For information, write Deutschkurse für Ausländer, Adelheidstrasse 13. *This program offers good instruction for intermediate students of German, but suffers from its location in a big city where many people speak English and American tourists and GI's are plentiful.*

Münster

• **University of Münster Summer Program**

This three-week program, starting at the beginning of August and designed especially for specialists in *Germanistik,* offers a monographic course in German literature which deals with a different field every year (drama, poetry, novel, and so on). Cost for tuition, room, and board, about $80. For further information, write Auslands-Kommittee, University of Münster, Münster. *This program is especially suited for advanced students and teachers interested in a refresher course in German literature, rather than phonetics and intonation.*

Rothenburg

• **Summer Vacation Course in Art**

This program, sponsored by the Tourist Association of Rothenburg, offers a series of two-week sessions in painting from May through September. Entrance requirements include a minimum age of eighteen and a knowledge of German. For information, write Verkehrsverein e.V. Rothenburg o/d Tauber.

Stuttgart

• **Stuttgart Technical University Summer Program**

This one-month program, starting late in June, consists of a series of lectures on science and technology, architecture, economics, philosophy, and literature; plant visits and excursions; and courses in the German language for beginners and advanced students. The entrance requirements are junior standing at least and some knowledge of German. Cost for tuition, room, and board, about $80. For information, write Büro für Ferienkurse, Technische Hochschule Stuttgart, Keplerstrasse 11, Stuttgart.

GREAT BRITAIN*

Bangor

• **University of Wales Summer School**

Subjects taught at this school, which runs from mid-July to early August, are British life and institutions, the culture of Wales, music, and Russian language. Cost, about $110. For information, write Summer Schools Secretary, University College of Bangor, Wales.

Birmingham

• **Birmingham University of Roman Villa Excavation Courses**

Birmingham sponsors four courses in excavation techniques in Romano-British digs. One course, held near Cirencester, Gloucester, runs three weeks, from early to late July. The other three, each two weeks in duration, are held in Wroxeter, Shropshire, in July and August. Cost for two weeks, about $60. For information, write Department of Extra-Mural Studies, Birmingham University, Edgbaston 15, Birmingham.

* For more details on British summer programs, see the annual listings "Short Courses and Summer Schools in Britain" prepared by the British Information Services References and Library Division, 845 Third Avenue, New York, N.Y. 10022.

Chester

• **University of Liverpool International Summer School**

This university offers short courses in literature, languages, art, architecture, and other subjects, from late July to early August. Applicants must be eighteen years of age or older. Students take only one course per week, working in groups in the mornings and listening to general lectures in the evenings. Cost for tuition, room, and board, about $45 per week. For information, write Director of Extra-Mural Studies, University of Liverpool, 9 Abercromby Square, Liverpool 7. *Chester is a city of much historic interest. Because of the brevity of the individual courses, however, little academic benefit may be expected.*

Durham

• **University of Durham Summer School**

Durham offers a course in archaeological excavation at Corbridge, in Northumberland. The program lasts two weeks, beginning in late July. Minimum age, eighteen. Cost for tuition, room, and board, about $40–$70. For information, write Director of Adult Education, Durham University, 32 Old Elvet, Durham.

Hull

• **Hull University Summer Programs**

Hull University sponsors a program in drama and another in various aspects of history and historiography. Both programs are held in York in late July and early August. Cost for tuition, room, and board, about $50. For information, write Department of Adult Education, Hull University, 195 Cottingham Road, Hull.

Leeds

• **Leeds University Course in Medieval Archaeology**

The field work for this course is done at Sandal Castle, near Leeds, and the course runs for a week in late August. For information, including costs, write Department of Extra-Mural Studies, The University, Leeds 2.

London

• **City of London College Summer Program**

A three-week program of courses in English and international law, running from mid-July to mid-August. Participants must be at least eighteen years of age. Cost for tuition, about $30. For information, write Head of Summer School, City of London College, Moorgate, London, E.C. 2.

• **London University Course in Medieval Art**

This course is held in France and England for two weeks in mid-July. For information, including costs, write Mrs. C. J. Robertson, Combe Hay Manor, Nr. Bath, Somerset.

Manchester

• **University of Manchester**

This university offers a two-week course in liberal arts subjects during the last half of July. A number of excursions are included. Cost for tuition, room, and board, about $40 per week. For information, write Director of Extra-Mural Studies, University of Manchester, Manchester.

Various Cities

• **Four British University Summer Schools**

The universities of Birmingham, London, and Oxford and the Scottish universities (held at Edinburgh) sponsor programs running from early July to mid-August. These are graduate-level courses of top quality, and only highly qualified upperclassmen are eligible. Each program covers a different topic, and these topics vary from year to year. For instance, the topics in 1968 were: Birmingham (at

Stratford on Avon), Shakespeare and Elizabethan Drama; London, Twentieth Century English Literature; Oxford, Seventeenth-Century English History, Art, and Literature; and Edinburgh, the Enlightenment in Britain. Birmingham: cost for tuition, about $130; all-inclusive, $375. London: cost for tuition $180; all-inclusive, $375. Oxford: cost for tuition, $140; all-inclusive, $400. Edinburgh, cost for tuition, $175; all-inclusive, $350. For information, write Information and Reference Division, Institute of International Education, 809 United Nations Plaza, New York, N.Y. 10017.

SCOTLAND

Edinburgh

• **Edinburgh University Summer School in Drama**

Running from mid-August to early September, this program is held in picturesque "Aulde Reekie." Cost for tuition, room, and board, about $140. For information, write Department of Adult Education, Edinburgh University, 11 Buccleuch Place, Edinburgh 8.

Glasgow

• **Glasgow University Summer Programs**

Glasgow University sponsors two summer programs, one in art and music and the other in marine biology. For information, write Glasgow University, Glasgow, W.2.

IRELAND (Eire)

Dublin

• **Trinity College Summer Program**

A course of lectures and tutorial sessions on Irish civilization and Anglo-Irish literature, given in a two- and a four-week session in July. Cost for tuition, about $35, with room and board about $70. For information, write The Registrar, International Summer School, 6 Trinity College, Dublin.

• **University College Summer School**

A course in Irish history and civilization, offered during the last half of July. Tours and excursions are included. Those attending must be at least seventeen years of age. Cost for tuition, $30. For information, write Brian Farrell, Secretary, University College Summer School, 86 St. Stephan's Green, Dublin.

Sligo

• **Yeats International Summer School**

A series of lectures and seminars on the life and works of W. B. Yeats is given by various scholars in a two-week session during the last half of August. Cost for tuition, about $60. For information, write Secretary, Yeats International Summer School, 12 Stephan Street, Sligo. *This program consistently attracts important scholars, although anyone interested in Yeats may attend.*

ISRAEL

Jerusalem

• **Hebrew Union College Summer Institute on Near East Civilizations**

Courses in Hebrew language and literature and archaeology (at excavations at Tel Gezer). Students study in Israel from late June to early August and then spend five days in Greece, where the program ends. The program is conducted in English. Prerequisite: B.A. degree. Cost for tuition, room, board, and tours, about $1,620. For information, write Hebrew Union College Biblical and Archaeological School, 40 West 68th Street, New York, N.Y. 10023.

• **Hebrew University Summer Program**

Running from mid-July to late August, this program has courses in the archaeology of the Holy Land, the Dead Sea Scrolls, government and politics of Israel, education in Israel, and modern Hebrew literature. Prerequisite: one year of college. Conducted in English.

Cost for tuition, $40–$80 per course; room, $40. For information, write American Friends of the Hebrew University, 11 East 69th Street, New York, N.Y. 10021.

Ramat Gan

• **Bar-Ilan University Summer Session**

This program runs from early July to late August and features courses in Jewish thought, Israeli politics, Hebrew language and literature, and English literature. Classes are conducted in English; housing is in dormitories. Cost for tuition, room, board, and transportation, about $950. For information, write Office of Admissions, Bar-Ilan University, 641 Lexington Avenue, New York, N.Y. 10022.

ITALY*

Aosta

• **University College of Federal Studies**

Running from early July to mid-September, this is a program in economics, sociology, European studies, and development aid, conducted in French. The program is mainly for graduate students. Cost for tuition, $70. For information, write Centre International de Formation Européenne, 6 Rue de Trevise, Paris 9.

Bressanone

• **University of Padua Summer Program**

This program, located in the majestic mountain country of South Tyrol, consists of several sessions from July through September in Italian language and civilization. Open to foreign students who are high-school graduates, it runs concurrently with the summer session for Italian students regularly enrolled at the University of Padua.

* For more details on Italian summer courses, see the annual *Summer Courses in Italy*, which can be obtained by writing to the Italian Cultural Institute, 686 Park Avenue, New York, N.Y. 10021.

Cost for tuition, about $10. For information, write Segretaria dei Corso Estivi per Straniere, Università de Padova, Padova. *Though this program offers little classroom language instruction, it provides students who have some knowledge of Italian with an excellent opportunity to observe Italian university life. Each foreign student shares a dormitory room with three Italians and can participate fully in all student activities. Rarely is any English heard on the summer campus.*

Cumae

• Vergilian Society Summer Program

This program offers four 2-week sessions and a 6-week session running from late June to early September for teachers and advanced students of classical civilization. Located in the historic region of ancient Campania around Naples, the program consists of guided tours to archaeological sites, plus lectures on classical literature, history, and art. (All lectures are in English.) The program is open to upper-level college students and graduates. An optional supplementary tour of southern Italy, Sicily, and the Rome area follows the first session and lasts about six weeks. Cost for tuition, room, board, and trips, $350 and/or $850. For information, write Classics Department, University of Georgia, Athens, Georgia.

Florence

• University of Florence Summer Program

This seven-week program, starting at the beginning of July and offered in one of Europe's most renowned art centers, consists of courses in the Italian language at various levels of difficulty, as well as lecture courses on Italian art, literature, music, and politics. Cost for tuition, about $35. For information, write Secretary of the Centro di Cultura per Stranieri, Via S. Gallo 25/A, Florence. *Despite the advantages of Florence for art students and art historians, the high percentage of American participants detracts from the language section of the program.*

- Dante Alighieri Language School

The summer semester at this school runs from early July to late November. Courses are given in Italian language, art, history, and culture. Cost for tuition, about $60. For information, write Centro Linguistico Italiano "Dante Alighieri," Via Magliabechi 7, Sante Croce, Florence.

Gargnano

- University of Milan Summer Program

This program, situated in a small town on Lake Garda, consists of two one-month sessions in July and August. Courses in the Italian language at various levels of difficulty are supplemented by lectures on Italian civilization. Cost for tuition, about $30. For information, write Segretaria dei Corso Internazionali della Università di Milano, Via Festa del Perdono 7, Milan. *This course offers good language instruction in small classes. There is close contact between the students and the Italian faculty. Despite the distractions of its attractive location, the program is serious and academically oriented.*

Milan

- The International School of Milan

The International School gives courses in all levels of Italian language in three- and four-week sessions from late June to late September. Cost for tuition, about $50. For information, write The International School of Milan, Via Senato 28, Milan.

Naples

- International Center for Archeological Studies

This is a program consisting of four 2-week sessions (in July and August) on Greek, Italic, and Roman civilization in Campania, conducted in Italian with some English translation. Cost for tuition, about $70. For information, write "Europa," Centro Relazioni e Scambi Culturali con l'Estero, Via Mezzocannone 119, Naples.

Perugia

• **Academy of Fine Arts**

This organization provides instruction in painting and sculpture in two one-month sessions from July through August. Students who complete three sessions receive a diploma. Interpreters are provided to assist students who do not speak Italian. Cost for tuition, about $40. For information, write Academy of Fine Arts, Piazza S. Francesco al Prato 5, Perugia.

• **Italian University for Foreigners**

Although this university maintains no special summer program, one of its three sessions each year runs from early July to the end of September. Courses are offered in Italian at various levels of difficulty and in Italian history and culture. Students must be at least fifteen years old; they may enroll for periods of one, two, or three months. Cost for tuition, about $20 per month. For information, write Secretary, Italian University for Foreigners, Palazzo Gallenga, Perugia. *Although a wide variety of courses is offered at this large institution, the high percentage of Americans enrolled is an important disadvantage.*

Ponza

• **International Center of Mediterranean Culture**

This program is held on the Island of Ponza, off Anzio. Courses are given in all levels of Italian language. Students take three-week programs from early July to late September. Cost for tuition, about $20. For information, write Centro Internazionale di Cultura Mediterranea, Via Silvio Pellico 8, Milan.

Ravenna

• **International Center of Mosaic Studies, Ravenna**

There are four twenty-day programs held between late June and early August, each consisting of courses in the history and style of mosaics, with studio work. For information, including costs, write Segretaria del Centro Internazionale di Studi per l'Insegnamento del Mosaico, c/o Azienda Autonoma di Soggiorno e Turismo, Via San Vitale 2, Ravenna.

Rimini

• **University of Bologna Language Course, Rimini**

This program offers two 4-week courses during July and August in art history and Italian for beginners and more advanced students. A series of lectures on Italian culture is also provided. Cost for tuition, about $35. For information, write Segretaria, Corso Estivo per Stranieri dell'Università di Bologna, Via Cairoli 69, Rimini. For reservations at the dormitory, which are limited, write Casa della Gioventù Studiosa, same address.

Rome

• **American Academy Summer Session**

A six-week course in Roman civilization that runs from late June to early August. The course is intended for graduate students and teachers, and although classes are held in English, a good knowledge of Latin is essential. Cost for tuition, $150. For information, write American Academy in Rome, 101 Park Avenue, New York, N.Y. 10017.

• **Catholic University of the Sacred Heart**

The Catholic University offers various courses in Italian language (all levels), business, and (in English) classical, Renaissance, and medieval studies. The program runs from late July to late August.

Cost for tuition, $40; for room and board, $150. For information, write Università Cattolica del Sacro Cuore, Summer Courses, Via della Pineta Sacchetti 644, Rome.

• Dante Alighieri Society Summer Program

This program offers two one-month summer sessions during June and July consisting of an intensive course in the Italian language at various levels of difficulty and a course in the history of art. Cost for tuition, from $10 to $20 per course. For information, write Secretary, Società Nazionale Dante Alighieri, Piazza Firenze 27, Rome.

Sante Margherita Ligure

• University of Genoa Summer Program

Running from mid-August to mid-September, this program offers courses in Italian language and culture. Cost for tuition, $20. For information write, Segretaria dei Corsi Internazionale di Studi Italiani, Università degli Studi, Via Balbi 5, Genoa.

Siena

• Academia Musicale Chigiana Summer Program

This academy offers courses in instrumental music, voice, conducting, and composition for advanced students, the program running from mid-July to mid-September. Only highly qualified students are accepted. Courses are conducted in English, Italian, and French. Cost, for tuition, about $30. For information, write Academia Musicale Chigiana, Palazzo Chigi, Saracini, Siena.

• University of Siena Summer Program

This eight-week program, running from mid-July to mid-September, offers courses in the Italian language at various levels of difficulty, along with a series of lectures on Italian literature, history, and art. Cost for tuition about $15 per month. For information, write Segretaria della Scuola per Stranieri, Università de Siena, Siena. *One advantage of this program is its location in an area where "proper, pure, and harmonious" Italian is spoken.*

Urbino

• **University of Urbino Summer Program**

A four-week program (in August) in Italian language at all levels of difficulty. Cost for tuition, about $20. For information, write University of Urbino, Via Saffi 2, Urbino.

Varenna

• **Summer Courses in Physics**

Three courses in advanced physics running from late June to late July and from late July to mid-August. For advanced graduate students, conducted in English. Cost for tuition, room, and board, $120. For information write Società Italiana di Fisica, Via Irnerio 46, Bologna.

Venice

• **Benedetto Marcello Conservatory**

A program, running from early August to mid-September, in Italian opera and instrumental music. For information, including costs, write Benedetto Marcello Conservatory, Venice.

• **Giorgio Cini Foundation**

Contemporary art and culture in Italy, taught from early to late September. For information, including costs, write Fondazione Giorgio Cini, Isola de San Giorgio Maggiore, Venice.

• **"Musical Vacations" Program**

Although this program in Italian music is primarily intended for musicians and advanced students, it may be audited by others.

Each year the works of one Italian composer are featured. Cost for tuition, about $30. For information, write Segretaria delle Vacanze Musicali, c/o Conservatorio di Santa Cecilia, Via dei Greci 8, Rome.

Viareggio

• **University of Pisa Summer Program**

This program, offered in a small seaport on the coast of Tuscany, consists of two 3-week sessions between mid-July and late August. Courses in Italian at various levels of difficulty are supplemented by lectures on modern Italian culture. No academic qualification is needed for admission, but students must register for a complete three-week session and must attend classes regularly. Cost for tuition, about $20. For information, write Segretaria dei Corso per Stranieri, Università di Pisa, Pisa.

Vincenza

• **International Center of Architecture**

This program, dealing with Palladio and his influence on architecture in Venice, is for advanced students and runs for three weeks in August. Cost for tuition, about $30. For information, write Centro Internazionale di Architettura "A. Palladio," Corso Fogazzaro 16, Vincenza.

JAPAN

Tokyo

• **International Christian University Summer Seminar on Japanese Area Studies**

Japanese art, religion, and politics taught in English in July and August. Cost for tuition, room, board, and transportation, about $800. For information, write Summer Seminar, International Christian University, Mitaka, Tokyo.

• **Sophia University Summer Program**

This program offers courses in Japanese history, civilization, and related subjects, held in English from early July to mid-August. A ten-day "study observation" tour is included in the program. Low cost transportation from Vancouver to Tokyo is available to groups. Cost for tuition, room, board, and transportation, round-trip from West Coast, $1,200. For information, write Sophia University Associates, 211 East 87th Street, New York, N.Y. 10021.

LEBANON

Beirut

• **American University Summer School**

From mid-June to mid-August a program of courses in the liberal arts is offered in the school of arts and science. For information, including costs write Registrar, American University, Beirut.

MEXICO

Acapulco

• **Acapulco Summer School**

Courses in Spanish languages at all levels and in Spanish and Mexican culture, in July and August. For information, including costs, write Escuela de Verano de Acapulco, Quebrada 68, Acapulco.

Chihuahua

• **Mexican–North American Institute of Cultural Relations**

This program, which lasts from June through September, provides a variety of courses in Spanish at various levels of difficulty. In addition there is a course in Mexican civilization held in Spanish and English. Cost for tuition, about $50. For information, write Director of Courses, Instituto Mexicano Norteamericano de Relaciones Culturales, Aldama 9, Altos Chihuahua.

Cuernavaca

• **Cidoc Summer Program**

The Centro Intercultural de Documentación offers courses throughout the summer in Spanish language and linguistics and in Latin American institutions, running from early June to late August. Courses are taught by local and visiting scholars. Cost for tuition, about $170 per month; room, $80–$120. For information, write Centro Intercultural de Documentación, Apartado 479, Cuernavaca.

Guadalajara

• **Mexican–North American Cultural Institute**

The Institute offers courses in all levels of Spanish language in a six-week program running from mid-June to late July and in an intensive three-and-a-half-week session running from early to late August. For information, including costs, write Instituto Cultural Mexicano-Norteamericano de Jalisco, A. C. Guadalajara, Jalisco.

• **University of Guadalajara Summer Program**

This four-week program, which lasts from early July to early August, offers courses in Spanish literature, Mexican civilization, and arts and crafts, held in Spanish and English. The only requirement is a minimum age of fifteen years. Cost for tuition, about $100; room and board, about $155. For information, write Secretary for the Summer Courses, Belen 120, Guadalajara.

Mexico City

• **Iberian–American University Summer Program**

This program for both undergraduates and graduate students is held from mid-June to late July and features courses in Spanish at all levels and Latin American culture and other subjects. There is also a teachers' program. Cost for tuition, about $170; with room and board, about $300. For information, write Summer School,

Universidad Iberoamericana, Cerro de las Torres 395, Mexico 21, D.F.

- **Institute of Comparative Law, National Institute of Mexico**

Courses in Mexican law for advanced students, conducted in English and Spanish in July and August. Cost for tuition, about $100. For information, write Institute of Comparative Law, Torre de Humanidades, Ciudad Universitaria, Mexico 5, D.F.

- **Institute of Modern Languages**

This institute offers intensive courses in Spanish language in three 4-week sessions in the summer. These courses are intended mainly for businessmen and others who need short, intensive work in spoken Spanish. For information, write Instituto de Lenguas Modernas, S.A., Reforma 509, Mexico, D.F.

- **Interpretors and Translators Institute**

Courses at all levels in Spanish language and in Mexican culture and history are offered in a six-week session running from early July to mid-August. Classes are given for 15 hours a week. For information, including costs, write Instituto de Interpretes y Traductores, Tiber 113, Mexico 5, D.F.

- **Mexican–North American Institute of Cultural Relations**

This institute offers four 3-week sessions from mid-June to mid-September, each offering 15 hours of classes per week in all levels of Spanish language. Cost for tuition, about $50. For information, write Instituto Mexicano Norteamericano de Relaciones Culturales, Hamburgo 115, Mexico 6, D.F.

- **National University of Mexico School for Foreign Students Summer Program**

This school offers courses in the Romance languages as well as courses in the civilizations of Spain, Mexico, and Latin America, some conducted in Spanish, some in English. The program runs from late June to late August, and a great many Americans attend. Those attending must be at least eighteen years of age. Cost for tuition, about $130. For information, write Summer School, Ciudad Universitaria, Mexico 5, D.F.

• **University of the Americas Summer Program**

This college is an American-type institution offering summer courses in the Spanish language and in Mexican civilization (held in English and Spanish). A course for teachers of Spanish is also offered. For information, including costs, write University of the Americas, Kilómetro 16, Carretera México-Toluca, Mexico 10, D.F.

Monterrey

• **Monterrey Institute of Technology Summer School Program**

Courses in the Spanish language at various levels of difficulty. Additional courses are available in Spanish and Latin American literature and a variety of other subjects—some held in Spanish, some in English. Students take from 10 to 20 hours of classes per week, and an M.A. degree is available. The program runs from mid-July to late August. Cost for tuition, room, and board, about $360. For information, write Escuela de Verano, Instituto Tecnológico de Monterrey, Sucursal de Correos J, Monterrey.

• **University of Nuevo Leon Summer Program**

Spanish language and culture, taught in July and August. For information, write Universidad de Nuevo León, Monterrey.

Morelia

• **University of Michoacan Summer Program**

Courses in the Spanish language at various levels of difficulty, in the teaching of Spanish, and in Mexican civilization. Concerts and lectures are arranged, and credits for transfer may be earned. Enrollment is limited to 100. The program runs from late June to early August. Cost for tuition, about $90. For information, write Secretaria de la Escuela de Verano, University of Michoacan, Santiago Tapia 403, Morelia.

Morelos

• **University of Morelos Summer Program**

Students in this program may earn up to 8 credits in courses in Spanish (all levels) and Mexican history and art. The program runs from early July to mid-August. For information, including costs, write Cursos Temporales, Humboldt 306, Cuernavaca, Morelos.

San Miguel de Allende

• **Institute Allende Summer Program**

Courses in painting, sculpture, photography, drama, writing, and other arts and in Mexican history. Instruction is given in English, but a course in Spanish language is available. The program runs from mid-June to late August. Cost for tuition, $50 per month; room and board, $3 per day. For information, write Director, Institute Allende, San Miguel de Allende, G.T.O.

• **Spanish American Academy Summer Program**

This program consists of courses in Spanish at various levels of difficulty and courses in Spanish literature and Mexican civilization, running from late June to early September. Cost for tuition (ten weeks), about $190; room and board, about $5 per day. For information, write Director, Instituto Hispano Americana, Apartado 150, San Miguel de Allende, G.T.O.

Saltillo

• **Institute for Spanish American Studies**

This is a one-month program in intensive Spanish and Latin American culture held in two sessions, late June to late July and late July to early September. There is a teacher workshop in the first session. Cost for tuition, room, and board (ten weeks), about $500. For information, write Director of Admissions, Instituto de Estudios Iberamericanos, Apartado 358, Saltillo, Coahuila.

• **International University Summer Program**

Here courses are offered in Spanish language and literature and Mexican history and culture. The program runs from mid-June to late August in six-, four-, and two-week sessions. Students live with local families. Cost for tuition, room, and board (six weeks), about $360. For information, write Universidad Internacional, Apartado 293, Saltillo, Coahuila.

• **Jaime Balmes University Summer Program**

This program runs from mid-June to mid-August and is conducted in nine-, six-, and three-week sessions. Classes are taught by local instructors. Courses include Spanish language at all levels, Spanish literature, and archaeology. An M.A. is offered. Students live with local families. Cost for tuition, room, and board, about $480 (nine weeks). For information, write Department of Spanish Languages and Literature, Apartado postal 477, Saltillo, Coahuila.

Toluca

• **University of the State of Mexico Summer School**

This program offers courses in the Spanish language and in Mexican civilization, some of which are given in Spanish, some in English. The program runs from late June to mid-August. For information, write Director of the Summer School, University of the State of Mexico, Toluca.

Xalapa

• **University of Veracruz Summer Program**

Courses in the Spanish language at various levels of difficulty and in anthropology, archaeology, and Mexican civilization, some conducted in Spanish, some in English. The program runs from late June to mid-August. Approximately seventy American students attend. For information, write School of Foreign Students, University of Veracruz, Juarez 55, Xalapa, Veracruz.

THE NETHERLANDS

Amsterdam

• **Netherlands Universities Foundation Summer Course**

Each year one of the Dutch universities sponsors a series of lectures, held during the last half of August on some aspect of world affairs. Lectures are in English. For information, including costs, write Netherlands Universities Foundation for International Cooperation (NUFFIC), Molenstraat 27, The Hague.

Nijmegen

• **Academy of International Law**

Two 3-week series of lectures on international law, open to advanced students and practicing lawyers. Lectures are in English. A diploma is awarded after examination. Cost for registration (six weeks), $20. For information, write Academy of International Law, Peace Palace, The Hague. *These are high-level lectures for specialists, but are not organized around the systematic study of a particular subject.*

• **Summer Course in Dutch**

This program consists of a course in the Dutch language, together with a series of lectures on Dutch civilization. It is geared primarily to French students or persons who can speak French, and it runs for three weeks in August. Excursions are included. For information, write Secretary, Summer Course, Ministry of Education and Science, Nieuwe Uittleg 4, The Hague.

NORWAY

Bergen

• **University of Bergen Summer School**

Running from mid-July to early August, this is a program in Norwegian language and culture. Prerequisite: one year of Norwegian. Cost for tuition, room, and board, about $100. For information, write Nordisk Institute, Allegaten 33, Bergen.

Oslo

• **University of Oslo Summer School**

Courses in the Norwegian language, civilization, social studies, and arts are given from late June to early August. In addition, there are graduate courses on Norwegian education, public health, and other topics. All classes are in English, but there is a modern language laboratory. Excursions, field trips, and social events are integrated into the programs. Participants must be college students with at least sophomore standing. Cost for tuition, room, and board, about $420. For information, write Oslo Summer School, St. Olaf College, Northfield, Minnesota. *This is a large, well-organized program on the American model, providing credits for transfer to United States colleges. Despite the fact that courses are held in English, there is considerable contact between Americans, Norwegians, and other foreign students.*

PORTUGAL

Coimbra

• **University of Coimbra Summer Program**

From mid-July to late August, courses are offered in the Portuguese language at various levels of difficulty. In addition there are classes in Portuguese literature and civilization. Cost for tuition, about $20. For information, write Secretario do Curso de Férias, Faculdade de Letras, University of Coimbra, Coimbra.

Lisbon

• **University of Lisbon Summer Program**

During July and August, classes are offered in the Portuguese language at various levels of difficulty. In addition, there are courses in Portuguese civilization, some of which are held in English. Cost for tuition, about $20. For information, write Direcção do Curso de Férias, University of Lisbon, Rua da Academia dos Ciências, Lisbon.

ROMANIA

Sinaia

• **University of Bucharest Summer Program**

A four-week program, running from late July to late August, in Romanian language and culture, for advanced teachers and students of Romance philology. For information, including costs, write Universitatea Bucuresti, secretariatul cursurilor de vara Str. Pitar Mos 7–13, Bucharest.

SPAIN*

Alicante

• **University of Valencia Summer Program**

This 2-month program, held in two sessions, June–July and August-September, organized by the Cátedra Mediterráneo of the University of Valencia, is held at the Mediterranean seaside resort of Alicante. Courses in Spanish language at various levels of difficulty are supplemented by lectures on Spanish civilization and "monographic" courses in literature, art, and music. Cost for tuition,

---

* For more details on Spanish programs, see the annual *Courses for Foreigners in Spain*, copies of which can be obtained by writing to the Office of Cultural Relations, Spanish Embassy, 1629 Columbia Road, N.W., Apt. 625, Washington, D.C. 20009.

about $20. For information write Secretario de los Cursos para Extranjeros, Universidad de Valencia, Cátedra Mediterráneo, Valencia.

Barcelona

• **University of Barcelona Summer Program**

This program is more oriented toward the serious student than the University of Barcelona's analogous program held at Palma de Mallorca. Given on the home campus of the university in the capital of Catalonia, this is a three-week program offering courses in elementary, intermediate, and advanced Spanish. It begins in early August and awards certificates on examination. There is a small charge for use of the University's swimming pool and beaches. Cost for tuition, about $20. For information, write Director del Curso de Verano, Universidad de Barcelona, Barcelona 7.

Bilbao

• **University of Deusto Summer Program**

This program offers elementary, intermediate, and advanced courses in Spanish language and culture. The program runs from the beginning of July to the middle of August. A diploma of Profesor de Español is awarded to students who complete the advanced course. Cost for tuition, about $30. For information, write Director of Summer Courses, Apartado 1, Bilbao.

Cádiz

• **University of Seville Summer Program**

This one-month program (late July to late August) is held in the ancient and fascinating port city in southwest Spain. Courses in Spanish language, literature, and art are offered. Cost for tuition, about $30. For information, write Secretario del Curso para Extranjeros, Apartado 151, Cádiz.

Granada

• **University of Granada Autumn Course**

This five-week program (mid-August to mid-September) features courses in Andalusian and Hispano-Moslem culture. Also taught are Spanish language, literature, history, and art. For information, including costs, write Curso para Extranjeros, Universidad de Granada, Granada.

Jaca

• **University of Zaragoza Summer Program**

Held in the heart of the Pyrenees, this program consists of two 4-week sessions given between mid-July and early September. Classes are offered in elementary and advanced Spanish language and in Spanish literature, culture, art, and music. Cost for tuition, about $20. For information, write Secretaría de los Cursos de Verano, Ciudad Universitaria, Zaragoza.

León

• **University of León Summer Program**

A one-month program starting in mid-July and organized by the Spanish Cultural Affairs Department. Advanced courses in Spanish literature, history, and art are offered. Both high-school and college teachers are eligible to participate. For information, including costs, write Secretario General de los Cursos de Verano para Extranjeros, Avda General Sanjurjo 2, León.

Madrid

• **Central Language School Course for Foreigners**

The Central Language School sponsors an intensive summer program in elementary, intermediate, and advanced Spanish from mid-June to mid-September. Classes are held in the evening; certificate is awarded on passing an examination. For information, including costs, write Secretaría de la Escuela Central de Idiomas, Calle de Jesús Maestro, Madrid 3.

• **Summer School Course for Foreigners**

This program is organized by the Cultural Relations Department of the Ministry of Foreign Affairs and runs from the beginning of July through the middle of August. Courses are given in Spanish language, literature, art history, and culture. For information, including costs, write Dirección General de Relaciones Culturales, Secretaría del Curso Español para Extranjeros, Plaza de la Provincia 1, Madrid 12.

• **University of Madrid Summer Course for Foreigners**

This program runs from early July to the third week in August and offers diplomas and certificates for studies in Spanish language, literature, art, philosophy, geography, and culture. Language instruction is given in classes of fifteen to twenty-five but the lecture sections are large. Cost for tuition, about $30. For information, write Facultad de Filosofía y Letras, Cursos para Extranjeros, Ciudad Universitaria, Madrid 3. *The instruction in this program is excellent, and the serious student is exposed to fewer distractions than he would be in other programs in Spain.*

• **University of Madrid Summer Course for North Americans**

Organized in part by the Institute of Hispanic Culture, this program consists of two month-long sessions, in July and August. Courses in all levels of Spanish language and in Spanish literature, art, folklore, and culture are offered. In addition, there are studio courses in art. For information, including costs, write Sección Estados Unidos Instituto de Cultura Hispánica, Ciudad Universitaria, Madrid 3.

Málaga

• **Consejo Superior De Investigaciones Científicas Advanced Course in Spanish Philology**

This six-week course (mid-July to early September) is for advanced students only. The student has his choice of a medieval or a modern program. Students are given training in historical and sociological research techniques. Registration is small, and the faculty is distinguished. For information, including costs, write Dr. Antonio Quilis, Duque de Medinaceli 4, Madrid. *Registration must be completed by late May.*

• **University of Granada Summer Course for Foreigners**

This program runs from early July to late August and includes courses in all levels of Spanish language, in Spanish culture, and in Andalusian culture. American credits are offered. For information, write Curso para Extranjeros, Cátedra "Vicente Espinel," Alcazabilla 2, Málaga.

Oviedo

• **University of Oviedo Summer Program**

This program offers one-month courses in elementary and advanced Spanish and in Spanish culture. A certificate or diploma may be earned by passing an examination. Cost for tuition, about $20. For information, write Director del Curso para Extranjeros, Universidad de Oviedo, Oviedo.

Palma de Mallorca

• **University of Barcelona Summer Program**

A three-week program which offers courses in Spanish at all levels and in Spanish culture. Cost for tuition, about $20. For information, write Director del Curso de Verano, Universidad, Barcelona. *The resort militates against serious study.*

Pamplona

• **University of Navarra International Summer Program**

This program includes elementary, intermediate, and advanced Spanish-language courses and a general course in Spanish culture. It is held through August. Cost for tuition, about $70. For information, write Secretario del Curso Internacional, Universidad de Navarra, Pamplona.

Peñíscola

• **Castillo de Peñíscola Institute Summer Program**

This program offers two one-month sessions, July and August, and consists of courses in the Spanish language at various levels of difficulty as well as lectures on Spanish civilization. Cost for tuition, about $20. For information, write Director de Estudios "Castillo de Peñíscola" (Castellón de la Plana). *A distinctive characteristic of this program is that bull-fighting lessons are available!*

San Sebastián

• **Peñaflorida Institute Summer Course for Foreigners**

This three-week program, running from mid-July to mid-August, is organized by an official institute of the Spanish Institute of Education. Courses are offered in elementary and advanced Spanish and literature. Located in a favorite summer resort on the Bay of Biscay, not far from the French border, the program is open only to students with some prior knowledge of Spanish. Cost for tuition, about $25. For information, write Secretaria del Curso de Verano para Extranjeros, Instituto Nacional "Peñaflorída," Plaza de Pio XII, Ateno Guipuzcoano, Andia 13, San Sebastián.

Santander

• **"Menendez Pelayo" International University Summer Program**

Staffed by professors from other Spanish universities, "Menendez Pelayo" offers two and three-week sessions at the famous seaside resort of Santander. The first, given during July, is an intensive course including 3 hours of language instruction six days a week, in classes of fifteen students each, as well as 2 hours of lectures on literature, art, and culture. "Monographic" lecture courses are offered by some of Spain's leading professors. Only students over seventeen years of age are admitted. Cost for tuition, $20; with room and board, $125. For information, write "Menendez Pelayo" International University, Pabellion de Gobierno, Ciudad Universitaria, Madrid 3. *This program draws some top-flight professors, many of whom are in residence at Santander for the summer. A further advantage is the small size of language classes. However, the attractions of the seashore may prove too much for less determined scholars!*

Santiago de Compostela

• **University of Santiago de Compostela Summer Course**

A one-month program running from early July to early August, offering courses in Spanish language, history, culture, and art. Cost about $14. For information, write Director del Corso de Verano de la Universidad de Santiago de Compostela, Plaza de la Universitad 4, Santiago de Compostela.

Segovia

• **Diego de Colmenares Institute Course for Foreigners**

This program has three sessions, each lasting a month, and is held from late June to mid-September. Courses in the first two sessions include Spanish language, history, art, and literature. The third session, beginning in mid-August, includes the same courses as well as a painters-in-residence program. Cost for tuition, about $15 per session. For information, write Secretaría de Cursos para Extranjeros, Students and Painters Residence, Plaza del Conde de Cheste 8, Apartado 42, Segovia.

Seville

• **University of Seville Autumn Course for Foreigners**

Given in September, this one-month program offers courses in Spanish language, literature, culture, and history. Cost for tuition, about $20. For information, write Secretario de Cursos para Extranjeros, Facultad Filosofía y Letras, Universidad de Sevilla, Sevilla.

Valencia

• **University of Valencia Summer Course for Foreigners**

A four-week program in elementary and advanced Spanish, literature, art, history, and culture is offered in July. Cost for tuition, about $30. For information, write Secretario de los Cursos de Verano para Extranjeros, Cátedra "Mediterráneo," Universitad de Valencia, Valencia.

Valladolid

• **University of Valladolid Course for Foreigners**

This program, which runs through August, is intended for foreigners and includes courses in all levels of Spanish language and in Spanish literature, history, and art. At least three excursions to Spanish monuments and places of historical and artistic interest are organized by the program. A proficiency certificate is awarded on examination. Cost for tuition, about $25. For information, write Secretario de los Estudios para Extranjeros de la Universidad de Valladolid, Valladolid.

SWEDEN

Lund

• **University of Lund**

A series of lectures in English on Sweden and modern international issues held for two weeks in late August. Excursions, discussions, films, and visits with local families are arranged. Minimum age: twenty. For information, including costs, write International Student Course, Akademiska Föreningen, Lund.

Stockholm

• **Swedish Institute Course in Design**

This is a two-week course in August for professional architects, designers, and city planners. Courses in these fields are given in English. For information, including costs, write Swedish Institute, Box 3306, Stockholm 3.

Uppsala

• **International Seminar on Modern Sweden**

Sponsored by the Swedish Institute, this program is mainly for graduate students, journalists, and scholars with interests in Swedish society. It is held for two weeks in August in Uppsala. Cost for tuition, room, and board, about $150. For information, write Swedish Institute, Box 3306, Stockholm 3.

• **Swedish Institute Summer Program**

This program, running from late July to late August, offers a course in Swedish language and culture. Students must have had one year of Swedish and be at least twenty years of age. Cost for tuition, room, and board, about $150. For information, write Swedish Institute, Box 3306, Stockholm 3.

SWITZERLAND*

Corcelles and Churwalden

• **Albert Schweitzer College Summer Program**

This program is held in Corcelles, where the language taught is French and in Churwalden, where it is German. There are two 10-day sessions at each location, in July and August. Along with

---

* For more details on Swiss courses, see the annual *Holiday Courses and Camps in Switzerland,* which can be obtained by writing to the Swiss National Tourist Office, 608 Fifth Avenue, New York, N.Y. 10020.

language instruction (at all levels), lectures on contemporary issues are given. For information, including costs, write Summer Program, Albert Schweitzer College, Corcelles-sur-Chavarny.

Geneva

• **Applied Linguistics Center**

French language at all levels is taught in five 4-week sessions running from early May to late September. Audiovisual methods are used. Cost for tuition (eight weeks), about $300. For information, write Applied Linguistics Center, 20 Rue de Lausanne, Geneva.

• **University of Geneva Seminar on International Institutions**

This program provides a series of lectures, discussions, field trips, and individual research dealing with the subject of international organizations. Lectures are in French, but facilities are provided for simultaneous translations into English and other languages. The course runs for three weeks beginning in mid-July. A certificate useful in obtaining credit at United States colleges is available to students who submit a thesis after attending a special seminar. Cost for tuition, about $35. For information, write, Secrétariat des Vacances, Université, Geneva. *Although there are no formal entrance requirements, this is primarily a course for advanced students and specialists. Admission is restricted by the limited facilities for simultaneous translation.*

• **University of Geneva Summer Program**

This program runs in a series of five 3-week sessions from mid-July to mid-October. A wide variety of courses in French language and literature is offered at various levels of difficulty. Students must be at least seventeen years of age and must enroll for at least three weeks. Persons with no knowledge of French are admitted only at the first session. There is a special seminar on international institutions and organizations, conducted in French and with simultaneous translation into English. An extensive program of excursions and social events is arranged. Of the thousand-odd students in the program, 20 to 30 per cent are Americans. Cost, for tuition (six weeks), about $120; room and board, about $7 per day. For information, write Secrétariat des Cours de Vacances, Université 1211, Geneva 4. *Although a very large program, classes are small and supervision of students' work close. Students are placed according to their knowledge of French as determined by a preliminary examination.*

Lausanne

• **University of Lausanne Summer Program**

This program consists of a series of five 3-week sessions from mid-July to mid-October, with a wide variety of difficulty. Students must be at least seventeen years old; those with no previous knowledge of French are admitted only at the first session. An extensive program of excursions and social events is arranged. Of the 1,500-odd students, fewer than 10 per cent are Americans. Cost for tuition, about $30; room and board, about $5 per day. For information, write Secrétariat des Cours de Vacances, Cité P, Lausanne. *Although a very large program, classes are small and supervision of students' academic work close. A fine program in a charming city in the heart of French Switzerland.*

Leysin

• **International Festival of Young Artists**

This program is for musicians who are between fifteen and twenty-two years of age and is held in two sections; two weeks late June and early July in jazz; and four weeks from late June to late July in orchestra and chorale music. Conducted in English. For information, including costs, write "La Fauvette," Leysin.

Neuchâtel

• **University of Neuchâtel Summer Program**

A single four-week session running from mid-July to early August. Courses in French language and literature are offered at various levels of difficulty, with a language laboratory for those in the beginners course. There is also a course for teachers of French, and an extensive program of excursions is available. Cost for tuition, about $40; room and board, about $120. For information write Secrétariat de Cours d'Eté Université de Neuchâtel, Rue de 1ier Mars, Neuchâtel. *In this program, classes are small and supervision of the students' academic work is close.*

TURKEY

Istanbul

- **University of Istanbul Summer Program in Turkish Language and Culture**

This program runs from early July to late September. Cost, about $28. For information, write Türk Dili ve Kültürü Yas Kurlari Bürosu, Istanbul Üniversitesi, Istanbul.

YUGOSLAVIA

Zagreb

- **University of Zagreb Summer Program**

This is a four-week program held in August in Yugoslav languages and culture for advanced students and teachers of Slavic studies. For information, including costs, write Seminar za strane slviste pro filozofskom facultetu u Zagrebu, Dure Slaaja b.b., Zagreb.

CHAPTER 10 ～～～～～～～～～

Programs Sponsored by American Colleges and Universities: Regular Academic Year

85 year-programs for undergraduates . . . 19 programs for graduate students

The number of overseas programs organized by American institutions is expanding rapidly; the following listing is therefore probably far from complete. Furthermore, there are many programs open only to students of the sponsoring college or university. Since students at these institutions presumably can easily familiarize themselves with the programs, we have not included any of them here. The programs open to college students vary greatly in entrance requirements, size, and quality. Interested students are therefore urged to write for the brochures and catalogues of several before making formal application. It is wise, when asking for information, to request the names of students from one's area who have participated in the program and to consult with them when possible. It is also essential for students seeking to obtain academic credit for participating in any of these programs to obtain the approval of the authorities at their own college before enrolling.

We would very much appreciate hearing from participants in any of these programs about their experiences, especially if they note any inaccuracies in our program descriptions. Please write *The New Guide to Study Abroad,* 49 East 33rd Street, Sixth Floor, New York, N.Y. 10016.

GRADUATE PROGRAMS

The following universities and colleges sponsor graduate programs abroad. In these programs the student may satisfy a part or all of the requirement for a graduate degree (usually the M.A.) from the sponsoring institution. For detailed information, the student should write the graduate admissions office of the institution in which he is interested.

Language Programs

French

Central College, Pella, Ia. (Paris)
Middlebury College, Middlebury, Vt. (Paris)
Queens College, Flushing, N.Y. (Montpellier, Nancy, Nice, Reims)
University of Rochester, Rochester, N.Y. (Paris)
University of Southern California, Los Angeles, Calif. (Tunis)

German

Middlebury College, Middlebury, Vt. (Tübingen)
Queens College, Flushing, N.Y. (Kiel)
Tufts University, Medford, Mass. (Tübingen)

Italian

Middlebury College, Middlebury, Vt. (Florence)
Rosary College, River Forest, Ill. (Florence; women only)

Portuguese

Queens College, Flushing, N.Y. (Lisbon)

Spanish

Middlebury College, Middlebury, Vt. (Madrid)
New York University, New York, N.Y. (Madrid)

- **Michigan State University American Language Education Centers**

Michigan State University sponsors language-study programs in several countries with the Foundation of European Language and Educational Centers. The general requirements for entrance into the programs are two years of college-level study of the language used and standing of sophomore or higher. Courses are given in the language at special centers. Credit is determined by examination on return. Students may take any combination of three 12-week terms, fall, winter, and spring. Cost, about $800 per term, plus transportation. For information, write American Language Education Center, Michigan State University, East Lansing, Michigan. Programs are located in France (Paris), Germany (Cologne), Italy (Florence), Spain (Barcelona and Madrid), Switzerland (Lausanne and Neuchâtel).

International Affairs

Johns Hopkins University Center of the School of Advanced International Studies, Washington, D. C. (Bologna)

Area Studies

Stanford University Japanese and Chinese Area Studies, Stanford, Calif. (Tokyo and Taipei)

State University of New York at Albany, Albany, N.Y. (Central European Area Studies of Würzburg, Germany)

Fine Arts and Theater

Syracuse University, Syracuse, N.Y. (fine arts; Florence)

Tyler School of Art, Temple University, Philadelphia, Penna. (art; Rome)

University of California, Santa Barbara, Calif. (archaeology, classics, drama; Delphi, Greece)

UNDERGRADUATE PROGRAMS

AUSTRIA

Bregenz

- **Wagner College Year in Bregenz**

Open to juniors with good records (previous German courses not prerequisite), this program offers liberal arts courses in English as well as elementary, intermediate, and advanced courses in French, German, Italian, and Russian. Cost, about $3,000 for tuition, room, board, and round-trip transportation from New York. Students are housed in a hotel. For information, write Wagner College Study Program in Bregenz, Wagner College, Staten Island. N.Y.

Vienna

- **Central College Year in Vienna**

This is a twelve-month program for juniors and seniors. Prerequisites are two years of college German with a B average. Students take intensive German courses in the summer at the Goethe Institute and then study German language, literature, and culture through the following June at the University of Vienna. Up to 48 credits may be earned. Students live in hotels. Tuition, about $2,200. For information, write Vienna Study Program, Central College, Pella, Iowa 50219.

- **Institute of European Studies European Year**

This is a program open to sophomores and juniors of all colleges with a C-plus average or better. Students assemble in New York, then engage in a three-week field trip en route to Vienna. In Vienna classes are conducted in English at the Institute, which is attached to the University of Vienna. Those who understand German may attend regular university lectures. Students may enroll for the entire academic year or for the spring semester. During vacations, field trips are made to Italy and Spain. Students live in furnished rooms or with families, but eat at the Institute. A maximum of 30 credits may be earned. Cost, all-inclusive, about $3,400. For information, write Institute of European Studies, 35 East Wacker Dr., Chicago, Ill. 60601.

• **University of Puget Sound Semester in Vienna**

Mainly for Puget Sound juniors and seniors, this program offers courses in English (except for German-language courses) at the junior level. A speaking knowledge is prerequisite. Cost, all-inclusive, about $2,200, fall or spring. Students live in pensions and earn 15 credits. For information, write Vienna Program, University of Puget Sound, Tacoma, Wash. 98416.

• **Wesleyan University Program in Vienna**

This program runs from September to early November and is limited to a very few students. German majors should have had at least two years of college German, nonmajors at least one. Language instruction is in German. Cost, $275, not including transportation. For information, write Chairman, German Department, Wesleyan University, Middletown, Conn. 06457.

BELGIUM

Brussels

• **Drew University Semester on the Common Market**

This is a spring semester program held in Brussels and is primarily for economics majors. Instruction is in English, although qualified students with adequate language preparation may enroll in some courses at the Free University of Brussels. Students are housed with families and earn 15 hours' credit. Cost, about $1,600, plus transportation. For information, write Director, The Brussels Semester on the Common Market, Drew University, Madison, N.J. 07940.

COLOMBIA

Bogotá

• **Syracuse University Semester**

This program is held in conjunction with the University of the Andes in Bogotá and is open to students at the advanced level of

Spanish language. The program is held only in the fall semester. Students live with local families and in dormitories. Cost, for tuition, room, board, and round-trip transportation from Miami, about $1,740. For information, write Foreign Study Program, Syracuse University, 335 Comstock Avenue, Syracuse, N.Y. 13210.

COSTA RICA

San José

• Beloit College Overseas Seminar

This program is given in the fall semester only and is open to students with at least a year of college Spanish. Students live with local families. For information, write World Affairs Center, Beloit College, Beloit, Wis. 53511.

• University of Kansas Junior Year

Open to upper-level sophomores of all colleges with a C-plus average or better and 16 credits of college-level Spanish. After a period of orientation in Washington, students attend regular classes at the University of Costa Rica from February to December. They live with families. Credits are determined on an individual basis. Cost, all-inclusive, about $1,850. For information, write College of Liberal Arts and Sciences, University of Kansas, Lawrence, Kans. 66044.

DENMARK

Copenhagen

• Washburn University Spring Semester in Copenhagen

Open to sophomores, juniors, and (infrequently) seniors with a B average, this program offers courses (in English) on European and Scandinavian culture and history. Students live with local families and earn 15 credits. Cost, all-inclusive, about $1,500. For information, write Washburn Semester in Copenhagen, Washburn University, Topeka, Kans. 66621.

- **Whittier College in Copenhagen**

This is a fall semester program conducted in English and open to sophomores, juniors, and seniors of Whittier, although others are also accepted. Special classes are conducted by the Director, a Whittier professor, and by members of the staff of the University of Copenhagen in European and Scandinavian political science, economics, and culture. Study projects and field trips are included in the curriculum. To qualify, students must have a B average or better. Students live in boardinghouses and earn 12 to 15 credits. Cost, all-inclusive, about $3,000. For information, write Whittier College in Denmark, Whittier College, Whittier, Calif. 90608.

Various Cities

- **American–Scandinavian Foundation**

This foundation offers a program for Americans to go to Scandinavian countries as trainees in various professions. A good knowledge of the country's language is required. For information, write the American-Scandinavian Foundation, 127 East 73rd Street, New York, N.Y. 10021.

- **Scandinavian Seminar**

The Seminar offers a program in which American students live with Danish families and study at folk schools. For information, write The Scandinavian Seminar, 140 West 57th Street, New York, N.Y. 10019.

FRANCE

Aix-en-Provence

- **Michigan–Wisconsin Junior Year in France**

This program, which runs from mid-September to late June, is primarily for students of the two sponsoring universities, but a limited number of other students will be accepted. Applicants must be juniors with the equivalent of two years of college French and a B average. After an intensive four-week language program, students attend regular classes at the University of Aix-Marseille. Students earn 30 credits for the year's program. They live in dormitories and with families. The cost for residents of Wisconsin and Michigan amounts to about $2,100; for others, about $3,000. For information, write Office of International Studies, University of Wisconsin, Madison, Wis., or Office of Study Abroad, University of Michigan, Ann Arbor, Mich. 48104.

• Institute for American Universities

This program is run under the auspices of the University of Aix-Marseille and is held in two semesters from September to June. Courses in European culture and history are taught in English at the Institute, and all students are expected to take two courses each semester in French at the University. There are no prerequisites. Housing is in local homes and in student hostels. Cost for tuition, about $1,000 (year); room and board with family, $100 per month. For information, write Director, Institute for American Universities, University of Aix-Marseille, 2 bis Rue du Bon-Pasteur, Aix-en-Provence.

Besançon

• Knox College Study Program

A program for college students with two years of college French and a B average. The courses include French history, literature, and culture. Housing is in dormitories, and 30 credits may be earned. Cost, all-inclusive, about $3,200. For information, write Chairman, Modern Language Department, Knox College, Galesburg, Ill. 61401.

Lyon

• University of North Carolina

This program is for students who have reached an advanced level in French and have B averages in both French and other courses at their colleges. A month of intensive language study in the summer is followed by two semesters of study in history, political science, and French language and literature at the University of Lyon. Students may earn up to 30 points of credit and live either in dormitories or with French families. Cost, all-inclusive, about $2,100 if a North Carolina resident, $3,700 if not. For information, write University of North Carolina Year in Lyon, Chapel Hill, N.C. 27514.

Montpellier

• **West Chester State College**

Priority is given to students at Pennsylvania colleges by this program. Students must have a B average through two years of college French. Cost, about $1,600; students live in dormitories. For information, write Junior Year at Montpellier Program, West Chester State College, West Chester, Penna. 19380.

Paris

• **Alma College Year in France**

Open to college juniors who have finished second-year French with a B average. Students may study (1) for a summer and a school year or (2) for a school year alone. Costs, (1) about $2,600 and (2) about $2,280. Courses are held in co-operation with the Alliance Française. Up to 30 points of credit may be earned. Students live in private homes. For information, write Alma College Studies in France, Alma, Mich. 48801.

• **Central College Year in France**

This is a twelve-month program for juniors and seniors from any college. Prerequisite: two years of college French with a B average. Students take intensive French courses in the summer and then study French language, literature, and culture at the University of Paris until July, living in dormitories. Up to 44 credits may be earned; cost, about $2,200. For information, write Paris Study Program, Central College, Pella, Iowa 50219.

• Hamilton College Junior Year

Open to juniors of all colleges with a B average or better and two years of college French. After a preliminary language-training period at Biarritz, the students study at the University of Paris and in special classes organized by Hamilton. Emphasis is on French language and civilization. Students live with families and earn 30 credits. Cost, about $3,100. For information, write Director, Junior Year in France, Hamilton College, Hamilton, N.Y. 13346.

• Sarah Lawrence Junior Year

This program is for juniors with reasonable fluency in French. Students attend a special class in French language and civilization and regular classes in other subjects at different institutes. They live in boardinghouses, dormitories, and with families and receive 30 credits. Cost about $3,1000, plus $200 per month living expenses. For information, write Director for Foreign Studies, Sarah Lawrence College, Bronxville, N.Y. 10078.

• Smith College Junior Year

This is a program open to junior girls with two years of college French. After a preliminary period of language study at Aix-en-Provence, the students attend special classes in French language and civilization in Paris. They live with families and earn 30 credits. Cost, all-inclusive, about $4,100. For information, write Chairman, Committee on Foreign Study, Smith College, Northampton, Mass. 01060.

• Sweet Briar College Junior Year

This program is open to juniors of all colleges with a B average or better and two years of college French. After a period of pre-liminary language study in Tours, students attend both special and regular university classes in Paris in subjects of their major interest. They live with families and earn 30 credits. Cost, all-inclusive, about $3,000. For information, write Director, Sweet Briar Junior Year in France, Sweet Briar College, Sweet Briar, Va. 24595.

Poitiers

• **Syracuse University French Study Program**

This program is given in both the spring and fall semesters and is open to juniors from all colleges. Applicants should have studied French through the second-year college level. Instruction is in French. Cost, about $1,700, not including return transportation. Students live with families or in dormitories. For information, write Foreign Study Program, Syracuse University, 335 Comstock Avenue, Syracuse, N.Y. 13210.

• **Beloit College Overseas Seminar**

Students in this program, held at the University of Rennes, take courses in French art, civilization, and language. Prerequisite: two years of college French. Students live with local families. For information, write World Affairs Center, Beloit College, Beloit, Wis. 53511.

Strasbourg

• **Otterbein College Junior Year**

This program is for juniors with a B average in advanced French. Courses (in French) are taken at the Institut d'Etudes Françaises Modernes, and students may earn up to 32 points of credit. Cost, about $2,100; students live in rooming houses, in dormitories, and with local families. For information, write Coordinator, Strasbourg Year Abroad Program, Otterbein College, Westerville, Ohio 43081.

• **United College for Foreign Study and Exchange Intensive Course**

This intensive course in French language is held at Strasbourg. Prerequisites are two years of college French with a B average. Students can earn 30 credits. Cost, about $2,300, not including return transportation. For information, write Director, United College for Foreign Study and Exchange, P.O. Box 665, Tiffin, Ohio 44883.

Tours

• **Bowling Green State University**

Held from March to July, this program offers 15 credits for studies in French language and culture. Applicants should have studied two years of college French with a good average. Cost, about $1,850. For information, write Department of Romance Languages, Bowling Green State University, Bowling Green, Ohio 43402.

• **Rutgers University Junior Year**

Students in this program spend the first six weeks in Paris taking intensive French courses. They then move to Tours for two semesters of courses (30 points of credit). Applicants should be at the advanced level in French and should have good records. Cost (New Jersey resident) about $2,000; others, about $2,200. For information, write Director, Rutgers Junior Year in France, Milledoler Hall, Rutgers—The State University, New Brunswick, N.J. 08903.

GERMANY

Berlin

• **Beloit College Overseas Seminar**

Courses in this program are given at Schiller College and include German language, literature, and history. Prerequisite: beginning German. For information, including costs, write World Affairs Center, Beloit College, Beloit, Wisc. 53511.

Freiburg

• **De Pauw University Spring Semester**

This program consists of a three-week European tour, followed by two months' study in Freiburg under faculty from Freiburg University and by two and a half months' work in independent study projects in a British or a European university. Instruction at Freiburg is in English, except for the required German course. Prerequisites include junior standing and two years of college German with a B average. Cost, about $1,700. Students live in dormitories with German students and earn 15 credits. For information, write Semester in Freiburg, De Pauw University, Greencastle, Ind. 46135.

• **Wayne State Junior Year**

Juniors and seniors of all colleges with a B average or better and two years of college German are eligible. There are two groups, one at the University of Munich, the other at the University of Freiburg. After a period of preliminary language study, students attend a mixture of special classes and regular university lectures. They take German language and civilization and courses in their major fields, live in dormitories, rooming houses, and with families, and earn 30 credits. Cost, about $2,600. For information, write Director, Wayne State Junior Year in Germany, Wayne State University, Detroit, Mich. 48202.

Hamburg

• **Purdue University—Indiana University Foreign Study Program**

In this program, a six-week intensive German course is followed by an academic year at Hamburg University, where students follow a course of regular instruction. Open to sophomores, juniors, and seniors with two years of college German and a B average. Cost, out-of-state residents, about $2,400; Indiana residents, $1,800 for tuition and transportation. Students live with families or in dormitories. For information, write Foreign Study Program, Purdue University, Lafayette, Ind. 47907, or Foreign Study Program, Indiana University, Bloomington, Ind. 47405.

• **Smith College Junior Year**

This program is open to juniors of all colleges (both men and women) with two years of college German. After a preliminary period of language study, students attend classes at the University of Hamburg. They live with families and earn 30 credits. Cost: about

$4,100. For information, write Chairman, Committee on Foreign Study, Smith College, Northampton, Mass. 01060.

Heidelberg

• **Heidelberg College Junior Year at Heidelberg**

This program is open to juniors of all colleges with two years of college German (B average or better). Students attend regular classes in German civilization at the Interpreter's Institute of the University of Heidelberg. They live with families and in dormitories and earn a maximum of 34 credits. Cost, about $1,600. For information, write Director, Heidelberg Junior Year, Heidelberg College, Tiffin, Ohio 44883.

• **Pepperdine College Year in Heidelberg**

Courses in this program are taught in English, and there are no language requirements. Those with knowledge of German may sit in on courses at the University of Heidelberg. One-quarter of the year is spent traveling as a group. Cost, about $3,500. For information, write Pepperdine College Year in Heidelberg, Pepperdine College, South Vermont at 79th Street, Los Angeles, Calif. 90044.

Kleiningersheim

• **University of Dubuque Year in Germany**

Open to juniors with a B average, with no language prerequisite, this program offers a liberal arts program at Schiller College at Kleiningersheim/Neckar. All instruction is in English except modern language courses. Cost, about $2,500. For information, write Dubuque in Germany, University of Dubuque, Dubuque, Iowa 52002.

Marburg

• **Millersville State College Year in Marburg**

This program is intended for German majors who plan to teach German after graduation. A 2-month intensive course in German language (6 credits) is followed by two semesters of study at the University. Courses are taught in German and subjects include history, literature, psychology, music, and political science. Tutors give instruction in German language. Cost, about $2,000. For information, write Junior Year in Marburg, Millersville State College, Millersville, Penna. 17551.

Munich

• **Wayne State Junior Year in Germany**

[See this program in the Germany listings under Freiburg, above.]

Oldenburg

• **University of Oregon Center for International Music Education**

This program is for seniors and graduate students. Instruction is by University of Oregon faculty members, and there is no language prerequisite, although study of German is required. The program runs through the academic year. Cost, all-inclusive, about $2,600; students live with families. For information, write German Center for International Music Education, University of Oregon, Eugene, Ore. 97403.

GREAT BRITAIN

London

• **Beaver College Semester Abroad**

Students in this program take courses at City of London College in the liberal arts. There are also lectures in literature and art by Beaver faculty members. Housing is in dormitories or with families, and the cost, per semester, is about $1,700. Applicants should have a B average in the social sciences. For information, write Director of International Programs, Beaver College, Glenside, Penna. 19038.

Wroxton

• **Fairleigh Dickinson University Semester Abroad**

Participants in this program live and study in a Tudor abbey located near Stratford on Avon. Courses are given in Shakespeare, sixteenth-century literature, English political institutions, and English culture. Summer graduate programs are given in Shakespeare and the English theater. Cost, about $1,350 per semester, for tuition, room, and board. For information, write Admissions Office, Fairleigh Dickinson University, Rutherford, N.J. 07070.

GREECE

Athens

• **American School of Classical Studies**

Admission to this institution is limited to college graduates with a major in classics, classical archaeology, fine arts, or ancient history. Qualified students in Byzantine and modern Greek studies are also eligible. The program consists of field trips, seminars, individual research, participation in excavations, and occasional lectures. There is no course work, and there are no credits or degrees. For further information, including costs, write Professor Mabel Lang, Department of Greek, Bryn Mawr College, Bryn Mawr, Penna. 19010.

• **College Year in Athens**

This is a privately administered program recognized by a number of American colleges and universities. Designed mainly for college juniors, it includes courses in Greek history, literature, art, and philosophy. Students live in supervised houses and apartments. For further information, including costs, write Mrs. George N. Hatsopoulos, Stonehedge, Lincoln, Mass. 01773.

Delphi

• **University of California Study Center for Classical Drama**

This program is open to undergraduates and graduate students and is held from late March to late August. Students study modern and classical Greek, classical drama, and play production. Housing is in a small local hotel. Applicants should have a B average and an interest in theater. Cost, California residents, about $1,850; others, about $2,100. For information, write Education Abroad Program Office, South Hall, University of California, Santa Barbara, Calif. 93106.

INDIA

Various Cities

• **University of Wisconsin Year in India**

Following intensive language or area courses in the United States, the student studies at the University of Delhi, at Banaras Hindu University, or at Osmania University. Courses include the second year of the language studied in the intensive session and individual field projects. Students work with local teachers. Languages include Hindi and Telegu. Tuition is the same as that at the University of Wisconsin, and a United States government grant covers travel and living expenses. For information, including costs, write Director, Undergraduate Year in India, University of Wisconsin, Madison, Wis. 53706.

ISRAEL

Jerusalem

• **Brandeis University Semester in Jerusalem**

Held from July through December, this program has no language prerequisite, although participants are required to take a Hebrew language course in the first months. Classes are taught by Brandeis faculty members in English. Cost, all-inclusive, about $2,000; students live in rooming houses. Prerequisite: B average. For information, write Jacob Hiatt Institute Program, Brandeis University, Waltham, Mass. 02154.

ITALY

Bologna

• **Dickinson College Center for International Studies**

This program is intended for juniors majoring in political science. Courses in international relations, economics, and comparative government are given at the Center for International Studies and at the Johns Hopkins University Graduate Center. Applicants should have had one semester of college or two of high-school French or Spanish and have passed basic college courses in political science with at least a B average. Cost, about $3,200. For information, write Political Science Department, Denny Hall, Dickinson College, Carlisle, Penna. 17013.

• **Indiana University Italian Study Center**

Courses in this program, including a six-week intensive Italian course, are taken at the University of Bologna. Up to 30 credits may be earned. Two years of college Italian are prerequisite. Cost for tuition and transportation, about $2,000. For information, write Director, the Italian Study Center in Bologna, Ballantine Hall 642, Bloomington, Ind. 47405.

Florence

• **Gonzaga University Year Abroad**

Courses in this program are taught in English by members of the Gonzaga faculty. Students live at the Gonzaga student center. Prerequisites: B-minus average and one semester of Italian. Students with sufficient preparation in Italian may audit courses at the University of Florence. The program features tours in Europe and the Middle East. Cost is about $3,100 for tuition, room, board, and one-way transportation. For information, write Gonzaga in Florence, Gonzaga University, Spokane, Wash. 99202.

- **Smith College Junior Year**

This program is open to junior girls of all colleges with two years of college Italian. After a preliminary period of language study, the students attend special classes in Italian language and civilization in Florence. They live with families and earn 30 credits. Cost, about $3,300. For information, write Committee on Foreign Study, Smith College, Northampton, Mass. 01060.

- **Syracuse University Semesters in Italy**

This program is open to sophomores and juniors of all colleges with a B average or better. Students attend special classes held in English in Florence, studying Italian and European history and civilization. They live with families. Students may enroll for one or two semesters; there is also a summer session. Cost, about $1,800 per semester, plus return passage. For information, write Foreign Study Programs, Syracuse University, 335 Comstock Avenue, Syracuse, N.Y. 13210.

Naples

- **Tufts University Overseas Program**

This program is mainly for classics majors, both graduate students and undergraduates. Graduate students may do work toward an M.A. in Italian studies in this program. Cost, about $3,400. For information, write Director, Tufts University Overseas Program, Tufts University, Medford, Mass. 02155.

Pavia

- **Oregon State System of Higher Education Year in Pavia**

This program features courses in the liberal arts and business administration in English and in Italian. Students not proficient in Italian take intensive language courses. Sophomores, juniors, and seniors are eligible. Cost, $2,300 to $2,800. For information, write Italian Studies Center, Portland State College, P.O. Box 751, Portland, Ore. 97207.

Rome

• Loyola University Year Abroad

This program is open to sophomores, juniors, and seniors with a C average. There is no language prerequisite. Students take courses taught in English by Loyola faculty members. Students may participate in the program for a semester (cost, about $1,000) or for the full academic year (about $2,800, all-inclusive). For information, write Director of Foreign Studies, Loyola University, 320 N. Michigan Avenue, Chicago, Ill. 60611.

• Sarah Lawrence Junior Year

This is a program for juniors with reasonable fluency in Italian. After preliminary language instruction, students attend special classes in Italian language and civilization and regular courses at the University of Rome. They live in boardinghouses, dormitories, and with families and receive 30 credits. Cost, about $2,600. For information, write Director of Foreign Studies, Sarah Lawrence College, Bronxville, N.Y. 10708.

• Temple University—Tyler School of Art

Sponsored in conjunction with the Experiment in International Living, this program includes field trips, a three-week stay with an Italian family, art history and Italian language courses, and studio classes. Students must be at least nineteen years old and have junior standing. They should also have taken 18 credits in art courses. Graduate students are also accepted and may count their courses toward the M.F.A. degree at Tyler. Students live in boardinghouses. Cost, about $3,600. For information, write Temple Abroad, Tyler School of Art, Beech and Penrose Avenues, Philadelphia, Penna. 1912. *Although no Italian is required for admission, the language instruction in this program is minimal. Students interviewed expressed the opinion that more stress should be placed on language training; the art instruction, however, is excellent.*

JAPAN

Tokyo

• **California Western University Quarter in Asia**

This is an eleven-week program with six weeks of study and five weeks of course-related travel. Classes are in English and include political science, fine arts, history, and spoken Japanese. Students live with families and in dormitories and hotels. Cost, about $2,300. For information, write California Western Quarter in Asia, California Western University, San Diego, Calif. 92106.

• **Stanford University Center for Japanese Studies**

This is a full-year program for undergraduate and graduate students with at least two years of Japanese. The emphasis is on oral language, taught by trained nationals. Students live with families or in rented quarters. Cost, about $3,800–$4,000. For information, write Center for Japanese Studies, Stanford University, Stanford, Calif. 94305.

MEXICO

Guadalajara

• **Washington University**

Students, who should have a thorough knowledge of Spanish, take courses at the University of Guadalajara. A short intensive Spanish course precedes study at the University. Students live in dormitories and with families. Cost, about $2,400. For information, write Director, Year in Guadalajara, Washington University, St. Louis, Mo. 63130.

Mexico City

• **University of Nebraska Year in Mexico City**

Students in this program study at the College of Mexico, beginning in February. Prerequisite: three years of college Spanish. Cost, about $1,200. Students live with local families. For information, write University of Nebraska year in Mexico City, Lincoln, Nebr 68508.

THE NETHERLANDS

Amsterdam

• **Syracuse University Semester Abroad**

A one-semester course in home economics, taught in English, which can be taken in either the fall or the spring. Cost, about $1,740, plus return passage. For information, write Foreign Study Programs, Syracuse University, 335 Comstock Avenue, Syracuse, N.Y. 13210.

Breukelen

• **University of Oregon European Program**

This program is for male majors in business administration. Students take courses in English at the Netherlands School of Business, near Amsterdam. Prerequisite: one year of college French, German, or Spanish. Cost, Oregon residents, about $3,000; out-of-state, about $3,600. For information, write European Program in Business Administration, University of Oregon, Eugene, Ore. 97403.

NORWAY

Various Cities

• **American–Scandinavian Foundation**

This foundation offers a program for Americans to go to Scandinavian countries as trainees in various professions. A good knowledge of Norwegian is required. For information, including costs, write the American-Scandinavian Foundation, 127 E. 72nd Street, New York, N.Y. 10021.

• **Scandinavian Seminar**

The Scandinavian Seminar offers a program in which American students live with Norwegian families and study at folk high schools. For information, including costs, write The Scandinavian Seminar, 140 West 57th Street, New York, N.Y. 10019.

SPAIN

Madrid

• **Bowling Green State University Semester Abroad**

This program, held from March to July, is open to students with a C-plus average and two years of college Spanish. Up to 15 credits may be earned. Courses are taught by Bowling Green faculty members and by native teachers. Courses (in Spanish): Spanish language, art, and culture. Cost, all-inclusive, about $1,850. For information, write Department of Romance Languages, Bowling Green State University, Bowling Green, Ohio 43402.

• **Georgetown University Junior Year**

A program for juniors of all colleges with a C-plus average or better and two years of Spanish. After an intensive Spanish course in September, students attend special classes in Spanish language and civilization at the University of Madrid. They live in a dormitory or with families and earn 30 to 36 credits. Cost, about $2,700. For information, write Rector, Institute of Languages and Linguistics, Georgetown University, Washington, D.C. 20007.

• **Lake Forest Fall Term Abroad**

This program is open to sophomores and juniors able to use written and spoken Spanish. Held in the fall term only, the program offers courses in Spanish culture taught in Spanish by local teachers. Cost about $1,000 for tuition, room, and board. Students live with families. For information, write Director, Fall Term in Madrid, Lake Forest College, Lake Forest, Ill. 60045.

• **Marquette University Year Abroad**

Sophomores, juniors, and seniors with two years of college Spanish are eligible for this program. After an intensive course in Spanish language, students study at the University of Madrid; they also are tutored by a University of Madrid teacher. Cost is about $2,500, and students live with families or in boardinghouses. For information, write Director, Study Center in Madrid, Marquette University, 1309 W. Wisconsin Avenue, Milwaukee, Wis. 53233.

• **Mary Baldwin College Year Abroad**

This is a nine-month program of courses taught in Spanish by Mary Baldwin faculty. Students, who must be women, should have completed a course in Spanish literature. Thirty credits may be earned. Students live with local families. Cost, about $2,700. For information, write to the Dean, Mary Baldwin College, Staunton, Va. 24401.

• **New York University Junior Year**

This program is open to juniors of all colleges with a B average or better and a good knowledge of Spanish (at least two years of college Spanish or the equivalent). Students attend special classes in Spanish language and civilization at the University of Madrid. They live in dormitories, boardinghouses, and with families and receive up to 33 credits. Cost, about $2,600. For information, write Director, Junior Year in Spain, New York University, New York, N.Y. 10003.

• **Smith College Junior Year**

This program is open to juniors of all colleges with two years of college Spanish. After a preliminary period of language study at Santander the students attend special classes in Spanish language and civilization in Madrid. They live with families and earn 30 credits. Cost, all-inclusive, about $4,000. For information, write Chairman, Committee on Foreign Study, Smith College, Northampton, Mass. 01060.

• **Vanderbilt University Semester in Spain**

In this program, instruction is given in Spanish by members of the faculties of Vanderbilt and the University of Madrid. Students may choose either semester and should have had two years of college Spanish with a B average. Housing is in private homes. Cost, all-inclusive, about $2,100. For information, write Vanderbilt in Spain Program, College of Arts and Sciences, Vanderbilt University, Nashville, Tenn. 37203.

Valencia

• **University of Valencia Junior Year**

Sponsored until recently by the University of San Francisco, this program is intended partly for teachers on sabbatical. Students may study for either one semester or the entire academic year and may earn 15 credits a semester. Housing is in private homes in Valencia, and the cost is about $1,300 per semester, $1,900 per year. Students should be at the third-year level in Spanish. For information, write Institute of Spanish Studies, 1315 Monterrey Boulevard, San Francisco, Calif. 94127.

SWEDEN

• **American-Scandinavian Foundation**

This foundation offers a program for Americans to go to Scandinavian countries as trainees in various professions. A good knowledge of Swedish is required. For information, including costs, write The American-Scandinavian Foundation, 127 East 73rd Street, New York, N.Y., 10021.

• **Scandinavian Seminar**

The Seminar offers a program in which American students live with Swedish families and study at folk high schools. For information, including costs, write The Scandinavian Seminar, 140 West 57th Street, New York, N.Y. 10019.

SWITZERLAND

Fribourg

• **Georgetown-at-Fribourg**

This is a program for male juniors of all colleges with a B-minus average or better and a knowledge of German or French. Students travel independently to Switzerland and attend special classes in social science, philosophy, literature, and classics at the University of Fribourg. They live in a dormitory and earn 32 to 36 credits. Cost, about $1,900. For information, write Moderator, Georgetown-at-Fribourg, Georgetown University, Washington, D.C. 20007.

• **Rosary College Foreign Study Plan**

A program for junior-class women of all colleges with a C average or better and two years of college French. Participants study French in special Rosary-organized classes and lectures at the University of Fribourg. They live in a Rosary center, the Villa des Fougères, and with local families. They earn 36 credits. During vacations, organized tours are arranged. Cost, all-inclusive, about $2,700. For information, write Director, Junior Year Abroad, Rosary College, River Forest, Ill. 60305.

Geneva

• **Sarah Lawrence College Year**

Students in this program take courses at the University of Geneva and are tutored by local teachers. Students live with families. Cost for tuition, about $2,600. For information, write Director of Foreign Studies, Sarah Lawrence College, Bronxville, N.Y. 10708.

• **Smith College Junior Year**

This program is open to junior girls of all colleges with one year of college French. The students attend classes in history, social science, and international relations at the University of Geneva and the Institute of International Studies. They also study

French in special classes. They are housed with local families and earn 30 credits. Cost, all-inclusive, about $4,000. For information, write Chairman, Committee on Foreign Study, Smith College, Northampton, Mass. 01060.

TAIWAN

Taipei

• **Beloit College Overseas Seminar**

This program features courses in Chinese culture, history, and language. Students live with local families. For information, including costs, write World Affairs Center, Beloit College, Beloit, Wis. 53511.

• **Stanford University Inter-University Program for Chinese Language Studies in Taipei**

This is a full-year program for undergraduate and graduate students with at least two years of Chinese. The emphasis is on oral language, taught by trained nationals. Students live with families or in rented quarters. Cost, about $3,800–$4,000. For information, write Inter-University Program for Chinese Language Studies in Taipei, Stanford University, Stanford, Calif. 94305.

TUNISIA

Tunis

• **University of California Year in Tunis**

Cosponsored by the Experiment in International Living and the American Friends of the Middle East, this program includes intensive study of French in France, followed by a four-week stay with a Tunisian family and by study at the University of Tunis, where courses are held in French. Credit is arranged individually. Cost, about $1,700. For information, write Coordinator of Year at the University of Tunis, School of International Relations, University of Southern California, Los Angeles, Calif. 90007.

CHAPTER 11 ∿∿∿∿∿∿∿∿∿

Programs Sponsored by American Colleges and Universities: Summer

89 summer programs for undergraduates and graduate students

Summer programs operated by American colleges and universities are uniformly more expensive than those run by foreign institutions and in many cases employ exactly the same facilities—even the same teachers. In most instances, however, they provide more intense instruction and closer supervision. They also make it easier for students to obtain academic credit at American institutions for the work covered.

AUSTRIA

Salzburg

• **Georgetown University Summer Program**

This is a six-week course in German language, taught by Georgetown faculty and by local instructors. Instruction is in English except for language classes. Cost for tuition, room, board, about $310. For information, write Georgetown-Salzburg Program, Georgetown University, Washington, D.C. 20007.

- **Ohio Wesleyan University Summer Program**

This program is limited to students with at least one year of German. Instruction is by local teachers, and students live with local families. For information, including costs, write Ohio Wesleyan Summer Program in Salzburg, Ohio Wesleyan University, Delaware, Ohio 43015.

- **Salzburg Summer School**

Courses in German language at all levels, Austrian culture, and European economics and politics, running from early July to mid-August and conducted in English. Prerequisite: one year of college. Cost for tuition, room, and board, about $320. For information, write Austrian Institute, 11 East 52nd Street, New York, N.Y. 10022.

Vienna

- **Hope College Vienna Summer School**

A program of travel and study of European civilization, with German-language instruction also included. After a preliminary study tour, students attend classes at the Institute of European Studies. Instruction is in English, and the students live with families. Classes run for six weeks, and the entire program lasts from early June to early September. Cost, all-inclusive, $1,250. For information, write Director, Vienna Summer School, Hope College, Holland, Mich. 49423.

- **Oberlin College German Summer School**

A program in German language, literature, and art, open to undergraduates with at least one year of college German. There is an advanced class for properly qualified students. Students attend classes at the Institute of European Studies and live with families. The program runs from June to September and includes nine weeks of classes. Cost, all-inclusive, $1,200. For information, write

Department of German, Oberlin College, Oberlin, Ohio. 44074. *This program uses American methods, but employs Austrian instructors who speak German. An academic level comparable to the high standard set at the home campus is maintained.*

• **Wooster College in Vienna Program**

The Wooster Program runs for three months, with nine weeks of courses and the remaining time spent in supervised and independent travel. Instruction is in German. Prerequisite: one year of college German. Cost, all-inclusive, about $1,250. For information, write Wooster in Vienna, College of Wooster, Wooster, Ohio. 44691.

CANADA

Quebec

• **Kutztown State College French Summer Session**

This program is for students with at least two years of college French. Instruction is by local instructors, and the program runs for about six weeks. For information, including costs, write French Summer Session in Canada, Kutztown State College, Kutztown, Penna. 19530.

COLOMBIA

Various Cities

• **Students for Understanding**

This program is part of an exchange program with Colombian universities. Students spend eight weeks in Colombia, living with local families and taking courses in Spanish language and Latin American culture. Prerequisite: some facility in Spanish. For information, including costs, write Students for Understanding, Our Lady of Cincinnati College, Edgecliff, Ohio 45206.

DENMARK

Copenhagen

• **George Washington University Summer Arts Program**

Here, courses are given in the theory of design, and a design workshop is available to students. Applicants must have studied design for at least one year. Travel makes up 25 per cent of the program. For information, including costs, write Summer Arts Program in Scandinavia, George Washington University, Washington, D.C. 20006.

ECUADOR

Various Cities

• **University of Oregon Summer Session**

This program lasts one month and may be taken in July or August. Students take courses in elementary and intermediate Spanish and Ecuadorian culture. Field trips are a part of the program. For information, including costs, write University of Oregon Summer Session in Ecuador, 109 Education, University of Oregon, Eugene, Ore. 97403.

EL SALVADOR

San Salvador

• **Council of Mennonite Colleges El Salvador Seminar**

All instruction is in English in this program, which includes three weeks of travel and four of courses. Students live with families. Cost, all-inclusive, about $600. For information, write El Salvador Seminar, Goshen College, Goshen, Ind. 46526.

FRANCE

Aix-en-Provence

• **Oberlin College Summer Session in France**

Of the nine weeks of resident study in this program, five are spent at Aix, one at Avignon, and three at Paris. There are two levels of instruction, one for students with two years of French, another for those with three years. Students live in local homes and in dormitories. Cost, all-inclusive, about $1,200. For information, write Oberlin College Summer Session in France, Oberlin, Ohio. 44074.

Aubigny or Clémont

• **University of Mississippi Summer School in France**

After six weeks' resident study at Aubigny or Clémont, students spend three weeks in supervised travel. Prerequisite: two years of college French. Cost, all-inclusive, about $1,350. For information, write Summer School in France, University of Mississippi, University, Miss. 38677.

Avignon

• **Bryn Mawr Avignon Institute of French Studies**

A six-week program of study at Avignon, with an additional week of travel. Housing is with local families. Cost for tuition, room, and board, about $700. For information, write Institut d'Etudes Françaises d'Avignon, Bryn Mawr College, Bryn Mawr, Penna. 19010. *This is a large, high-quality program for students with high academic standing and three years of college French.*

Brive, Corrèze

• **George Washington University Summer Program**

This is a nine-week program consisting of resident study and course-related travel. Prerequisites: two years of college French with a B average. For information, including costs, write Summer Program in France, The George Washington University, Washington, D.C. 20006.

Dijon

• **Georgetown University Program in Dijon**

Students in this six-week program take courses in the University of Dijon and live either in dormitories or with local families. Some knowledge of French is required. Cost for tuition, room, and board, about $315. For information, write Georgetown in Dijon, Georgetown University, Washington, D.C. 20007.

Fontainebleau

• **American School of Art**

Painting, sculpture, architecture, engraving, and music are taught in this program, which runs from early July to late August. Cost for tuition, room, and board about $700. For information, write Director, Fontainebleau School, 122 East 58th Street, New York, N.Y. 10022.

Grenoble

• **University of Oklahoma Summer Session**

Students study for six weeks at the University of Grenoble and take a two-week tour of France. Cost, all-inclusive, except board, about $1,000. For information, write Summer Session in France, University of Oklahoma, Norman, Okla. 73069.

Montpellier

• **University of Louisville Summer Study of French**

Students study at Montpellier for six weeks before traveling for another three weeks. Arrangements can be made to take courses at the University of Montpellier. Prerequisite: two years of French. Cost, all-inclusive, about $900. For information, write Summer Study of French, University of Louisville, Louisville, Ky. 40208.

Paris

• **Academic Year Abroad Summer Program**

Students in this program, which runs from late June to early August, may take courses in three general areas, French language and civilization, art history, and political science, at various institutions in Paris. Housing is with local families. A tour of Belgium and England held in August is optional. Cost for tuition, room, and board, about $800. For information, write Academic Year Abroad, 225 East 46th Street, New York, N.Y. 10017.

• **American Center for Students and Artists**

This program, which runs from early July to mid-August, offers courses in painting, graphics, drawing, and art history. All are held in English. Tours and special lectures are included. Cost for tuition and board, about $600. For information, write Director, College Art Study Abroad, American Center for Students and Artists, 261 Boulevard Raspail, Paris xiv, France.

• **Kansas State University Summer School Abroad**

Participants in this program live in student residences and with families and take courses at the Cours de Civilisation at the Sorbonne. Prerequisite: two years of French. Cost, all-inclusive, about $1,000. For information, write Summer School Abroad, Kansas State University, Manhattan, Kans. 66504.

• **Michigan State University American Languages and Education Center**

The AMLEC summer program offers 8 weeks of study in Paris and one of supervised travel. Students live in hotels. All courses are taught in French. Prerequisite: two years of college French. Cost for tuition, room, partial board, and transportation, about

$800. For information, write American Language and Education Center, Michigan State University, East Lansing, Mich. 48823.

- **Sarah Lawrence College Summer Session**

This is a six-week program for women of high academic standing. Courses on modern France are given by American instructors, although language classes are led by French teachers. Classes and living quarters are in the Cité Universitaire. Cost for tuition, room, and board, about $700. For information, write Summer Session in Paris, Sarah Lawrence College, Bronxville, N.Y. 10708.

Strasbourg

- **MacMurray College Summer Abroad**

This is a small, 8-week program made up of 6 weeks of study at the University of Strasbourg's course for foreigners and 2 weeks of travel. Housing is in dormitories. Cost, all-inclusive, about $1,000. For information, write Summer Abroad, MacMurray College, Jacksonville, Ill. 62650.

- **Rutgers University Summer Program**

In this program students enroll in courses for foreigners at the University of Strasbourg and live in dormitories. Prerequisites: proficiency in French and a B average. For information, including costs, write Rutgers Summer Program at Strasbourg, Rutgers— The State University, New Brunswick, N.J. 08903.

GERMANY

Cologne

- **Michigan State University American Languages and Education Center**

This is a nine-week course for students with at least two years of college German. Instruction is by Michigan State and local teachers. Students live with families. Cost, all-inclusive, about

$800 (credit program). For information, write American Languages and Education Center, Michigan State University, East Lansing, Mich. 48823.

Munich

• **University of Oklahoma Soviet Area and Language Summer School**

This is a ten-week program in Germany and the Soviet Union in co-operation with the Institute for the Study of the USSR. There are three programs for intermediate and advanced Russian-language students. Instruction, in Russian and English, is by Soviet and American teachers. Cost, all-inclusive, about $1,200. For information, write Soviet Area and Language Summer School, University of Oklahoma, Norman, Okla. 73069.

Singen

• **University of Louisville Summer Program**

Three weeks of this nine-week program are spent in travel. During the academic period, students live in dormitories or with families. Prerequisite: two years of college German. For information, including costs, write Summer Program in Germany, University of Louisville, Louisville, Ky. 40208.

GREAT BRITAIN

London

• **Oklahoma Baptist University Overseas Study Program**

This program consists of four weeks of study in London and six of supervised travel in Europe. Instruction is by Oklahoma Baptist University faculty. One year of a foreign language is suggested, but not required. Cost, all-inclusive, about $1,500. For information, write Overseas Study Program, Oklahoma Baptist University, Shawnee, Okla. 74801.

- **University of Michigan Interdisciplinary Program**

Students in this six-week program take courses in several topics. They live in hotels. Cost, about $700, plus transportation. For information, write Interdisciplinary Program for Study in Great Britain, University of Michigan, Ann Arbor, Mich. 48104.

- **Susquehanna University Oxford Seminar**

Students in this program take a specially arranged five-week course on contemporary Britain at Pembroke College. Applicants should have good academic standing. Cost, all-inclusive, about $1,160. For information, write Oxford Seminar Program, Susquehanna University, Selinsgrove, Penna. 17870.

Oxford

- **University of Massachusetts Summer Seminar**

This large program runs for six weeks. Students live in dormitories. Cost, all-inclusive, about $800. For information, write Oxford University Seminar, University of Massachusetts, Amherst, Mass. 01002.

- **Western Michigan University Social Studies Seminar**

This ten-week program is held every three years (1969, 1972, 1975, etc.). A four-week study program is followed by two weeks of travel-study in Britain and four weeks on the Continent. Prerequisites: at least junior standing and a B-minus average. Cost, all-inclusive, about $1,270 (nonresidents). For information, write Oxford Social Studies Seminar, Western Michigan University, Kalamazoo, Mich. 49001.

GREECE

Athens

- **American School of Classical Studies Summer Program**

A course in Greek civilization, held in English, for teachers and advanced students of the classics. It runs from late June to early

August, with excursions and field trips included in the program. Those attending must have the appropriate educational background in the subject. Cost for tuition, room, and board, about $600. For information, write Classics Department, Rutgers—The State University, New Brunswick, N.J. 08903.

• **University of Colorado Hellenic Institute**

Courses offered in this program include Greek art, literature, and history. After seven weeks of resident study, students travel for three weeks. Housing is at a local college. Cost, all-inclusive, about $1,500. For information, write University of Colorado Hellenic Institute, Boulder, Colo. 80302.

ITALY

Bologna

• **University of Massachusetts Summer Seminar**

Students in this eight-week program take various courses taught by University of Massachusetts instructors. They live in dormitories or with local families. Cost, all-inclusive, about $850. For information, write Bologna Summer Seminar, University of Massachusetts, Amherst, Mass. 01002.

Florence

• **Gonzaga University Summer Session**

Six weeks of this two-month program are spent in study in Italian language and culture, given in English. The remainder of the time is spent in supervised travel. Students live in dormitories. Cost, about $1,200. For information, write Gonzaga-in-Florence Summer Session, Gonzaga University, Spokane, Wash. 99202.

• **Michigan State University American Languages and Education Center**

Courses in this nine-week program are taught in Italian, and students live with families. One week is spent in supervised travel. Prerequisite: two years of college Italian. Cost, all-inclusive, about

$650. For information, write American Languages and Education Center, Michigan State University, East Lansing, Mich. 48823.

• **Sarah Lawrence College Summer Session**

This program offers courses on Italian language and on the Renaissance in Italy taught by Sarah Lawrence faculty. Housing is in villas rented by Sarah Lawrence. Prerequisite: B average. Cost for tuition, room, and board, about $700. For information, write Summer Session in Florence, Sarah Lawrence College, Bronxville, N.Y. 10708.

Rome

• **Temple University Tyler School of Art Summer Program**

This program has two sessions, one running four weeks and the other eight weeks. Classes are given in print-making, drawing, and other art fields. Students live in pensions. Prerequisite: 18 credits of art courses. Cost for tuition, about $200 (four weeks) and $350 (eight weeks). For information, write Tyler School of Art in Rome, Temple University Tyler School of Art, Philadelphia, Penna. 19126.

Siena

• **University of Oklahoma Summer Session**

This program offers six weeks at the University of Siena in courses in Italian language and history. A two-week tour of Italy follows. For information, including costs, write Summer Session in Italy, University of Oklahoma, Norman, Okla. 73069.

JAPAN

Tokyo

• **Georgetown University Summer Session**

This five-week program is given by Sophia University faculty members. Students live in dormitories and hotels. There are no prerequisites. Cost for tuition, room, and board, about $570. For information, write Summer Session in Tokyo, Georgetown University, Washington, D.C. 20007.

• **Gonzaga University Summer Program**

Students in this small program study for seven weeks at Sophia University and spend a week in supervised travel. There are no prerequisites, and students live in dormitories. For information, including costs, write Gonzaga-in-Tokyo, Gonzaga University, Spokane, Wash. 99202.

MEXICO

Guadalajara

• **Georgetown University Summer Session**

Students in this six-week program study at Guadalajara University, but English is used in all but language classes. Prerequisite: good academic standing. No previous knowledge of Spanish necessary. Housing is with local families. Cost for tuition, room, and board, about $300. For information, write Georgetown in Mexico, Georgetown University, Washington, D.C. 20007.

• **Gonzaga University Summer Program**

Six weeks of this two-month program are spent in resident study at Guadalajara University, where courses are taught in English. The rest of the program is spent in supervised travel. There is no language prerequisite. Students live with local families. For information, write Gonzaga-in-Mexico, Gonzaga University, Spokane, Wash. 99202.

• **University of Arizona Summer School**

This program, extending from late June to early August, offers courses in Spanish at various levels of difficulty and courses in Latin American civilization and the arts in both Spanish and

English. Graduate credits can be earned. Cost for tuition, room, and board, about $330. For information, write Professor Juan B. Real, Box 7227, Stanford, Calif. 94305.

• **University of San Francisco Summer Program**

Courses in this program are taught by local and American instructors. The program runs for five weeks. For information, write Summer Session in Guadalajara, University of San Francisco, San Francisco, Calif. 94117.

Guanajuato

• **St. Francis College Summer Program**

Students in this seven-week program must have had at least two years of college Spanish. The program consists of six weeks of resident study at the University of Guanajuato, where courses are given in English and Spanish, and one week of supervised travel. Housing is with families. For information, including costs, write Summer Study in Guanajuato, St. Francis College, Brooklyn, N.Y. 11201.

• **University of Guanajuato Great Lakes Colleges Association Summer School**

This program, which is held from early July to mid-August, offers courses in Spanish language and literature as well as Mexican literature, art, and history. Classes are held in Spanish and English. Excursions, lectures, dances, and other activities are provided. Cost for tuition, about $300. For information, write Latin American Program, Antioch College, Yellow Springs, Ohio. 45387.

Mexico City

• **Brigham Young University Summer Program**

This program is restricted to students adhering to Latter-day Saint standards and consists of seven weeks of courses taught in

English and Spanish by Brigham Young faculty members. In addition, there is one week of supervised travel. Housing is with local families. For information, including costs, write Mexican Residence Program, Brigham Young University, Provo, Utah 84601.

• Indiana Intercollegiate Study Project

Open to students of sixteen Indiana colleges who have a reading knowledge of Spanish and are recommended by the appropriate dean. Program participants take six weeks of courses in Spanish at University of the Americas. They live with families and can earn six credits. Cost, all-inclusive, about $550. For information, write Department of Spanish and Portuguese, Indiana University, Bloomington, Ind. 4740.

• MacMurray College Summer Program

In this six- or ten-week program, students follow the course of regular instruction at the University of the Americas. Courses are taught in English and Spanish, and students live with local families. Cost for tuition, room, and board, about $400 (six weeks). For information, write MacMurray Summer Abroad, MacMurray College, Jacksonville, Ill. 62650.

• San Diego State College Summer Session

Here, too, students take courses at the University of the Americas and live with local families. Other courses are taught by San Diego State faculty members. The program runs for six weeks, and students live with local families. Cost for tuition, about $170; room, board, and air transportation optional. For information, write Summer Session in Mexico City, San Diego State College, San Diego, Calif. 92115.

• Western Kentucky State College Summer Quarter

This three-month program offers courses taught by faculty members from the sponsoring college and from the University of the

Americas. Courses are taught in English, except for Spanish-language classes. Students live with families and in hotels and pensions. Cost for tuition, about $160. For information, write Summer Quarter in Mexico Program, Western Kentucky State College, Bowling Green, Ky. 42102.

• **West Virginia Wesleyan College Summer Session**

Students in this five-week program take courses (in English) at the University of the Americas. Cost, all-inclusive, about $650. For information, write Study-Abroad Summer Session in Mexico, West Virginia Wesleyan College, Buckhannon, W.Va. 26201.

Monterrey

• **Florida State University Summer Program**

Students in this six-week program take courses at the Mexican Technical University, taught by local and American instructors. Housing is in dormitories. For information, including costs, write Summer Program in Mexico, Florida State University, Tallahassee, Fla. 32206.

• **Kansas State University Summer School**

This program consists of six weeks of courses at Monterrey Technical Institute and one week of travel. Prerequisite: two years of college Spanish. Housing is in dormitories and with families. Cost for tuition, room, and board, about $300. For information, write Summer School Abroad, Kansas State University, Manhattan, Kans. 66504.

• **Mankato State College Summer School**

This six-week program offers courses at Monterrey Technical Institute taught in Spanish and English by Mexican instructors. Housing is in dormitories. For information, write Summer School for Students of Spanish, Mankato State College, Mankato, Minn. 56001.

• **Texas Christian University Summer School**

In this program students enroll at the Monterrey Technical Institute. They live in dormitories. Cost for tuition, room, and board, about $250. For information, write Summer School in Mexico, Texas Christian University, Fort Worth, Texas 76129.

• **University of Tennessee Summer Program**

This is a co-operative program with the Monterrey Technical Institute and runs for six weeks. For information, write Summer Study in Mexico, University of Tennessee, Knoxville, Tenn. 37916.

Veracruz

• **Southern Illinois University Travel–Study Course**

This is an eight-week program in which four weeks are spent at the University of Veracruz and the other four in travel in Mexico. At Veracruz, participants take courses (in Spanish) in liberal arts subjects and can earn up to 12 credits. Prerequisite: two years of high-school Spanish or one of college Spanish. For information, including costs, write Latin American Institute, Southern Illinois University, Carbondale, Ill. 62901.

OKINAWA

Various Cities

• **Michigan State University Exchange Program**

Students take five weeks of intensive courses, in English, at the University of the Ryukyus. There are also three weeks of travel in Japan. Cost, about $1,050. For information, write M.S.U. University of Ryukyus Exchange Program, Michigan State University, East Lansing, Mich. 48823.

PORTUGAL

Lisbon

• **Queens College Summer Program**

Students in this program take eight weeks of courses in Portuguese at the University of Lisbon. Housing is in student residences. Prerequisites: one semester of Portuguese and a B average. Cost, about $400, plus transportation. For information, write Summer Program in Portuguese, Queens College of the City University of New York, Flushing, N.Y. 11367.

PUERTO RICO

Rio Piedras

• **Council of Mennonite Colleges Caribbean Seminar**

This program is for students at the ten-member colleges of the Council of Mennonite Colleges. Students study for six weeks at the University of Puerto Rico. Courses are taught in English. Prerequisite: high academic standing. Housing is with local families. For information, including costs, write Caribbean Seminar, Council of Mennonite Colleges, Goshen College, Goshen, Ind. 46526.

SPAIN

Barcelona

• **Michigan State University American Languages and Education Center**

Instruction in this nine-week program is given in Spanish by American and foreign instructors. Prerequisite: two years of college Spanish. Students live with local families. Cost, all-inclusive except transportation, about $550. For information, write American Languages and Education Center, Michigan State University, East Lansing, Mich. 48823.

Bilbao

• **Boston College Summer School**

This eight-week program is held at the University of Duesto. Courses are taught in Spanish by the Jesuit staff of the University. No previous knowledge of Spanish is required. Prerequisite: sophomore standing. Housing is in dormitories. For information, including costs, write Summer School in Spain, Boston College, Chestnut Hill, Mass. 02167.

Granada

• **Oberlin College Summer Session**

In this nine-week program, courses are taught in Spanish by local instructors. Students live with families. Prerequisites: 10 semester hours of college Spanish and a B average. Cost, all-inclusive, about $1,200. For information, write Spanish Summer Session, Oberlin College, Oberlin, Ohio 44074.

Madrid

• **Augustana College Summer School**

In this six-week study-travel program, courses are taught in Spanish by instructors from the Centro Cultural Hispánico-Francés. Prerequisite: one year of Spanish. Cost, all-inclusive, about $850. For information, write Summer School in Spain, Augustana College, Rock Island, Ill. 61202.

• **Bryn Mawr Center of Spanish Studies**

This program is for advanced students of Spanish. Courses in liberal arts subjects and in Spanish language are offered, all conducted in Spanish. Housing is with families. Prerequisite: three years of college Spanish and high academic standing. Cost for tuition, room, and board, about $650. For information, write

Center of Spanish Studies, Bryn Mawr College, Bryn Mawr, Penna. 19010.

• **Michigan State University American Languages and Education Center**

Courses in this nine-week program are taught by American and local instructors. Students live with families. Prerequisite: two years of college Spanish. Cost, all-inclusive (credit enrollment), about $720. For information, write American Languages and Information Center, Michigan State University, East Lansing, Mich. 48823.

• **Rollins College Summer Session**

In this program, American and Spanish instructors teach courses in Spanish language and culture. The program runs for seven weeks. Prerequisite: one year of Spanish and a C average. Students live with families. Cost, about $1,000. For information, write Summer in Madrid Program, Rollins College, Winter Park, Fla. 32789.

• **University of Louisville Summer Program**

Students in this program take courses at the University of Madrid and live in dormitories or with families. Prerequisite: two years of Spanish. Cost, all-inclusive, about $900. For information, write Summer Program in Spain, University of Louisville. Louisville, Ky. 40208.

• **University of Oklahoma Summer Session**

Students in this program take courses at the University of Madrid. The program consists of seven weeks of study and two of travel. Cost, all-inclusive, about $950. For information, write Summer Session in Spain, University of Oklahoma, Norman, Okla. 73069.

Palma de Mallorca

• **University of San Francisco Summer Session**

Courses in this six-week program are taught by a staff of local instructors. There is no language prerequisite. Housing is with local families and in hotels. Cost, all-inclusive, about $1,000. For information, write Summer Session in Mallorca, University of San Francisco, San Francisco, Calif. 94117.

Santander

• **Academic Year Abroad Summer Study Program**

This program, which runs from late June to early August, offers, after an orientation program in Madrid, four weeks of intensive language study at Menendez-Pelayo International University. Advanced language students also study Spanish history and literature. Students live in dormitories. Cost for tuition, room, and board, about $540. For information, write Academic Year Abroad, 225 East 46th Street, New York, N.Y. 10017.

• **Loyola University Summer School**

Students in this two-month program enroll in the summer course for foreigners at the University of Santander; all instruction is in Spanish. Housing is in dormitories. Prerequisite: two years of high-school Spanish. Cost, about $950. For information, write Summer School in Spain, Loyola University, Chicago, Ill. 60626.

Valencia

• **University of San Francisco Summer Session**

In this five-week program, the courses are taught by local instructors and the students live in dormitories, hotels, or with local families. There is no language prerequisite. For information, including costs, write Summer Session in Valencia, University of San Francisco, San Francisco, Calif. 94117.

Various Cities

• Trinity College Travel-Study Program

This is a full-summer program for women students in which four weeks are spent in resident study and the remainder is spent in supervised travel. Prerequisite: one year of college Spanish. For information, including costs, write Travel-Study Program, Trinity College, Washington, D.C. 20017.

SWEDEN

Uppsala

• California State College at Long Beach Summer Session

Scandinavian literature, history, and culture and Swedish language are taught in this program, which runs for five weeks from late June to late July. Cost for tuition, room, and board, about $400. For information, write Coordinator of International Programs, California State College, Long Beach, Calif. 90804.

SWITZERLAND

Bern

• Loyola University Summer Session

This six-week liberal arts program offers courses at three levels: elementary, advanced, and graduate. They are taught by local and American instructors. There is no language prerequisite. Cost, all-inclusive, about $1,900. For information, write Summer School in Europe, Loyola University, Los Angeles, Calif. 90045.

Lausanne

• Michigan State University American Languages and Education Center

In this nine-week program, courses are taught in French by American and local instructors. Housing is with families. Prerequi-

302 • THE NEW GUIDE TO STUDY ABROAD

site: two years of college French. Cost, all-inclusive, about $620.
For information, write American Languages and Education Center,
Michigan State University, East Lansing, Mich. 48823.

Neuchâtel

• **Michigan State University American Languages and Education Center**

This program is similar to the AMLEC program in Lausanne
just described.

UNION OF SOVIET SOCIALIST REPUBLICS

Moscow

• **Dartmouth Summer Language Program**

This is a two-month program for advanced students in Russian
language. Students study in Moscow and spend two weeks in independent travel in Europe before returning. Cost, all-inclusive,
about $1,550. For information, write Russian Summer Program,
Department of Slavic Languages, Dartmouth College, Hanover,
N.H. 03755.

• **Oberlin College Summer Session**

Half of this twelve-week program is spent in resident study, the
remainder in supervised travel. Prerequisite: 10 semester hours of
Russian with a B average, or four semesters of Russian. Students
take special courses at Moscow State University in Russian language. Housing is in dormitories. Cost, all-inclusive, about $1,550.
For information, write Russian Summer Session Abroad, Oberlin
College, Oberlin, Ohio 44074.

• **Universities of Colorado and Kansas Summer Language Institute**

In this program, six weeks are spent in resident study with
faculty from the sponsoring universities and three weeks are
spent in supervised travel. Prerequisites: 12 semester hours of

Russian for admission to intermediate courses, 18 hours for advanced courses. Cost, all-inclusive, about $1,550. For information, write Summer Language Institute in Russian, University of Colorado, Boulder, Colo. 80302, *or* Summer Language Institute in Russian, University of Kansas, Lawrence, Kans. 66044.

Various Cities

- **Indiana University Slavic Workshop**

This ten-week program for advanced students in Russian language is held for five weeks on the campus of Indiana University in Bloomington and for five weeks in the Soviet Union. The session in Indiana consists of intensive courses in Russian, and all students must pledge to speak only that language. Prerequisite: two years of college Russian. Cost, all-inclusive, about $1,700. For information, write Slavic Workshop, Department of Slavic Languages, Indiana University, Bloomington, Ind. 47401.

- **University of Oklahoma Soviet Area and Language Summer School**

For a description of this program, see Munich, Germany, above, p. 288.

UNITED ARAB REPUBLIC

Cairo

- **American University Summer Institute in Arabic Studies**

Conducted from mid-July to late August. Cost for tuition, about $400. For information, write Center for Middle Eastern Studies, Portland State College, Portland, Ore. 47207.

PART III

The Precollege and Secondary-School Student Abroad

Precollege and High-School Programs: Regular Academic Year

Study abroad gives the recent high-school graduate a good jump when he enters college . . . keeping an eye on the draft . . . American-sponsored precollege programs generally the best-tailored to the needs of American students . . . some precollege programs profiled . . . regular high-school programs are of three types: (1) those for dependents of Americans abroad; (2) the private boarding schools; (3) the international and experimental programs

Study abroad has traditionally been associated with higher education but there is no overriding reason why the younger student should not also enjoy its benefits. The needs of such a student, of course, are somewhat different; it makes no more sense to enroll the average high-school junior in an overseas college program than it would to expect him to profit from a year at an American university. But if a program has both extracurricular and academic aspects tailored to the secondary-school level, it can provide a valuable experience to nearly any young American. In a recent interview, Lily Von Klemperer, former head of the Counseling Division of the Institute for International Education, observed:

"Overseas study at the high school and post-high school level is somewhat of a burning issue. There is more demand at present than there are programs of real educational value. There are, of course, some good programs, but parents should look very carefully into programs before they let their children participate."

PROGRAMS FOR PRECOLLEGE STUDENTS

It is important to note that Miss Von Klemperer distinguishes "high-school" and "post-high school" education. The latter type refers in this context to the so-called precollege year abroad for students who have graduated from a secondary school but have not yet formally enrolled in college.

There are at least three important arguments favoring study abroad at the precollege level. In the first place, a year of formal study in a country such as Spain or France may well improve a young person's chances of being admitted to a good American university. Provided that the student can show that he has attended a bona fide school or university abroad and has passed necessary examinations, most American college or university admissions officers will consider the experience a definite asset.

In the second place, for serious language students, an academic year of supervised study abroad provides an unparalleled opportunity for attaining fluency in the foreign language. As we have seen, training in such circumstances is practically on a round-the-clock basis. Virtually every experience will be a form of language education, particularly if students have the good fortune to live in university dormitories occupied by their European counterparts, few of whom are likely to speak much English.

For students intending to major in a foreign language at college, fluency in that language gives a tremendous head start. Instead of wrestling with the technical linguistic details, they will be able to focus their efforts on such advanced subjects as the philosophy, history, and literature of their country of specialization. Moreover, having lived in the culture, they will have insight into the subtleties of much of this material that other students are likely to miss.

Last, a period of study abroad can help develop a young student's maturity and self-confidence. "Travel is fatal to prejudice, bigotry and narrow-mindedness—all foes to real understanding," Mark Twain remarked. "Likewise, tolerance or broad wholesome charitable views of men and things cannot be acquired by vegetating in one little corner of the earth all one's lifetime." While this is true for anyone, for a youth just graduating from high school, a year abroad can also serve to build character by providing him with a breathing space, a time for reflection and re-examination before he plunges into college life.

Most good precollege study-abroad programs emphasize individual guidance and attention. This type of environment encourages the development of self-confidence and removes many of the ungrounded but still very real fears students commonly experience in their freshman year of college. Indeed, some students returning to the United States after a year abroad find American colleges rather restrictive and prosaic. One student of the postgraduate course at the American school in Lugano told a reporter of the *Wall Street Journal,* "Going to college in the United States after a year abroad was a tremendous letdown."

There are, of course, many problems involved in studying abroad at the precollege level, particularly since most programs available fail to offer the benefits just mentioned. This is particularly true of the majority of foreign-sponsored programs, which tend to fall short of meeting the special needs of American students. Thus, aside from gaining some language competence, most American high-school graduates cannot hope to profit from attending a foreign secondary school; the course of study is commonly rigid and heavily weighted toward subjects like Latin, which are not widely taught in the United States. Certainly foreign universities might serve better, but most of these will not admit American students unless they have had two years of college. The special programs for foreigners do enroll United States high-school graduates, of course, but since they concentrate almost exclusively on language instruction, an American cannot obtain the balanced program of general courses that colleges in the United States expect freshmen to take.

These curriculum difficulties aside, there remains the question of credit. A young high-school graduate who wishes to study abroad without "losing" a year—that is, one who hopes to enter college as a sophomore after returning to the United States—may face great difficulties if he spends the year in a foreign university program. For many students, of course, "losing" a year would not be a disaster. But for young men subject to the draft, the question of credit is critical. If a student is going to reach his eighteenth birthday during the year abroad, he must register with his local Selective Service before his departure. And to secure exemption from the draft, he must convince the board that his course of study overseas will earn him sufficient credit to satisfy 25 per cent of the requirements for an undergraduate degree at an American college. In other words, he must show the board evidence that he will be accepted as a sophomore upon his return home.

There is also, for young students fresh from high school, the problem of supervision and guidance. As has been pointed out, foreign universities pay relatively little attention to the personal problems of students, and the student-teacher ratio is such that very little could be done for any individual in any event. Thus, for a variety of reasons most precollege students cannot really profit from participating in the ordinary programs offered by foreign institutions for students from other countries. They must rely on programs sponsored by American institutions which are tailored to their particular needs.

We give here a listing of the most important programs of this type currently available. Whichever one a student chooses, he should first obtain the approval of whatever American college he hopes to attend upon his return. This is not as difficult as it may seem. Most college admissions officers are sympathetic in principle to the idea of study abroad. If the student can show that the foreign program is of high quality, that he will be properly guided in his studies and held to standards comparable to those of the American college he expects to enter, and that properly attested records of his work will be submitted, these admissions officers will probably agree at least to consider his application the following year without prejudice. Male students should obtain a letter to this effect to present, again before departure, to their local draft boards.

• **Academic Year Abroad**

This program acts as a kind of clearing house and administrative center in Paris and Madrid. It provides hand-tailored educational programs for individual high-school graduates, the actual classes being conducted by various local institutes. Students live with families. The Paris program runs from mid-September to mid-June; that in Madrid from early September to late June. Costs, approximately $3,650, including transportation, tuition, and room and board, along with an extensive program of excursions and theater visits. While the program is designed primarily for high-school graduates, some students with previous college experience are admitted. For information, write Academic Year Abroad, 225 East 46th Street, New York, N.Y. 10017. *This is an excellent program, which concentrates on language training and the local culture. Students are placed in language courses according to their individual abilities, and adequate attention is paid to maintaining standards and providing American-type examinations. Graduates have been regularly accepted with appropriate standing in a variety of good American colleges.*

• **American College in Paris**

This program offers high-school graduates the first two years of a college liberal arts curriculum. Graduates may transfer as juniors to four-year colleges in the United States. Except for advanced language classes, instruction is in English, and American methods and grading procedures are followed. Students live with families and eat in French student restaurants. Cost, approximately $1,000, not including transportation or room and board. The program runs from early September to late May. For information, write American College in Paris, 65 Quai D'Orsay, Paris 7, France. *This is a college primarily for Americans who have attended European secondary schools and whose families are resident in Europe, but some graduates of United States high schools are admitted. Classes are small and the level of instruction good. However, the variety of courses offered is somewhat limited.*

• **American Institute for Foreign Study**

A program focusing on foreign languages, English literature, and history, offered in Britain, France, Austria, Italy, and Spain. The program stresses integrating American students into ongoing foreign institutions but also offers courses in European history, art, and other subjects, taught in English. Students live in regular dormitories; thus contacts with foreign students are encouraged. In some classes, students with sufficient language competence may attend regular university courses. The French center is located in Grenoble (the University), the German in Salzburg (the University), the Italian in Perugia (Italian University for Foreign Students), the Spanish in Salamanca (the University), and the British in Bournemouth (the University) and Bangor (the University). Cost, about $2,500, including tuition, room and board. The program runs from mid-September to late June. For information, write American Institute for Foreign Study, 102 Greenwich Avenue, Greenwich, Conn. 06830. *This is a new program. For an evaluation of the Institute's extensive summer program, which is run on the same principles, see p. 327.*

• Fleming College

A two-year liberal arts program offering courses in history, international relations, language, mathematics, art, and other subjects, taught in English. A one-year program concentrating on European political and economic affairs is also available. The school is located at Lugano, Switzerland; students are housed in a villa adjoining the school. Cost, including one-way transatlantic passage, tuition, room and board, and an extensive six-week tour of Europe, approximately $4,600. For information, write Fleming College, 326 East 69th Street, New York, N.Y. 10021.

• Schiller College

This is a liberal arts college run by a German staff but following an American-type curriculum. In addition to its program for college students (see above p. 266), it provides freshman-level instruction in a variety of subjects, including most modern European languages. Students with competence in German may audit courses at the Stuttgart Technische Hochshule. Students live in two castles located in small villages outside Stuttgart. The program runs from late September to late May. Cost, including transatlantic transportation, tuition, room and board, and an extensive program of excursions and tours, $2,500. For information, write Schiller College 7121 Kleiningersheim Neckar, Germany.

PROGRAMS FOR HIGH-SCHOOL STUDENTS

There are also many schools and special programs in foreign countries that accept American students who have not yet completed their secondary education. These are difficult to classify, but they may be divided into three main types.

Schools for Dependents of Americans Abroad

Since World War II there has been a steadily increasing number of Americans who move abroad for extended periods, either because they are on duty with the Armed Services or some other branch of the federal government or because they are assigned to overseas posts by an American corporation. Such people usually do not see themselves as permanent residents of the country in which they are living; yet they expect to remain abroad for a fairly protracted time. They bring their families with them and want to make sure that their children's schooling is not disrupted. Thus, there has been an increasingly heavy demand for American-type secondary and even primary education overseas. For children in the lower grades, it is often possible to rely on the ordinary local schools, but in most countries it is unrealistic to expect older students to adjust to a different system in a short period, and in many it is actually impossible to enroll such students in the local systems. Ideally, these Americans want schools in which the "normal" American curriculum is followed but which also provide some taste of the foreign environment, such as intensive study of the language and courses in the history and culture of the host nation.

The number of schools abroad that seek to fulfill these needs is very large. More than 160,000 American children are currently enrolled, for example, in some 290 military dependents schools set up by the Department of Defense throughout Europe and the Middle East. In addition, thousands of other children are attending American-sponsored schools in some ninety nations. The central clearinghouse for schools that cater to the needs of American families abroad is the International School Services (392 Fifth Avenue, New York, N.Y. 10018). Founded in 1955, it is a private nonprofit organization dedicated to meeting the educational needs of American children overseas, and it provides several important services. First, it has a program for corporations with overseas branches under which it establishes and operates schools for the children of company employees. For example, ISS is in the process of establishing a school in Great Yarmouth, England, for children of employees of the American oil companies engaged in developing the North Sea gas fields. In addition, ISS screens and recommends teachers and administrators for other overseas schools. Its staff interviews and reviews the records of more than 2,000 applicants each year. Nearly 400 teachers were placed in positions abroad in 1968. The organization also arranges recruiting trips for overseas administrators who are able to return to the United States for staff selection, and it runs for schools serving Americans abroad a number of conferences and workshops designed to help overseas school people keep in touch with current trends in American educational thought. Finally, ISS acts as a kind of general secretariat for widely scattered associated schools. Its staff answers hundreds of questions each year concerned with curriculum, administration, fund raising, and so on. The organization also publishes a useful pamphlet, *Overseas Schools Serving American Students*, which is updated annually. This brochure gives a complete list of overseas schools and includes information on the size, cost, and grade range of each institution.

Private Boarding Schools

In addition to schools established primarily for the dependents of Americans living overseas, a limited number of schools abroad also enroll students from the United States. A complete listing of these schools can be found in the volume *New Horizons in Education*, published by Pan American Airways. Copies can be obtained from the Manager of Publications, Pan American Airways, Pan American Building, New York, N.Y. 10017. The cost is $3.95. This guide gives details of schools suitable for American students in Austria, France, India, Italy, Japan, Korea, Lebanon, Malaysia, the Netherlands, Nigeria, Pakistan, the Philippines, Singapore, Spain, Switzerland, Taiwan, Thailand, the United Arab Republic, and the United Kingdom.

The greatest concentration of these schools is found in Switzerland. Formerly known as "finishing schools," these Swiss schools have expanded considerably, both in numbers and courses offered, in recent years. In nearly all cases, they are boarding schools with both a junior and a senior section. They cater to an international clientele, and they vary widely. Some offer a curriculum similar to those of secondary schools in the United States; a few are modeled on British secondary schools. Many have multitrack systems, in which the English-speaking section will prepare students for university entrance in either the United States or Great Britain. The French-speaking section may include French and/or Swiss university preparation, courses leading to French-language proficiency certificates, and a "finishing school" program consisting of traditional subjects, home economics, and perhaps some commercial subjects. The German-speaking section offers similar courses.

All these schools generally stress language instruction. Those in Switzerland have developed a reputation for excellence in this field and attract language students from many different countries. The academic year in the Swiss schools generally starts in the middle of September and continues to the end of June. Most of the schools follow a trimester system, with the first term ending at Christmas time, the second at Easter, and the third around the first of July.

Costs range from $1,500 to $3,500 annually for full board and tuition, the majority charging between $2,000 and $2,500. A complete listing of Swiss boarding schools, *Private Schools in Switzerland*, can be obtained from the Swiss Tourist Office, 608 Fifth Avenue, New York, N.Y. 10020. The French Cultural Services, 972 Fifth Avenue, New York, N.Y. 10021, publishes a similar volume, *Private Schools in France*, but with a handful of exceptions, all located in and around Paris, these conduct classes exclusively in French.

In addition to the famous Swiss and French boarding schools, there are, of course, many distinguished boarding schools in Great Britain. These schools, known as "public schools," are usually highly selective in their admissions policies. Generally, applicants are required to pass what is known as the Common Entrance Examination. This examination is usually given during the last year at preparatory school (the equivalent of preprep schools in the United States), when students are about thirteen. It covers such subjects as English, Latin, French, mathematics, geography, and history. The best of these boarding schools belong to an association called the Headmasters' Conference; these include Eton, Harrow, Winchester, Marlborough, Torbridge, Rugby, and Shrewsbury, which are schools for boys, and Roedean and Cheltenham, which are girls' schools.

Educational standards in these schools are very high. Generally, classes are small. While the curriculum for many years stressed the classics, recently more emphasis has been placed on the sciences. Students are prepared for the British General Certificate of Education (both levels) which is required for university entrance in Great Britain. As with the Continental schools, a trimester system is followed, with the first term ending with Christmas. Tuition fees for these schools come to approximately $1,500.

In addition to the more famous schools, there are numerous other boarding schools which are less restrictive in their admissions policies. An excellent guide to these schools is published by J. J. Paton, 63 Queen Victoria Street, London, E.C. 4, England. Parents wishing to enroll their children in British boarding schools should get in touch with one of the educational placement agencies situated in London rather than write individual schools. These agencies have complete files on admissions policies and help many students obtain entrance in good schools every year. The two largest are Gabbitas and Thring, 6 Sackville Street, London, W. 1, England, and Truman and Knightley, Educational Trust, Ltd., 93 Baker Street, London, W. 1, England. Both these organizations are nonprofit educational trusts recognized by the British Ministry of Education.

International and Experimental Programs

The schools for dependents are primarily American schools in a foreign setting, and the foreign boarding schools are primarily foreign schools that accommodate themselves to American students. There are, however, also a number of interesting schools and special programs which do not fit into either of these categories. The most important of these are described below.

• Schoolboys Abroad in Barcelona and Rennes

This program is organized in Barcelona, Spain, and in Rennes, France, by the Phillips Academy Schools of Andover and Exeter. The program is intended for high-school juniors interested in acquiring fluency in French or Spanish while satisfying the standard requirements for the eleventh grade in American high schools.

Courses are offered in English, mathematics, and history as well as Spanish and French.

Transfer credit is given by the sponsoring Phillips Academy Schools. Students live with local families and study in a central classroom building under the supervision of Phillips Academy staff. The program is restricted to boys. Cost, about $3,400, including transportation, tuition, room and board, and a number of excursions. For information, write Administrator, Schoolboys Abroad, George Washington Hall, Andover, Mass. 01881.

• **American Field Service**

This program, which functions in some twenty-eight countries, provides means for foreign students between sixteen and eighteen years of age to attend high schools and live with families for a year in the United States and for American high-school students to live with foreign families and attend school abroad for an academic year. There is also a summer program of similar character. Students are selected by the American communities which sponsor foreign students in the United States on the AFS program. Candidates must be juniors or seniors with at least two years of study of the appropriate foreign language. The minimum age is sixteen. Students are selected for their all-round achievement and adaptability. They are normally awarded scholarships covering tuition, room, and medical expenses abroad but usually pay their own travel expenses. For information, write American Field Service, 313 East 43rd Street, New York N.Y. 10017.

• **The American School in Switzerland**

This school, located near Lugano, is staffed and administered by Americans. It offers courses in English, several foreign languages, social studies, sciences, mathematics, art, and history. There are four grades of instruction, and classes are small. The student body is entirely American. The academic year runs from mid-September to early June. Cost, approximately $3,500, including room and board and tuition. For information, write American School in Switzerland, 326 East 69th Street, New York, N.Y. 10021.

• **American School of Paris**

This school, located in the suburbs of Paris, offers a general American-type primary- and secondary-school program. Classes are conducted in English, and the student body is chiefly American, but children of other nationalities are admitted. The academic year runs from mid-September to early June. Tuition ranges from about $500 to $725, according to the grade. Boarding students are not accepted, and students must have a parent or guardian living in the Paris area to be admitted. For information, write American School of Paris, 8 Rue de la Machine, Louveciennes (Yvelines), France.

• **English School of Paris**

This school, located eight miles from Paris, provides primary and secondary education of the British type. American students, however, are accepted, and the curriculum allows them to prepare for admission to American colleges. The academic year runs from mid-September to June. Tuition ranges from about $700 to $1,000, according to the grade. Some boarding students are admitted. For information, write English School of Paris, 38 Quai de l'Ecluse, Croissy-sur-Seine (Yvelines), France.

• **Atlantic College**

This school, located in Wales, attempts to provide an international educational system which meets the university entrance requirements of all the Atlantic Community nations. Courses are offered in languages, mathematics, science, and European and American history at the level of the last two years of high school. Cost, approximately $1,500 for tuition and room and board. For information, write Atlantic College, St. Donat's Castle, Llantwit Major, Glamorgan, Wales.

• **Marymount International Schools**

Affiliated with Marymount School in Tarrytown, N.Y., these international girls' boarding schools are conducted by the Sisters of the Sacred Heart of Mary (Roman Catholic Church). The schools are located in the suburbs of London, Paris, Rome, and Barcelona. They offer an American secondary-school curriculum with college-entrance requirements stressed. Special emphasis is given to language study. Cost, including board and lodging and tuition, but not transportation, ranges from $1,500 for the London program to $2,125 for the Paris program. For information, write as follows: London: Marymount International School, George Road, Kingston upon Thames, Surrey, England; Barcelona: Marymount International School, Calle San Pedro 17, Barcelona, Spain; Rome: Marymount International School, Via della Villa Laychl 180, Rome, Italy; Paris: Marymount International School, 72 Boulevard de la Saussage, Neuilly Sur Seine, France.

CHAPTER 13

Programs for High-School Students: Summer

Summer study abroad can be as inexpensive as camp and more stimulating . . . there are many programs, and the quality varies, so a close examination is in order . . . all about chaperons . . . 39 summer programs profiled

In the past few years, the number of summer study programs for high-school students abroad, especially in Europe, has increased dramatically. During the summer of 1968, nearly 20,000 young Americans studied in Europe under the auspices of more than fifty different programs.

One significant reason for this growth is the increasing availability of excellent programs at a reasonable cost. A typical program offers high-school students six weeks in Europe, including round-trip transportation by jet from New York, four weeks' study at a university in France, Britain, Spain, Italy, Austria, or Germany, two weeks' sightseeing in major cultural centers, and the services of American secondary-school teachers as chaperons, usually in the proportion of one teacher for every ten students—all for $750. This compares quite favorably with the cost of a typical summer camp in the United States. It is, therefore, not surprising that many students, and their parents as well, view the new summer programs with favor.

Such a remarkable educational bargain is made possible by a combination of circumstances. Transportation costs are minimal because the programs are able to book entire planes from the airlines. Overseas educational institutions welcome the programs because they simplify many of their registration and supervisory responsibilities. And since the European governments are committed to subsidizing summer schools for nationalistic and political, as well as economic, reasons, the costs of the academic side of these programs is also low. Furthermore, American supervisory personnel, usually called chaperons or counselors, serve, in most cases, with only nominal salary.

Benefits of High-School Programs Abroad

For students of high-school age, independent foreign study is, of course, impractical. Most parents (rightly, in our opinion) refuse to allow teen-agers to confront the strains and complications of living abroad unsupervised, and almost without exception the students themselves recognize the need for restrictions and controls that college students tend to rebel against. When properly run, these programs provide a fine balance of fun and hard work, excitement and stimulation, checked by guidance and support. The reaction of more independent-minded college students in junior-year programs—that they are isolated from contacts with the foreign culture and from academic life—is almost totally absent in the high-school group, as anyone who has talked to numbers of them will testify. A few weeks is not long enough to produce a dramatic increase in knowledge, although especially in the area of language instruction, remarkable results are often accomplished; but with highly motivated and impressionable youngsters, the impact of even this short period can be enormous. Horizons are broadened, independence stimulated, critical faculties force-fed. Here are a few typical coments:

"There is no question in my mind that my summer in England has been the most broadening experience of my life."

"Before I left the United States, practically everyone I talked to led me to believe that the French people were the most unfriendly and nastiest group of people that one could ever meet. To me, these conclusions have been totally untrue."

"I think the way the French people take pride in their land and conserve their beautiful buildings is wonderful. I feel ashamed, after seeing the way the French preserve their cities, at the way Americans are destroying or neglecting once beautiful cities. The French don't waste anything they can use. I'm afraid we, in the U.S.A., will be sorry in the future at the way we have squandered our resources."

"For the past month, I've had to wash and iron my own clothes, take a bus or walk instead of driving a car, and I've had to do without Mom's home cooking. I've had to make decisions and manage money without my parents to help me. I'm learning to get along on my own. Altogether, this has been the most educational, the most fun, and the most meaningful summer of my life."

For the American teachers who accompany the students, the experience is also almost ideal. At no out-of-pocket expense beyond what they need for gifts and personal items, they get six weeks abroad, usually with an opportunity to attend classes at the foreign summer school, and thus, especially if they are language teachers, to improve themselves professionally in the process. And those who design and operate the programs also benefit; the economics are such that these organizations can function without subsidy. Most of them are nonprofit corporations, but it is clear to anyone who has observed them closely that they are flourishing. They are well staffed, they are steadily expanding, and they are even developing modest scholarship programs and otherwise improving the scope and quality of their educational offerings.

But There Are Some Things to Think About

Despite these advantages, by no means all the summer programs for high-school students are worth while. Their very number and variety have caused much confusion. The National Council of State Superintendents of Foreign Languages stated in a recent bulletin, "The Council is alarmed by the rapid proliferation of so-called 'study' programs offered by hundreds of organizations, private, commercial, or 'non-profit,' which take advantage of the tremendous popularity of foreign travel." In 1965 the Council appointed a committee to investigate the situation and lay down guidelines to help educators evaluate these programs. Its report, drafted by the highly regarded authority Stephen Freeman, of

Middlebury College, deals broadly and in the main sensibly with the difficult question of how to select a good program.*

The report discusses first the question of sponsorship. Programs run by American colleges, public and private secondary schools, and religious organizations are nearly always reliable; these institutions are experienced and have reputations to protect. Thus, they may generally be counted on to do what they say they will do. At the other extreme, travel agencies and airline companies also offer summer study programs. These are seldom satisfactory for young students; the sponsors know little about education and tend merely to deposit the student in a foreign summer school, where he is left to his own devices. More difficult to evaluate are the private organizations devoted specifically to summer study programs. As Freeman points out, "The greatest problems and dangers lie in this category, since these private agencies are responsible only to themselves. Some are good; some are downright dishonest." Freeman urges students and parents considering these programs to check them out carefully by reading their literature with a critical eye and by insisting that the sponsors provide the names of students and teachers who have participated in the programs in previous years whom they may contact.

Freeman goes on to discuss the criteria that good programs should apply in selecting students and chaperons; the difference between foreign study and foreign travel; the proper housing of students; and related matters. "Caveat emptor," he concludes, "Be on your guard; be skeptical; ask questions until you are satisfied; do not enroll or pay money until then."

While this advice is sound, the general admonitory tone of the Council's bulletin should not discourage interested persons from enrolling in such programs, including those operated by private organizations. There is a built-in prejudice in the minds of many teachers against anyone who presumes to operate an educational institution without the proper educational credentials or who, admittedly or not, makes a profit out of running an educational enterprise. They forget that administration is an art in itself and

---

* Copies of this bulletin, which is called *Criteria for Evaluating Foreign Study Programs,* may be obtained from the State Supervisor of Foreign Language Instruction in any of the fifty state departments of public instruction.

that many educational administrators from college presidents on down, are, in fact, neither scholars nor unconcerned with balance sheets. The economics of overseas programs, as we have seen, are far different from those of American educational institutions. It is unrealistic to think that this fact can be ignored and illogical to assume that anyone who makes a profit out of overseas education must be either a thief or a mountebank.

Chaperons and Related Problems

These private organizations, however, face real problems of conflict of interest. They need large numbers of students and chaperons in order to function efficiently and are thus tempted to accept persons who are not qualified. Their method of recruiting presents particular dangers. In general, they rely on the interest of high-school teachers in foreign study and travel to obtain their participants. If such a teacher can persuade eight students to sign up, he himself becomes the leader of the group and receives a salary equal to his expenses. If he recruits additional students, he receives further payment for each. The possibility that teachers may accept students of low intellectual capacity or ones not psychologically mature enough for the experience cannot be ignored. Dr. Freeman goes so far as to state flatly: "The selection of the leader-chaperon should be totally separate from recruitment or financial considerations."

This statement, in our opinion, goes too far.* That the system creates a danger goes without saying, but the suggestion that recruitment be entirely separated from the selection of chaperons ignores both the advantages of the current policy and the weaknesses of the alternative. Prospective chaperons may be *tempted* to accept unqualified students, but they would be foolish indeed if they succumbed to that temptation. They are answerable to the parents of all the students in their group and to the authorities of their own school. If they take students into the group who are likely

---

* One of the authors of this book, Cyril J. H. Taylor, is the president of a private organization engaged in running such a program. Accordingly, this section has been written entirely by the other authors and represents their opinions, based on study of many of these programs.

to cause trouble or to weaken the academic side of the program, they are likely to find themselves in serious difficulties, not only while abroad but also after they return. Moreover, from the student's point of view, he is much less likely to abuse the freedom he gets from being far from home if he knows that his chaperon will report any serious misbehavior to his parents and be on hand to confront him if he tries to misrepresent the character of his actions.

Put positively, the fact that chaperons recruit their own students enables them to select ones they know well and in whom they have confidence and assures the students while abroad of the support and guidance of a person they know and respect. If chaperons, however well selected, do not have this personal contact with their charges before and after the foreign experience, their effectiveness is likely to be reduced.

Moreover, it is not easy for a teacher to convince parents that they should allow their teen-age children to study in Europe for the summer. It is naïve to think that all a teacher has to do is to indicate his willingness to take a group abroad and then sit back waiting for the applications to roll in. On the contrary, most parents tend to insist, whatever the reputation of the program, that a local teacher well known to them accompany their offspring on the great adventure. The teacher must also persuade his school principal and superintendent that his proposal is sound, and most of these officials are understandably reluctant to allow groups to be formed unless they can be assured that they are worth while and responsible. In a system where teachers were separately recruited, this would not be the case. Thus requiring prospective chaperons to form groups of their own students is an effective screening process, both for teachers and for students. A frivolous or unintelligent teacher is unlikely to be able to muster a group, and the serious and intelligent teacher is unlikely to accept unqualified students for the venture.

This is not to say that the chaperon recruitment system is perfect. Our observations of the best of these programs in the field have turned up some cases of chaperons who neglected their charges and of students who should never have been accepted in the programs. But in such organizations, these cases are rare. The long-range interests of the sponsors, as well as those of the chaperons and students, militate against irresponsibility. In any case—and here we are in agreement with the Freeman criteria—proper investigation by prospective students and their parents is the best protection against trouble. If the teacher forming a group has a good local reputation, if he has some familiarity with the foreign culture and at least a working knowledge of the language, he should make an excellent chaperon.*

Know Just What You're Getting

One other caveat raised in the Council's report merits discussion. This concerns the character of the foreign schools at which these programs are located. "Many programs speak deceptively of study in a foreign university, under university professors. The truth is that students may be enrolled in special courses for foreigners, or be taught by specially hired assistants in the otherwise empty classrooms." It is true that some high-school programs attempt to bask in the reflected glory of great institutions like the Sorbonne. In the case of high-school programs this is a foolish but relatively harmless exaggeration. It would indeed be disastrous if high-school students were thrown directly into a real foreign university. But the report errs in suggesting that the courses for foreigners are not well suited to the needs of these students. Quite the contrary; the very fact that they are not "real" university courses is what makes them desirable. As we have seen, the quality of instruction in such institutions is excellent. Furthermore, the better private organizations that send high-school groups to them provide the guidance and supervision that they themselves ignore.

We would very much appreciate hearing from participants in any of the programs described on the following pages about their experiences, especially if they note any inaccuracies in our program descriptions. Please write *The New Guide to Study Abroad,* 49 East 33rd Street, Sixth Floor, New York, N.Y. 10016.

---

* The Council's report suggests that a chaperon "should not expect to pursue studies or research of his own." We disagree. Since the students will be in class at least three or four hours a day, there is no reason why he should not take advantage of the opportunity to spend this time in advanced language and culture classes and thus improve himself professionally.

Some Leading Programs

By far the largest of the numerous private organizations that run summer study programs for high-school students are the American Institute for Foreign Study and the Foreign Study League. Each currently enrolls more than 7,000 students a summer in centers all over Europe. Their programs are similar in cost, in method of recruiting students, in length of stay abroad, in type of subject studied, and in most of the logistical details involved in transporting, housing, feeding, supervising, and otherwise caring for the students. They differ somewhat, however, in their educational policies and objectives.

• **American Institute for Foreign Study**

This program flies most of its students to London by chartered plane. After a few days of sightseeing in the London area, students are transported by bus to a number of university centers in Great Britain and on the Continent, where for four weeks they attend classes for three or more hours a day. The British programs concentrate on literature and contemporary society, but there are also classes in drama, archaeology, and a variety of other subjects at one or another campus.

In other countries the emphasis is on language study (French, German, Spanish, Italian, and Russian); the students are tested on arrival and assigned to classes according to their proficiency. In all cases, the instruction is conducted for the Institute by local nationals under the supervision of the local university or school. Chaperons (each of whom has responsibility for about ten students) are encouraged to attend the more advanced classes. Each campus has an AIFS American principal and a local national assistant principal who has charge of extracurricular activities. There is an extensive program of afternoon and week-end tours and excursions. Students and chaperons usually live in dormitories; in some cases foreign students studying at the school are also in residence. The academic program is followed by an additional week of travel, ending with several days of sightseeing in Paris, after which the students are returned to the United States by plane. Cost, about $775 from New York. For information, write American Institute for

Foreign Study, 102 Greenwich Avenue, Greenwich, Conn. 06830: *This program stresses integration of the students into the local situation. Conditions vary from center to center, but where possible they attend classes with students from other countries and share dining and housing facilities with them. At some centers young local "monitors" live with the Americans to help them with the language and assist in making other local contacts. Yet adequate supervision by the American chaperons is always provided. Academic standards are good. Considerable emphasis is placed on orientation before departure, and the Institute attempts to maintain student interest in international understanding through its quarterly magazine, the* Ambassador *(subscription $1 a year).*

• **Foreign Study League**

This program flies students directly to the country of study in chartered planes. In most cases, the academic program is divided into two three-week sessions at different localities. But there is considerable variety; in some instances there are four weeks of study at one center, with a week of travel at each end of the program. Classes are held five days a week, 4 hours a day. The British programs concentrate on literature and drama. In other countries the emphasis is on languge study (French, German, Spanish, Italian, and Russian). Most instruction is by *American* teachers, although advanced language classes are usually taught by local nationals. American textbooks are used. The American teachers, who are brought over with the group, are in addition to the chaperons (called counselors) and have no responsibilities beyond their academic duties. Each campus has an American principal, plus an assistant principal who has charge of extracurricular activities. There is an extensive program of afternoon and week-end tours and excursions. Students and counselors live in dormitories. At the end of the program students are returned to the United States by plane or ship. The cost varies with the particular program: most cost about $750–$800 from New York. For information, write Foreign Study League Schools, 164 East 3900 South, Salt Lake City, Utah 84107. *This program puts great emphasis on group unity and on maintaining continuity with American teaching methods. All groups are self-contained in classroom, housing, and dining facilities and while touring and making local excursions. Social contacts with local nationals are encouraged, but closely supervised. Considerable emphasis is placed on orientation before departure; for instance, textbooks used in the courses are distributed to students on enrollment. Academic standards are good.*

Some other organizations of this type are:

• **American International Academy**

This organization offers five-week programs: three weeks of classroom work (in Austria or France) and two weeks of travel. Open to both high-school and college students. It is affiliated with Westminster College, a small liberal arts institution, and also operates a travel-study program in "Social Studies–Humanities." Cost, about $770. For information, write American International Academy, 1840 South 13th Street, Salt Lake City, Utah 84105.

• **Work or Study Abroad Schools, Ltd.**

This institution offers six-week programs in a variety of countries, open to high-school and college students. Cost about $750, higher for Israel and Russia. For information, write Work or Study Abroad Schools, Ltd., Mitchell Building, Milwaukee, Wis. 53202.

• **World Academy Schools for Foreign Study**

This organization runs six-week programs in a variety of European centers, open to high-school and college students. It solicits individual as well as group applications. Cost, $800 to $1,000. For information, write World Academy Schools for Foreign Study, Box 1847, 123 East 6th Street, Cincinnati, Ohio 45202.

In addition to the organizations specializing in high-school summer study programs, many American schools and even a few American colleges run programs abroad for high-school students. The most important of these are listed below, along with a sampling of the foreign summer schools that make special arrangements for younger students.

AUSTRIA

• Austrian Committee for International Education

This is a four-week program of language study, open to students aged fourteen to nineteen, held in Vienna during August. For information, including costs, write Austrian Committee for International Education, Türkenstrasse 4, Vienna, Austria.

• College of Wooster

A program open to students with one year of German. It combines study in Vienna with a period of travel in Germany and Austria and runs from mid-June to early September. Cost, about $1,245, including transportation. For information, write German Summer Session in Vienna, College of Wooster, Wooster, Ohio 44691.

• Georgetown University

This program, which runs from early July to mid-August, is held at Salzburg. It is open to high-school juniors and seniors, on the recommendation of their principal or adviser. Cost, about $310. For information, write Georgetown University, 37th and O Streets, N.W., Washington, D.C. 20007.

• Lerchs International Language School

This school runs one-month classes in German language at Innsbruck from June through September; it is open to students at least fourteen years old. Cost for tuition, room, and board, about $40 per week. For information, write Lerchs Internationale Sprachschuler, Kapuzinerstrasse 10, Innsbruck, Austria.

FRANCE

• Academic Year Abroad

This six-week program, open to high-school seniors and college students, has sections in both Paris and Spain. The Paris program offers courses in art history, French language and culture, and political science. Cost, $785 for tuition, room, and board. The Spanish program offers courses in all levels of the language and in Spanish history, literature, and art history. Cost, $549. Transportation and a three-week August tour are additional for both programs. Academic credit is available. For information, write Miss Janelle Kleinschmidt, Registrar, Academic Year Abroad, 225 East 46th Street, New York, N.Y. 10017.

• American Pre-College Program

This is a six-week program in Paris, open to high-school juniors and seniors. A variety of courses in French language and culture are combined with excursions and theater visits. Students live in dormitories. Cost, about $565 for tuition, room, and board; transportation is extra. For information, write American Pre-College Program, 15 Boulevard Jourdain, Paris, France.

• American School in Switzerland

This program, held in southern France, is open to students between sixteen and twenty. Courses are offered in French language, art appreciation, and contemporary European affairs. Cost, about $1,800, including transportation. For information, write American School in Switzerland, 326 East 69th Street, New York, N.Y. 10021.

• Avon Public Schools

This is a seven-week study and touring program. Classes are offered in French language and culture, and students visit Spain and Italy. Students must be between fifteen and eighteen and have some knowledge of French. Cost, about $845, including transportation. For information, write Superintendent, Avon Public Schools, 50 Simsbury Road, Avon, Conn. 06001.

• Choate School

This program, running from mid-June to early August, combines four weeks of language study in Paris with a tour of France,

Switzerland, and Italy. Students must be sixteen years of age and have a good knowledge of French. Cost, about $1,500, including transportation. For information, write Choate School, Wallingford, Conn. 06492.

• College Cevenol Language Course

This is a program in French language, culture, and the arts, open to students aged fourteen to eighteen with two years of French. It runs from mid-July to mid-August. Cost, about $275 for tuition, room, and board; transportation is extra. For information, write Admissions Officer, American Friends of the College Cevenol, 47 Highland Avenue, East Northfield, Mass. 01360.

• Georgetown University

This program, which runs from early July to mid-August, is open to high-school juniors and seniors. It is held at the University of Dijon. Students must obtain recommendations from their local principal or faculty adviser. Cost, about $315; transportation is extra. For information, write Georgetown University, 37th and O Streets, N.W. Washington, D.C. 20007.

• Indiana University

This program, which runs from late June to late August, is located at Saint-Brieuc. It is open only to juniors of Indiana high schools who have had three years of French. Students live with families. Cost, about $950, including transportation. For information, write Honors Program in Foreign Languages, 101 Lindley Hall, Indiana University, Bloomington, Ind. 47401.

• University of Louisville International Center

This program, running from mid-June to mid-August, offers six weeks of classroom study at Montpellier or Paris and three weeks of travel. Students must be at least sixteen and have had one year of French. Cost, about $850, including transportation. For information, write University of Louisville International Center, Louisville, Ky. 40208.

GERMANY

• Indiana University

This program, which runs from late June to late August, is located at Krefeld. It is open only to juniors of Indiana high schools who have had three years of German. Students live with families. Cost, about $950, including transportation. For information, write Honors Program in Foreign Languages, 101 Lindley Hall, Indiana University, Bloomington, Ind. 47401.

• University of Louisville International Center

This program, running from mid-June to mid-August, offers six weeks of classroom study at Singen and three weeks of travel. Students must be at least sixteen and have had one year of German. Cost, about $850, including transportation. For information, write University of Louisville International Center, Louisville, Ky. 40208.

GREAT BRITAIN

• Corolla Summer School

A program in English literature, history, mathematics, and other subjects, held at the University of Reading. Students must be between fourteen and nineteen. Cost for tuition, room and board, and transatlantic transportation, $1,650. For information, write Corolla in England, Dyke, Va. 22935.

GREECE

• Pierce College

A six-week program, open to students between sixteen and eighteen, held at Athens. Courses are offered in elementary modern

Greek and (in English) in Greek literature, history, and classical art. Cost for tuition, room and board, and transatlantic transportation, $1,695. For information, write Pierce College Summer School, Simmons College, Boston, Mass. 02115.

ISRAEL AND NEAR EAST

• American Zionist Youth Foundation

A seven-week program held at the Israel Summer Institute, open to high-school juniors and seniors. In addition to classroom work, students live for two weeks on a kibbutz. Cost, abut $900, including transportation. For information, write American Zionist Youth Foundation, 515 Fifth Avenue, New York, N.Y. 10022.

• Choate School

A travel-study program, running from early July to late August, centered at Beirut. Students must be between sixteen and nineteen. Cost, about $2,000, including transportation. For information, write Choate School, Wallingford, Conn. 06492.

JAPAN

• Avon Public Schools

This program, running for ten weeks, concentrates on Japanese language and culture. Students must be between fifteen and eighteen and have some knowledge of Japanese. Cost, about $1,000, including transportation. For information, write Superintendent, Avon Public Schools, 50 Simsbury Road, Avon, Conn. 06001.

• Georgetown University

This program, running from early July to mid-August, is open to juniors and seniors with a B average. It is held at Sophia University in Tokyo. Cost, about $900 from San Francisco. For information, write Georgetown University, 37th and O Streets, N.W. Washington, D.C. 20007.

• **Sophia University**

This program runs from early July to early August. It is open to graduating seniors only and is held in Tokyo. Cost, about $400. For information, write Sophia University Associates of America, 211 East 87th Street, New York, N.Y. 10028.

MEXICO

• **Friends World Institute**

This is an eight-week study-travel program which includes three weeks of classes at the Mexican-American Cultural Institute. Cost, about $800. For information, write Friends World Institute, 5722 Northern Boulevard, East Norwich, N.Y. 11732.

• **Georgetown University**

This program, held at the Institute of Technology at Guadalajara, runs from early July to mid-August. It is open to juniors and seniors. Cost, about $295, plus transportation. For information write, Georgetown University, 37th and O Streets, N.W. Washington, D.C. 20007.

• **Gonzaga University**

This program, running from early July to mid-August, accepts juniors and seniors in its elementary Spanish courses. Recommendation of principal or adviser is required. The program is held at Guadalajara. Cost, about $300. For information, write Gonzaga University, 502 Boone Street, Spokane, Wash. 99202.

• **Indiana University**

This program, which runs from late June to late August, is located at San Luis Potosí. It is open only to juniors of Indiana schools who have had three years of Spanish. Students live with families. Cost, about $650, including transportation. For information, write Honors Program in Foreign Languages, 101 Lindley Hall, Indiana University, Bloomington, Ind. 47401.

SOVIET UNION

• Avon Public Schools

This is a seven-week study-tour of Russia and eastern Europe. It is open to students between fifteen and eighteen with some knowledge of Russian. Cost, about $1,000, including transportation. For information, write Superintendent, Avon Public Schools, 50 Simsbury Road, Avon, Conn. 066001.

• Choate School

This program, running from late June to late August, includes a month of Russian study at Choate and a month's tour of eastern Europe. Students must be between sixteen and nineteen and have had one year of Russian. Cost, about $2,000, including transportation. For information, write Choate School, Wallingford, Conn. 06492.

SPAIN

• Avon Public Schools

A six-week program, including four weeks of classes at the University of Madrid and travel in France, Italy, and England. Students must be between fifteen and eighteen and have some knowledge of Spanish. Cost, about $750, including transportation. For information, write Superintendent, Avon Public Schools, 50 Simsbury Road, Avon, Conn. 06001.

• Choate School

This program, running from late June to late August, includes four weeks' study in Madrid and travel in Spain and France. Students must be between sixteen and nineteen and have a good knowledge of Spanish. Cost, about $1,400, including transportation. For information, write Choate School, Wallingford, Conn. 06492.

• Rollins College

This program, running from late June to early August, provides a language and culture program in Madrid open to high-school seniors with a year of Spanish. Cost, about $1,000, including transportation. For information, write Chairman, Department of Modern Languages, Rollins College, Winter Park, Fla. 32789.

• University of Louisville International Center

This program, running from mid-June to mid-August, offers six weeks of classroom study at Madrid and three weeks of travel. Students must be at least sixteen and have had one year of Spanish. Cost, about $850, including transportation. For information, write University of Louisville International Center, Louisville, Ky. 40208.

SWITZERLAND

• National Student Association

This program, held at Neuchâtel, runs from early July to late August. It is open to students between fifteen and eighteen who have had a year of French. A touring program is included. Cost, about $1,500, including transportation. For information, write U.S. National Student Association, 265 Madison Avenue, New York, N.Y. 10016.

• Tutor Summer School

A six-week program providing intensive study of French for students between fifteen and eighteen. Classes are held in the Geneva area. Cost, about $1,500, including transportation. For information, write Tutor Summer School, 20 Rue de Lausanne, Geneva, Switzerland.

PART IV

The Teacher Abroad

CHAPTER 14

Study Abroad for Teachers

Many American teachers enroll in foreign universities . . . a rich variety of scholarship aid and grants aavilable . . . the Fulbright programs for graduate and postdoctoral study . . . other government grants in language and area study . . . grants from foundations and other private sources

The opportunities available to American schoolteachers for a period of study abroad are so varied that anyone who has reasonable academic qualifications and possesses the necessary determination and perserverance should be able in one way or another to arrange it.

First of all, teachers can simply enroll at their own expense in postgraduate courses at foreign universities. Aside from courses given at universities and colleges in English-speaking countires (generally in the Commonwealth), most will require fluency in the language of the country. Unfortunately, language teachers excepted, not many American schoolteachers have this ability. For those who do, the cost is quite low: approximately $1,500 in most countries for board, lodging, and tuition. This gives the idea a particular appeal for teachers on sabbatical leave. The half salary they receive while on sabbatical is usually sufficient to cover their expenses. It is interesting that an increasing number of school systems grant their teachers such sabbatical leaves for a bona fide study purpose.

Teachers interested in enrolling privately as individual students at foreign universities should study Parts I and II of this book for details on higher education outside the United States. Other valuable reference sources include the following:

Handbook on International Study for U.S. Nationals. Published by the Institute of International Education, 809 United Nations Plaza, New York, N.Y. 10017.

International Handbook of Universities, edited by H. M. R. Keyes. Copies may be obtained from the American Council on Education, 1758 Massachusetts Avenue, N.W. Washington, D.C. 20036.

Commonwealth Universities Handbook, edited by the Association of Commonwealth Universities in London. Copies may be obtained from the American Council on Education, 1758 Massachusetts Avenue, N.W. Washington, D.C. 20036.

New Horizons in Education. Published by Pan American Airways, Pan American Building, New York, N.Y. 10017.

Teachers interested in study abroad may also apply for scholarships or grants for a specific course of study or research. There are many thousands of such grants available. Competition, of course, is stiff; applicants must have first-rate academic records. But the prestige is great, and the economic advantages are certainly significant. A more easily achieved alternative is to apply for a position as a teacher abroad. In many ways this is both the most available approach and the most rewarding in terms of contact with a foreign culture. Available opportunities are discussed in some detail in the following chapter.

SCHOLARSHIP AND GRANTS

Because the number of scholarships and grants available to teachers is large, considerable time and research are necessary to unearth the many different opportunities available and discover which are best suited to the applicant's needs and talents. Candidates should start their investigations at least two years before their planned departure.

Most awards require the following qualifications from candidates: good academic record; excellent personal references; proven record of capacity for independent study; adequate command of the language of the country where studies are to be undertaken; good health. Many also require that candidates have at least a master's degree.

Although the field of study to be undertaken is seldom specified, applicants are usually required to submit a definite study plan. Therefore, certain restrictions, such as the availability of research facilities in the candidate's field, must be considered. It is up to the candidate to satisfy himself before applying for a grant that his plan is feasible in the country of his choice. Since applications are often quite involved and difficult to complete, teachers should seek as much assistance as possible before submitting them. Conversations with teachers who have already spent a year abroad on a grant will help considerably. Since competition is so intense, it is most important to obtain the widest possible range of information and advice.

The great number of individual awards and grants available precludes a complete listing. Only the largest programs will be discussed here. Applicants seeking complete information on the subject are advised to consult the following directories:

Study Abroad. Published by the Unesco Publications Center, 319 East 34th Street, New York, N.Y. 10016. The sixteenth edition (1966) contains information on over 170,000 individual opportunities for subsidized study abroad. Awards offered by 77 international organizations and 1,690 individual donors in 120 different countries are discussed in detail.

Handbook on International Study for U.S. Nationals. Published by the Institute of International Education, 809 United Nations Plaza, New York, N.Y. 10017. This gives a complete analysis of overseas study opportunities. Chapter 2 gives details of scores of scholarship programs.

The principal organizations making grants for study abroad are discussed below.

Government Grant Programs

• Fulbright Programs

The program for educational and cultural exchange of the United States Department of State was first authorized in 1946 by the Fulbright Act. The Mutual Educational and Cultural Exchange Act of 1961 (Public Law 87–256), known as the Fulbright-Hays Act, consolidated and expanded previous legislation governing the program. This Fulbright-Hays Act aims at increasing mutual understanding between the United States and other countries by promoting international co-operation for educational advancement. With the consent of the foreign governments concerned, the Department of State conducts each year educational and cultural exchanges involving persons from more than 120 foreign countries. Grants are awarded for the purposes of consultation and observation in specialized fields, study, teaching, university lecturing, and advanced research.*

Graduate Study. A grantee must hold a bachelor's degree or its equivalent, and he must present an acceptable plan of study lasting at least a year at an educational institution abroad. He must know the language of the host country sufficiently well to carry on the proposed study. However, some allowances are made in this matter for countries whose languages are not widely taught in the United States. Candidates should be in good health and should generally be under thirty-five years of age. All grants for graduate study are awarded on the basis of open competition. A primary factor in selection is the potential of the candidate to further understanding between the United States and the host country. A grant usually includes transportation, tuition, maintenance, and incidental expenses while overseas. Funds are paid in the currency of the foreign country or in dollars. Payments vary with the cost of living in different countries. No extra funds are provided to cover the expenses of dependents whom a grantee may wish to take with him. Concurrent benefits under the GI Bill are not, however, affected. In addition to full grants covering all expenses, a number of travel grants are provided under the Fulbright-Hays Act. These awards are intended to supplement maintenance and tuition scholarships granted by universities, private donors, and foreign governments. For information, teachers currently doing graduate work at an American university should get in touch with the Fulbright program adviser on campus. Those not enrolled in an American university should apply to the Institute of International Education, 809 United Nations Plaza, New York, N.Y. 10017, or one of its

---

* The amount of money available for Fulbright scholarships is, of course, subject to appropriations from Congress, and varies from time to time. For instance, funds made available for the 1968–69 academic year were sharply curtailed, with subsequent cancellation or reduction of programs in a number of countries. A prospective Fulbright candidate should be sure to inform himself on the current status of any program in which he wishes to make application.

regional offices. The annual competition for these awards opens in May. Completed applications are due by October 31.

Postdoctoral Study. In addition to the Fulbright grants for graduate study, scholarships are also available for advanced postgraduate research. A candidate must have a Ph.D. degree or an equivalent professional status. He should know the language of the country well and present a plan for a research project at a foreign university of at least six months' duration. Awards cover the cost of travel for the grantee himself and necessary living expenses for both him and his accompanying dependents. The amounts, payable in the foreign currency, vary according to the cost of living in the country. For information, write Conference Board of Associated Research Councils, 2101 Constitution Avenue, N.W., Washington D.C. 20418. Applications are reviewed by screening committees in the various academic disciplines and by the Committee on International Exchange of Persons of the Conference Board of Associated Research Councils. The Board of Foreign Scholarships makes the final selections. Those interested in research projects in Australia, New Zealand, or Latin America should apply between March 1 and April 15 of the previous year—approximately fifteen months in advance. Those who wish to conduct research elsewhere should apply between June 1 and August 1 of the previous year.

• **Other United States Government Grants**

Under the provisions of the Education Professions Development Act (Public Law 90–35), which superseded the National Defense Education Act of 1958, a substantial number of grants are available for study abroad by graduate students and teachers specializing in certain languages and in area studies related to these languages.

Language and Area Study. Approximately twenty-five grants a year for periods of nine to twelve months are available to teachers of modern languages. The main objective is the improvement of individual teacher competence. Grants include the cost of round-trip transportation, living and tuition expenses, and an allowance of $1,000 per year for up to two dependents. In the case of shorter-term grants, the allowance is $100 per dependent per month. Applicants must have outstanding reputations as teachers of modern foreign languages or area studies and must possess the potential for becoming future supervisors or curriculum directors. They must also have had at least five years of teaching experience. For information, write Teacher Exchange Section, Bureau of International Education, Office of Education, U.S. Department of Health, Education, and Welfare, Washington, D.C. 20202. Applications are due by October 15.

Summer Language Study. Under this program for teachers of modern languages, American colleges and universities organize summer study sessions both in the United States and abroad for secondary-school teachers. Teachers must apply to the sponsoring institution. The awards usually consist of $75 a week for living expenses and free tuition and transportation. For general information on these summer institutes, write to the Office of Education, U.S. Department of Health, Education, and Welfare, Washington, D.C. 20202, or the supervisor of modern languages in your home state.

Private Grant Programs

• Foreign Area Fellowship Program

These foreign-area fellowships, which number over one hundred annually, are made available through funds donated by the Ford Foundation. Their purpose is to help meet the need in the United States for the knowledge and understanding of foreign areas that are required for the effective discharge of the United States' increased international responsibilities. They cover graduate and postdoctoral training at foreign universities in the social sciences, law, education, and the humanities. The grants are available for study in most countries. Applicants must satisfy one of the following requirements: be a graduate student in social sciences or humanities who wishes to combine training in a major discipline with multidisciplinary foreign-area or language training; be a teacher with a doctorate in one of the social sciences who wishes to be trained in foreign languages; be a government employee who wishes to undertake specialized foreign-language and foreign-area training. Graduate students who are in the early stages of acquiring foreign-language competency are usually expected to work at universities in the United States. Applicants are usually given awards for study abroad only after they have acquired the necessary language competence. Grants usually cover all costs, including transportation, board and lodging, and tuition. Applications should be made by November 1. For information, write Foreign Area Fellowship Program, 444 Madison Avenue, New York, N.Y. 10022.

• **American Association of University Women Fellowships**

The American Association of University Women offers approximately fifty fellowships worth $3,000 to $5,000 each for women university graduates who hold a doctoral degree or its equivalent. The scholarships may be used for study abroad or in the United States. For information, write the American Association of University Women Educational Foundation, 20401 Virginia Avenue, N.W., Washington, D.C. 20037.

• **Institute of International Education**

In addition to its screening of candidates for the Fulbright-Hays graduate study awards, the IIE handles applications for approximately two hundred additional fellowships and scholarships offered by foreign universities, cultural societies, and governments and by private donors, corporations, and foundations in the United States. Awards are usually for one academic year. The IIE screening committees recommend candidates for the awards to sponsoring agencies which make the final decision. For information on these scholarships, write the IIE for its *Handbook of International Study for U.S. Nationals*, 809 United Nations Plaza, New York, N.Y. 10017.

• **Rotary International**

Approximately 135 fellowships are awarded annually by this organization, about half of them to Americans, for study abroad during an academic year. Grants cover tuition, maintenance, and round-trip transportation costs. Candidates must be twenty to twenty-eight years of age, male, unmarried, with a bachelor's degree or equivalent. They must have a good working knowledge of the language of the country to be visited and must be sponsored by a local Rotary Club. Applications must be made by April 15 of the year preceding the award. For information, write a local Rotary Club, or Rotary International, 1600 Ridge Avenue, Evanston, Ill. 60201.

CHAPTER 15 ~~~~~~~~~~~~~~

Teaching Positions Abroad

*There are many openings abroad for qualified American teachers
. . . conditions may sometimes be difficult, but the work is rewarding . . . opportunities to teach in government-sponsored programs
. . . schools for dependents of military personnel abroad . . . private
organizations also send many teachers abroad . . . a rich variety
of summer opportunities . . . serving as a group leader for high-
school student summer programs*

REGULAR ACADEMIC YEAR

Any good American teacher who wishes to teach
abroad for one or two years should find little difficulty in obtaining
a post, for the number available is large. However, these positions
vary considerably in attractiveness. Very few offer salaries and
fringe benefits as good as those for comparable positions in the
United States. Nevertheless, the professional benefits of a period
of overseas service can be great, especially for teachers of modern
languages or social sciences.

Before applying for an overseas position a teacher should undertake a careful survey of the field. Caution should be exercised before a contract is signed, since an unwise decision is usually difficult
to change. For example, many overseas schools require contracts
of at least two years' duration in order to offset the heavy travel
costs involved. Furthermore, few teachers abroad enjoy the same
benefits and protection given teachers in the United States by professional associations such as the National Education Association.
In many cases the applicant will unfortunately have to make his
decision on the basis of rather sketchy information on such crucial

matters as living conditions, school facilities, and size of classes. Obviously, a personal visit to the school before signing a contract is seldom possible.

Unless a teacher is applying for a position in western Europe or at a Defense Department school for the children of American servicemen, conditions are likely to be very different from those in the United States. In many countries, secondary-school teachers are likely to be expected to teach a wide range of subjects rather than one or two. Salary scales are lower than in the United States, although many teachers abroad receive housing. Living conditions, even in Europe, differ considerably from those in the United States, while "essentials" like central heating, refrigeration, electricity, and even running water may be absent in the underdeveloped countries. Only persons motivated by the service aspects of foreign teaching positions should, for example, apply for jobs in Africa or India.

Another problem which can cause considerable anxiety for American teachers abroad stems from political interference in such matters as curriculum and promotions. American teachers contemplating overseas service should remember that, except in the case of Defense Department and other purely American schools, they will be working for foreign governments. The degree of political interference can be considerable, especially in times of local political upheaval or when United States international policies may arouse local resentments—an all too frequent occurrence!

Teachers with families should exercise special caution when applying for a position abroad. Providing schooling for their own children may pose problems, and medical and recreation facilities are likely to differ considerably from those in the United States.

However, teaching has many compensations. In the first place, promotion prospects are likely to be good; a skilled American teacher will be given positions of high responsibility much more quickly abroad than at home. Second, teaching systems abroad, especially in the underdeveloped countries, are more flexible than those in the Uniter States, and the possibilities for experimentation are often excellent. Teachers who find some of the more restrictive customs of American schools irksome are likely to have considerably more freedom abroad. Institutions like parent-teacher associations are rare. Finally, a period of study abroad can increase a teacher's professional competence, especially if his field is the local language.

There are three major types of teaching jobs overseas: (1) the government-sponsored opportunities, such as the Peace Corps, or the Teacher Exchange Program sponsored by the Fulbright-Hays Act; (2) the Department of Defense schools for dependents of servicemen overseas; and (3) private opportunities, such as those offered by International School Services of New York.

Government-Sponsored Opportunities

• **Department of State Educational Exchange Programs**

Under the provisions of the Fulbright-Hays Act, a number of exchange teaching positions abroad are made available by the United States Department of State with the purpose of increasing mutual understanding between the United States and other countries. The programs are administered by the Bureau of Educational and Cultural Affairs of the State Department.

Candidates must be currently employed in an elementary, secondary, or teacher-training school, hold a bachelor's degree, and have at least three years' teaching experience; in most cases fluency in the language of the host country is required. Candidates must also be personally committed to the objectives of the program and have a serious interest in other cultures and other peoples. Emotional maturity and the ability to adapt easily to different living conditions are also important.

Two types of educational exchange grant are available. Under one, the interchange plan, American and foreign teachers actually trade places; under the other, no direct exchange is involved.

Direct exchanges of positions take place between the United States and the following countries:

Argentina	Luxembourg
Australia	Netherlands
Austria	Norway
Belgium	New Zealand
Chile	Peru
Denmark	Uruguay
Germany	

Approximately two hundred direct exchanges take place annually under the plan. The teacher must be able to secure a leave of absence, and his institution must be prepared to accept a foreign teacher in exchange. Normally, only teachers of English, mathematics, science, social studies, and education can qualify for the program. Grants provide for transportation, a maintenance allowance based on normal living expenses in the host country for both the teacher and dependents, and, in some countries, an allowance for books and supplies. A special program exists between the United States and Canada, Sweden, and Britain. Under this plan, teachers must be able to secure a leave of absence *with pay*.

Approximately one hundred "one-way" teaching assignments for elementary and secondary schools are available in the following countries:

Austria	Ecuador	India	Pakistan
Brazil	Finland	Iran	Paraguay
Chile	Germany	Italy	Peru
Cyprus	Greece	Japan	Sweden
Denmark	Iceland	Korea	Turkey

Grants cover travel and maintenance expenses while abroad.

For information, write Teacher Exchange Section, Bureau of International Education, Office of Education, Department of Health, Education, and Welfare, Washington, D.C. 20202. Applications should be submitted between August 1 and October 15 of the year preceding the award.

• **Peace Corps**

The Peace Corps recruits and trains volunteers to work as teachers in the developing countries of Asia, Africa, and Latin America. Assignments are usually for a minimum of two years, including the training period in the United States. All training, travel, and living expenses are paid. In addition, a readjustment allowance of $75 for every month spent overseas is paid in a lump sum on termination of Peace Corps service. Selection for the three-month training period in the United States is based on evaluation of the application on scores on a placement test, and also on character references. The minimum age is eighteen with no upper age limit. Application forms are available at post offices and campus liaison offices, or write Peace Corps, Washington, D.C. 20006.

• **United States Information Agency**

This program provides posts for teachers of English, librarians, activities directors, and administrators at binational centers in Latin America, Europe, Asia, and Africa. The salary depends on the responsibilities of the position, the cost of living in the country of the assignment, family status, and previous experience. The minimum assignment is for two years. For information, write Head of Personnel, United States Information Agency, Washington, D.C. 20547.

• **United Nations Educational, Scientific, and Cultural Organization (UNESCO)**

A number of primary- and secondary-school positions are available in various underdeveloped countries under the auspices of UNESCO. In addition, a number of supervisors are engaged each year to assist in teacher-education programs in South America, Africa, and Asia. For information, write Technical Assistance Branch, Bureau of International Education, Department of Health, Education, and Welfare, Washington, D.C. 20202.

• **Pädagogischer Austauschdienst**

This organization recruits candidates for about forty English-language assistantships in German secondary schools. The salary is $450 a month for approximately fifteen classes a week. Candidates must be aged twenty-one to thirty, be unmarried, have a bachelor's degree, be committed to a teaching career, and speak German fluently. Applications should be made by January 1 to the German Embassy in Washington or the nearest German Consulate.

• **Institute of International Education**

IIE administers a program of English-language teaching assistantships in French secondary schools and teacher-training institutions. For information, write Institute of International Education, 809 United Nations Plaza, New York, N.Y. 10017.

Schools Sponsored by the Military

• Department of Defense Overseas Dependents Schools

By far the largest source of teaching positions abroad is the Department of Defense: about 155,000 American school children are currently enrolled in some 290 military dependents schools set up by the Department throughout Europe and in the Middle East, North Africa, and several Asian countries. Each year about 2,000 teachers are hired. Positions are available for elementary-, junior-high, and secondary-school teachers in all subjects and also for counselors, librarians, and principals. Nearly 7,500 teachers and administrators are employed in any one year. Conditions vary widely, but the general atmosphere is usually similar to that found in an American public school of comparable size. Many of the schools are quite small; nearly all are located on American bases. Except for a few local language teachers, all teaching and supervisory personnel are American. Working conditions and salary rates in these schools have improved significantly in recent years. Federal law now requires that salaries be at least comparable to those offered in the United States for similar positions. Candidates must have a bachelor's degree and a teaching certificate from the state in which they are currently working. Two years' teaching experience is also required. Employment contracts are usually for two years. However, certain hardship posts require only one year. In addition to salary, teachers receive a housing allowance and transportation costs. For information, write Overseas Dependents School Program, Department of Defense, The Pentagon, Washington, D.C. 20301. *The problem of adjustment to foreign conditions is likely to be much less for an American teacher working in a Defense Department school than in a local school abroad, since the environment is so similar to that of schools in the United States. Naturally there are some disadvantages. Since the schools are situated on American bases, possibilities for contact with the local population are limited. Shifting school populations resulting from movements of military personnel often make continuity of instruction quite difficult.*

Private Opportunities

In addition to government-sponsored opportunities for teachers abroad, there are many private agencies and organizations which assist teachers in obtaining positions overseas. Naturally, some caution should be exercised in dealing with private organizations. If teachers have any doubts, they should contact the Institute of International Education in New York City for advice on the matter.

The following is a partial listing of private organizations offering assistance to American teachers seeking positions overseas.

- **International School Services**

This organization recruits teachers for some three hundred private elementary and secondary schools all over the globe. The types and sizes of the schools very widely. Many are community-sponsored, such as the American School in Paris and the American Community School of Athens. Some are privately operated, such as the American School in Lugano, Switzerland. Still others are company-sponsored, such as the Continental Oil School in Dubai, Arabia or the Caltex Schools in Rumba and Duru, Sumatra. In 1968, nearly four hundred teachers obtained posts abroad through ISS. Contracts are usually for two years, but some schools require a three-year commitment, and a few offer one-year contracts. Salaries are often lower than in school systems in the United States; most range between $3,000 and $8,000. Administrative positions pay from $5,000 to $15,000. Transportation costs are paid by the hiring school. Candidates must have a bachelor's degree and two years' teaching experience. A teaching certificate is not required, but it is helpful. Applicants for positions should send a complete résumé, several references, and academic transcripts to the New York office of ISS. Personal interviews, normally held in New York, are required. ISS prepares a useful list of the schools abroad, "Overseas Schools Serving American Students." For information, write International School Services, 392 Fifth Avenue, New York, N.Y. 10018.

- **Acción**

This organization pays living and travel expenses for persons with leadership and administrative abilities who are willing to serve as volunteers on community developments projects in Latin America. Participants must be prepared to work at least fifteen months. Among the activities are helping to organize community councils, form co-operatives, and build schools, hospitals, and dispensaries. For information, write Acción, Box 27, Cambridge, Mass. 02138.

• **American Friends of the Middle East**

This organization assists Americans going to the Middle East to make professional contacts there. It issues brochures listing teaching opportunities in both governmental and private educational institutions in the Middle East. For information, write Teacher and Professional Placement Service, American Friends of the Middle East, 1607 New Hampshire Avenue, N.W. Washington, D.C. 20009.

• **Papal Volunteers for Latin America**

This organization co-ordinates recruitment, training, and support for Catholic lay volunteers on three-year teaching assignments in Latin America. Candidates must be aged twenty-one to forty-five and must be sponsored by their local diocese or school. Travel costs and living expenses are usually paid. Nearly three hundred volunteers are currently in South America under the auspices of this organization. For information, write Papal Volunteers for Latin America, 1300 South Wabash Avenue, Chicago, Ill. 60605.

• **Teachers for East Africa**

Teachers College of Columbia annually recruits and trains nearly one hundred teachers for two-year assignments in the secondary schools of Kenya, Tanzania, and Uganda in the fields of physics, chemistry, biology, mathematics, English history, and geography. The program is financed by the Agency for International Development. Successful candidates receive training for several weeks at Columbia University. Salary varies with previous experience. Transportation is provided. For information, write Teachers for East Africa, Teachers College, Columbia University, New York, N.Y. 10027.

• **Near East College Association**

This placement agency recruits teachers at all levels for the following schools and colleges: Athens College; Anatolia College; American University of Beirut; International College, Beirut; Robert College, Istanbul; and the American College for Girls, Istanbul. Appointments are usually for three years. Nearly one hundred positions are open annually. For information, write Near East College Association, 548 Fifth Avenue, New York, N.Y. 10030.

• **United Church Board for World Ministries**

This is the central clearinghouse for Americans belonging to Protestant churches who wish to teach in junior and senior high schools and colleges in Asia, Africa, and the Near East. Teachers of English language and literature, mathematics, science, home economics, and physical education are required. Assignments are usually for three years. A moderate living allowance is paid, plus transportation. More than one hundred jobs are available each year. For information, write United Church Board for World Ministries, 475 Riverside Drive, New York, N.Y. 10027.

An up-to-date file on teaching positions abroad is maintained by the Institute of International Education, 809 United Nations Plaza, New York, N.Y. 10017. Its *Handbook on International Study* includes a summary of various opportunities available. In addition, directories of jobs abroad, including positions for teachers, are offered by the following:

United States Government Printing Office, Washington, D.C. 20402.

World Affairs Center, 345 East 46th Street, New York, N.Y. 10017.

Chamber of Commerce of the United States, 1514 H Street, N.W., Washington, D.C. 20006.

United States Department of Commerce, Washington, D.C. 20230.

Center for International Relations and Area Studies, University of Minnesota, Minneapolis, Minn. 55455.

Technical Assistance Information Clearing House, 44 East 23rd Street, New York, N.Y. 10010.

SUMMER

Nearly all the opportunities for summer teaching abroad are provided by the private organizations which run summer-school programs for high-school students (see Chapter 13, above). Since these organizations send about 20,000 students abroad each year and need about one teacher or chaperon for each ten students, in the neighborhood of 2,000 such positions are available each year. The advantages to secondary-school teachers of this type of summer employment are great. At little or no out-of pocket expense, they are able to spend six weeks abroad and usually to attend courses themselves. The sponsoring organizations handle all the details of travel and housing. The work involved is considerable, the responsibilities great; but the work is itself educational and satisfying, and the teacher usually has enough free time to enjoy himself too. Indeed, in a well-organized program, the teacher or chaperon undoubtedly sees more and has far more intimate contact with the foreign environment than he would if he simply went abroad on his own or joined a group.

Although the programs differ, it is not difficult to generalize about the routine of such a teacher. His basic responsibility is to act as a counselor and supervisor for his own group of from eight to fifteen students. He has to keep track of them while traveling, make sure that they are aware of the program for each day, and provide the support and guidance they require both in their academic work and in their adjustment to the foreign culture. He lives in the same dormitory with them, makes sure that they obey the rules, accompanies them on visits to local sights, and so on. In a smoothly functioning program many of these duties are shared by the teachers as a group; it is usual, for example, for one teacher to act as "duty officer" each evening in the dormitory, checking students out after the evening meal and making sure that they are all in their rooms at curfew time. It is seldom necessary for any teacher to have this duty more often than once a week. In addition, most chaperons are free during the morning hours when the students are in class. They may attend classes themselves or use these hours as they please. Conversely, in the programs that use Americans as teachers, it is normal for these persons to be free of supervisory functions as chaperons. They teach three or four hours each morning, grade papers, and perhaps accompany the group on afternoon excursions. In a good program, it should be emphasized, the chaperon or teacher will have an unending involvement with the students, but he will have enough time to himself to relax and enjoy life abroad too; this is the conclusion of the overwhelming majority of teachers we have interviewed in the field. The consensus is that the "work" is so satisfying that it is scarcely work at all.

The educational advantages for such teachers should be obvious. This is especially the case for language teachers, historians, and others particularly concerned with foreign cultures, but any teacher can profit from the experience. Aside from the benefits derived from studying the local language and culture with experienced native instructors, they are sure to find the time spent living in a foreign situation professionally stimulating. It is also possible for teachers to obtain academic credits by taking courses at many of these foreign institutions and to qualify themselves for salary increases at home in school systems that require additional course work for increments. Kenneth Coulter, Deputy Superintendent of the Greenwich, Connecticut, school system, points out that teachers have acquired from two to six credits toward M.A. degrees by attending classes at foreign institutes while serving as chaperons and that others who already have a master's have won exemption from the sixth-year level of training. It is essential, however, as Coulter explains, that those who wish to obtain credit in this way make arrangements *in advance* with the university at which they are working for a degree and provide their advisers with proper proof, upon returning to the United States, that they have actually done what they proposed to do.

How to Organize a Group

The American teacher who wishes to join one of these programs normally must recruit a group of students willing to enroll in it.

The teacher, as a matter of fact, must deal with three separate audiences: the sponsoring organization, the officials of his local school system, and the students and their parents. The organization will want to be sure he is a responsible person and that he is capable of recruiting at least eight students. Usually the teacher, in applying to an organization, must provide details about his teaching experience, language competence, and so on and also indicate which country he wishes to go to. Both the school officials and the students and their parents, on the other hand, will require assurances that the sponsoring organization is responsible and competent.

The organizations prefer that their chaperons know the foreign language well, or at least that they be teachers of the language (which, unfortunately, is not always the same thing). One of the marks of a good program is the degree to which its leaders insist upon this requirement.* In some cases they also accept chaperons who cannot recruit eight or more students. There are always a certain number of "extra" students who apply independently, and some teachers find that they can recruit more students than they can personally handle; these are assigned to chaperons who cannot muster a full group of their own. The usual practice is to pay the chaperon $50 for each student he recruits beyond eight, up to a maximum of about fifteen. This method of recruitment, as we have seen in Chapter 13, is highly controversial, but it is probably the best one available. Another mark of a good program is its willingness to refuse candidates for chaperon posts who lack proper educational and emotional qualifications, but for some reason are able to interest a group of students in participating; and still another is its refusal to put together too many groups of "stray" students, gathered in ones and twos from a variety of schools and headed by a chaperon who is not personally familiar with all of them.

In dealing with their academic superiors, teachers who wish to form groups must be prepared to explain in detail what the academic and cultural benefits of the program will be, both for themselves and (more important) for their charges. Most school officials will demand particular assurances about the financial soundness of the sponsoring organization and its capacity to handle all the complex arrangements involved in transporting, housing, feeding,

* This, of course, does not apply to programs in Great Britain.

and educating large numbers of persons. The better programs maintain regional representatives who will provide information and guarantees, both to school officials and to parents. Some even have made elaborate movies showing aspects of their activities in the field, which can be run off locally to convince the skeptical.

These local representatives of sponsoring organizations also provide materials that the teacher can use in recruiting students and persuading parents to allow their children to participate. The normal procedure is for the teacher to announce the plan to his classes and schedule a meeting at which interested students can discuss the program with someone familiar with its details. This meeting should be held as early as possible in the school year, certainly well before Christmas. Assuming that a sufficient number enroll, the teacher should count on devoting a considerable number of after-school hours to meetings with the group and with parents to discuss the program, digest the orientation materials provided by the sponsor, and stimulate his charges to learn about the country they are to visit. In general, it is most important to try to develop a group spirit in advance of departure. At every stage from his original decision to form a group to the actual time when the group takes off for Europe, it is helpful if the teacher and also his students can make contacts with former participants and with other persons who have studied abroad. Such informants can not only answer practical and specific questions but also do a great deal to develop confidence and stimulate curiosity. The time actually spent abroad is, after all, relatively short in these programs; it is vital to convince everyone concerned that it must be used efficiently.

PART V

Foreign Study Outside the Classroom

CHAPTER 16

Work and Travel Abroad Programs

Adding new dimensions to foreign study . . . the Experiment in International Living . . . work camps: demanding but satisfying . . . some sponsoring organizations . . . employment opportunities abroad and organizations that can guide you to the best jobs . . . students report their experiences . . . hints on choosing an educational tour . . . tour sponsored by student organizations

Many Americans go abroad not to study in the formal sense but to "learn by living" in a foreign land. They seek the nonacademic benefits that come from travel, from contact with a different culture, from getting to know people with other ideas and other systems of values.

The classroom is not for them. The student, they reason, is almost by definition a being apart. His interests require that he remove himself from the world and seclude himself with his books, laboratory tools, and research papers. How much better, they say, it is to spend one's precious weeks and months abroad actively participating in some community activity: living with a local family, holding down a job, helping unfortunates improve their lot, or taking part in some other socially constructive activity. An extremist of this school might even say that students are selfish, out to improve *themselves* above all else, journeying abroad to take rather than give or share.

All exaggeration aside, few will argue with the proposition that the student who goes abroad without his books, impelled simply by a desire to learn by living, may well achieve as much intellectually as the scholar who is closeted in a library. And he will be far more likely, too, to make a good impression on local people and thus contribute substantially to the development of international good will.

This being the case, there are, naturally enough, many organizations that try to aid students who want to live and work abroad. Some simply provide information, but a very considerable number conduct programs through which American students are placed in foreign homes and in foreign jobs for varying lengths of time.

The Experiment in International Living

Perhaps the best-known of these organizations is the Experiment in International Living, founded in 1932. The Experiment now sends more than two thousand young Americans each year to live with families in some forty nations. Approximately the same number of foreign youths come to the United States each year under Experiment auspices. The chief object of the Experiment is to enable participants "to make an enduring contribution to international understanding . . . by proving through individual action that different peoples of the world *can* learn to live together in mutual respect and understanding." Additionally, the organization believes its program will broaden the individual, too, and add greatly to his stock of factual information. Dr. Gordon Boyce, president of the Experiment (which has its headquarters in the small town of Putney, Vermont), has granted us permission to print the following official account of the nature and activities of the "Experiment."

> *Your Experiment* . . . starts almost from the moment you are accepted as a member. Your first step to membership is to submit an application (obtainable from any of the Experiment offices) telling about yourself in great detail. Your next step is to write a letter to your prospective family abroad—sometimes in their own language—according to instructions which will be sent to you. The Experiment also secures references from persons who know you especially well. These papers, together with a health report from your physician, are evaluated by experienced members of the Experiment staff in a rigorous "sizing-up" process which takes at least six weeks in all.
>
> Only those are accepted who are likely to cope successfully with the problems and challenges of an Experiment program, to contribute significantly to the experience of their group, and to be

worthy representatives of the United States abroad. Flexibility, adaptability, resourcefulness, and a genuine desire to make friends abroad are all essential qualifications. The candidates finally chosen are almost certain to be successful Experimenters—the kind who contribute to international understanding even under trying circumstances, and who come home feeling they have just had the best experience of their lives.

Even though an Experiment is a challenge, demanding the best that is in you, it is also an extraordinary brand of fun. Some members are so caught up in the spirit of Experimenting that they go abroad several times—each time to a different country. Many of them later qualify for leadership assignments and go abroad with the double advantage of an expense-paid Experiment and of superb training in the art of responsible, creative leadership. To all of these, and to a majority of all Experimenters, the program has proved its lasting value. In fact, a recent alumni survey revealed that two-thirds of all Experimenters in the United States are engaged in careers or part-time activities which contribute actively to international understanding. . . .

Once accepted as an Experiment member, you will begin almost immediately to prepare for the program ahead of you. A series of bulletins and brochures from The Experiment will provide the information you need on passports, inoculations, clothing, books to read, travel instructions, and other essential details. You will at all times have the help of a professional staff—even though you will quickly find yourself solving most of your problems on your own.

As your embarkation date approaches, you will be assigned to a group of about ten Experimenters going to the same country. The group may be mixed or all-girls; its members will all be about the same age as yourself. In all probability, they will represent a variety of geographic, academic, and professional backgrounds. Your group will have a mature leader—an experienced adult selected and trained for his position by The Experiment.* The eleven of you will make a "Matched group" only in the sense that all will show promise of becoming successful Experimenters. And that is how it should be, because in going abroad you will be demonstrating in a practical way the important truth that the United States is indeed "one from many."

You will first get acquainted with the members of your group at a predetermined meeting place or at the port of embarkation. From

---

* Leaders, who must be fluent in the local language, receive no salary, but all their expenses are paid. They must be between the ages of twenty-five and forty-five and are preferably experienced in teaching or camp work.

the beginning, you will have much to talk about. You may have completed a long and exciting journey already—perhaps with your parents—just in getting from your home to the point of assembly. Almost immediately, you will begin to compare notes with other group members and to discover points in common. Before the summer is over, you and the others in your group will be friends in that rare sense of comradeship which comes only when persons have shared in common problems and challenges and met them by working together.

Before, during, and after the program abroad, your leader will bring the group together in a series of discussions on the language, culture, customs, politics, manners, and other aspects of the country being visited. You will be encouraged at all times to state your personal views and to share any specialized knowledge you may have with other members of the group. The discussion method is used regularly by The Experiment as a means of achieving common goals.

Your group will be met at its destination by a representative of The Experiment, who will in most cases take you at once to your homestay community. There you will meet your host family—selected in advance by a Local Representative of The Experiment—and you will begin your fascinating new life in a strange and unfamiliar culture. One fact about your family is worth knowing in advance and remembering always. They will offer the hospitality of their home *on a voluntary basis*. They will ordinarily receive no compensation other than the considerable satisfaction of knowing that they, too, have made a useful contribution to international friendship and understanding. They share in your program because of their belief in Experiment ideals. By virtue of this spirit and willingness they are Experimenters also, just as you are.

During the homestay period you will meet occasionally with the other members of your group, and with host family members, to discuss matters of mutual interest, to meet key persons in the community, to visit local points of interest, and to enjoy spontaneous good times. Your group may witness the deliberations of a village *panchayat* or council in India, discuss West African politics or attend a tribal dance in Nigeria, join in a spectacular fiesta of fireworks and floats in Mexico, or chat informally with the burgomaster of a Dutch town.

At first, you may wonder whether the homestay and the group program—in which you are always expected to participate fully—are going to crowd out the pursuit of your individual interests. You will rapidly discover that, far from interfering with your personal interests, the activities of the family and group will tend to sharpen and define them—and to provide valuable contacts for following them up. In both your personal and group activities, you may at all times rely on the assistance of your Local Representative, a citizen of your host country who is dedicated to Experiment ideals and service and who knows his community well.

The end of the homestay marks the beginning of new adventure. Your group will now set out on its informal trip—an extended two-to-three-week journey by train, bus, bicycle, or hiking, generally within the host country. Along the way, you will stop to see sights of significance—the landmarks and ways of doing things which help to explain the spirit, heritage, and mode of life of the nation you are visiting. You may pause to explore an ancient cathedral in Spain, a "kibbutz," or communal farm, in Israel, a fishing village along a majestic fjord in Norway. In less than forty-eight hours, you will probably agree that the "informal trip" is aptly named. You may end a day's travels by sleeping in a railroad compartment speeding across India, a crowded youth hostel in Wales, a hotel room in Italy, a chalet on an Alpine slope in Switzerland. Each day will bring you face to face with the new and unanticipated. Small wonder that The Experiment cautions its members to "expect the unexpected.". . .

Often, however, these same adventures involve work and physical discomfort; and these realities can and should be expected. In Great Britain, for example, Experimenters hike or bike across rolling hills and spend their nights in youth hostels. In Norway, they explore the mountains on foot. In France, they cycle through the countryside and camp out. Experimenters to Denmark insist that they are always cycling against the wind, no matter in which direction they may go. In those countries in which Experimenters "rough it," they carry their own gear on bike and back. In most Experiment countries, transportation is by bus or second-class train, and overnight accommodations are found in youth hostels, pensions, dormitories, and small hotels. So "expect the unexpected"—and enjoy it!

In most Experiment programs you will have an unusual advantage far beyond reach of the ordinary tourist. Whenever possible, you will be accompanied by a member of your new family. He and his counterparts from the other host families will travel as guests of the group; and the Local Representative or a person he designates will serve as co-leader for the informal trip. The informal trip thus becomes a bi-national venture; and through the hospitality of the group you are able to repay in some measure the generosity of your homestay family. As you travel, you will talk together in the language of the host country (if you belong to a group requiring knowledge of a foreign language); and you will learn to see the country as your "brothers" and "sisters" see it.

In some programs, your month's homestay will be terminated by the informal trip; in others, divided by it. In either case, after these two phases of your program you will proceed to one of the major cities of the world for the concluding four or five days of your visit abroad. The city may be London, Stockholm, Paris, Warsaw, or Rome; it may be Lagos, Istanbul, New Delhi, or Tokyo. The city actually chosen will lie somewhere along the route to your point of departure for the United States.

During the city stay, members of groups of college age and above (at least one year out of high school) may have the option of traveling independently for four or five days at their own expense. This option is available to those who receive advance permission from The Experiment and, if minors, from their parents. *Independent travel is never permitted for members of high school groups.* If you travel independently during this period, you will be free to range as far afield as you wish, so long as you return in time to join the group for departure. If you remain with your group, you will enjoy a full schedule of cultural, sightseeing, and shopping activities, according to group preferences; and you will benefit from your group leader's guidance and assistance on where to go and what to see. . . .

The cost of participating in an Experiment program varies considerably according to the location, since transportation makes up a major part of the expense. The cost of programs in Europe vary between $900 and $1,100; those in India and parts of Africa run as high as $1,400; while in Mexico the basic expense is under $500.

The Experiment in International Living organizes its program around the ideas of an interchange of small groups of people from two nations. The emphasis is on selection and supervision of participants and a search for understanding through discussion and observation.

Wanted: Dedicated Persons for Work Camps

Work camps are more informal and more varied than the Experiment programs. Usually the participants are deeply dedicated to the effort to develop international good will. Indeed, they commit themselves to working long and hard for little or no pay, simply to promote socially useful projects (like the construction of homes for refugees) and to develop understanding among people. The spirit of the work camp can be sensed in this extract from an announcement of the Overseas Work Camps of the American Friends Service Committee.

> Work is universal. People of all countries and races must work, and tired muscles mean the same in any language. It is through doing constructive work, rather than merely reading or talking about human problems, that people come to understand the tensions and prejudices that separate individuals and nations.

The work camp movement began in 1920 after World War I, when there was dramatic need for reconstruction and rehabilitation in vast areas of Europe, coupled with a widespread belief that better understanding had to be developed with our former enemies if lasting peace were to be maintained. It is significant that the first camp was established near the war-shattered French city of Verdun. Germans and Frenchmen, along with volunteers from other countries, gathered in Verdun to help in the construction of housing for peasants whose homes had been destroyed in the war.

Such peace-oriented institutions as the American Friends Service Committee soon took up the work camp idea, and the movement expanded rapidly following the devastation of World War II. Nowadays, UNESCO sponsors a Coordination Committee for International Voluntary Work Camps which publishes annual lists of camps operating all over the globe.* The 1967 edition, for example, names more than 275 organizations sponsoring these camps.

It is impossible to describe a "typical" work camp because the camps vary greatly, depending on their size, the type of work, and the country in which they are established. Almost always volunteers must pay their own transportation costs and sometimes even part of

---

* There are separate lists for summer and winter programs. They can be obtained for $1.00 each by writing to the Coordination Committee for International Voluntary Work Camps, UNESCO, 6 Rue Franklin, Paris 16, France. UNESCO's annual *Vacations Abroad*, published in New York, also contains descriptions of work programs, but the volume is difficult to use because it is printed in four languages and mixes work programs, tours, and academic programs in the *same* listing.

the cost of their maintenance. If there is any compensation for work done, it is usually donated to the sponsoring agency.

Participants live in the simplest possible surroundings. A group in a Rhineland town near Bonn, for example, was housed in two small dormitories. The girls' building contained four rooms: a bare chamber with rows of mattresses on the floor, a recreation room containing a battered Ping-pong table and a few chairs, a kitchen, and a sort of laundry room. The boys' quarters were no more elaborate. Other camps may be still more simple. Participants often live in tents.

Work in these camps is generally unskilled and often strenuous. It may involve road repairing or ditch digging, the harvesting of crops or the scrubbing of floors in a hospital. On the other hand, it may consist of caring for poor children in a home or helping organize recreational activities in an urban slum. But always it means a full and active day. Here is the daily schedule of one typical camp.

5:30	Rise. Prepare breakfast, chop firewood, tidy living quarters
6:45	Breakfast (including quinine tablet)
7:10	Leave for work
8:30–12	Work
12–1:30	Lunch
1:30–4:30	Work
5:30	Return to billet
6:30	Supper
7:30	Group activities
9:30	Bed

Young students and teachers are willing to pay for the privilege of submitting for weeks on end to such a schedule because of their altruistic spirit. One reward they receive is an unparalleled opportunity to meet interesting young people from all over the world.

The following list, prepared by the Council on International Educational Exchange, includes some of the more important *American* organizations that sponsor work camps abroad.

American Friends Service Committee, 160 North 15th Street, Philadelphia, Penna. 19102.

American Zionist Youth Foundation, 515 Park Avenue, New York, N.Y. 10022.

Brethren Service Commission, 1451 Dundee Avenue, Elgin, Ill. 60120.

Ecumenical Voluntary Service/World Council of Churches, 475 Riverside Drive, Room 825, New York, N.Y. 10027.

The Lisle Fellowship, Inc., 3039 Pittsview Drive, Ann Arbor, Mich. 48104.

National Board of YMCA's, 291 Broadway, New York, N.Y. 10007.

National Student YWCA, 600 Lexington Avenue, New York, N.Y. 10022.

Unitarian Universalist Service Committee, 78 Beacon Street, Boston, Mass. 02108.

United Church of Christ, Specialized Ministries, United Church Board for Homeland Ministries, R.D. No. 2, Pottstown, Penna. 19464.

Other Employment Programs: AIESEC, IAESTE, ASIS, ISIS, and More

Many young people, of course, cannot afford to pay for the privilege of living with a foreign family or participating in a work camp. One obvious solution to this problem is the Peace Corps, but the Corps requires of its members a more extended period of service (at least two years) than the average student can afford to offer. Fortunately, however, it is possible to find remunerative short-term employment in many foreign countries, and many American students do so, especially during summer vacations.

It is by no means easy. Many governments require that foreigners obtain work permits before accepting any employment, and the procedures can be extremely time-consuming and complicated. Beyond that, as the Institute of International Education warns in its pamphlet *Summer Employment Abroad*, "In general most summer jobs available to American students abroad are menial and unskilled, the hours may be long, and the pay is low by American standards." An official of the United States Chamber of Commerce puts it more bluntly: "So you'd like to work overseas. May I offer counsel to the wise. Ye who would enter those uncertain climes, proceed with care!"

The best positions are those arranged through various university programs. Antioch College, which requires all its students to combine work with their studies, places many students in jobs abroad. Princeton has a program that puts small numbers of undergraduates into business concerns in foreign countries; the University of Louisville runs a nine-week summer program in France. These are all small operations, and chiefly for the students of the sponsoring colleges. More important are two international student organizations, The International Association of Students in Economics and Business (AIESEC) and the International Association for the Exchange of Students for Technical Experience (IAESTE).

AIESEC helps thousands of students obtain jobs abroad each year. Founded in 1948, it has more than 300 university branches in more than 40 countries, including 82 in the United States. In 1966, some 500 American college students found employment through AIESEC.

Local student committees at each member university, assisted by faculty advisors, solicit traineeship offers from business firms in their areas. Ideally, these traineeships are in administrative or managerial positions and vary in tenure from a period of two to six months, most of them during the summer holidays. At the International Congress, held annually in March, traineeship offers are matched with application forms of foreign students. After the Congress, each participating firm receives applications for approval. When a firm accepts an applicant, it commits itself to paying the trainee an adequate living allowance, generally from $70 to $90 per week. Each Local Committee has the responsibility of arranging for the reception and care of the foreign trainees in its own area— a task including travel arrangements, introductions to employer and landlord, arranging for receptions, lodging, meals, sightseeing, study tours, and providing social and cultural activities. Only upperclassmen or graduate students who intend to pursue a career in business or economics and have had some practical business experience are eligible to participate in the program. All applicants are carefully screened at member schools by joint student-faculty committees, which consider the candidate's academic and extracurricular records, his references, and his past business experience. Interested students should contact their local campus committee, or if none exists, write directly to AIESEC-US, 52 Vanderbilt Avenue, Suite 1110, New York, N.Y. 10017.

The IAESTE program, which operates in substantially the same way, places students specializing in engineering, science, and architecture. It too functions in some forty nations; in 1966 it placed 144 American students in jobs abroad. Applications may be obtained from campus committees or by writing to IAESTE, 866 United Nations Plaza, New York, N.Y. 10017.

The Jewish Agency, 515 Park Avenue, New York, N.Y. 10022, administers a similar program, Summer Work in Israel (PATWA), which finds positions for students interested in medicine, science, business management, and social work.

Other organizations specialize in jobs for which no particular skills are required. The United States National Student Association, for example, finds work in the British Isles, Germany, Switzerland, and other European countries each summer for college students. There is a $75 fee for this service, which covers a brief orientation program in each country after arrival. The NSA has also made special arrangements in Great Britain and Ireland which permit American students to find their own summer jobs in these countries without obtaining a work permit. For information, write to the NSA, 265 Madison Avenue, New York, N.Y. 10016. In Germany, the Zentralstelle für Arbeitsvermittlung, Zeil 57, 6000 Frankfurt/Main, runs a placement service that American students may use to find work on farms and construction projects and in restaurants, hotels, hospitals, and similar institutions.

There are also several private companies that specialize in locating jobs abroad for American students. Considerable concern has been generated among persons and organizations interested in international exchange and study by the activities of these companies. The Institute of International Education warns students to be "extremely cautious" about signing up in their programs. The Department of State, responding to many letters of inquiry, has even seen fit to issue a detailed set of criteria for evaluating these student employment agencies. This document contains much common-sense advice. It urges students to consult with persons who have previously employed the services of the organization, to read the fine print in all promotional literature, to make sure that the services offered are worth the price and that the organization is financially responsible.

Yet, as the Department says, there is little or no evidence which suggests that these companies are dishonest. Most complaints, it reports, appear to derive from "the kinds of normal breakdowns in arrangements which occur occasionally in international travel. The complaints which we have found most disturbing involve failure to make good on promises, refusal to make reasonable adjustments, and indifference about genuine misunderstandings." Nevertheless, many hundreds of students have taken these risks and emerged not only unscathed but convinced that the experience of working abroad was extremely rewarding.

The two largest organizations of this type are the American Student Information Service (ASIS) and the International Student Information Service (ISIS). ASIS, which has its headquarters at 27 Avenue de la Liberté, in Luxembourg, charges a basic fee of $36 for finding the student a job, arranging the necessary working permits, and helping him find a place to live. It also runs charter flights to Europe and back at reasonable rates. It requires, however, that those who use its services sign up for an "orientation" tour in Europe before beginning work. These tours vary in price from about $150 to $400. ISIS, located at 133 Rue Hôtel des Monnaies, Brussels, Belgium, operates somewhat differently. Its basic charge for finding the student a job and arranging the details is $150. This fee covers the cost of a brief overseas orientation program. The agency also offers optional transatlantic charter flights, but there are no compulsory tours.

The jobs arranged for through these organizations and others like them are primarily menial and low-salaried. Farm labor, hotel, resort and camp posts, hospital work, and jobs on construction projects make up the bulk of them. No one (as the organizations take pains to point out) can earn enough to pay for his whole summer. The chief purpose is to share in life and work abroad, not to make money; students are employed for from four to eight weeks and seldom earn more than $150 a month plus room and board. But even those sums help make it possible for many students and young teachers who would not otherwise be able to do so to spend the summer abroad.

The files of these agencies bulge with letters from students expressing great satisfaction with jobs obtained. Here are a few typical quotations:

A student from the University of California who worked on a farm: "I was placed with the Bürgermeister of a large village. He was also the owner of a vineyard, on which I worked. After a few weeks, I felt like part of his family. Through this homelike living I was able to discover the nature of the German people, which was my main purpose for taking this trip."

A girl from the University of Pennsylvania who worked in a hospital: "The working program was excellent; it gave us all an opportunity to meet and live with people from another country. No tour or brief visit could ever do for a person what a month or two of working in close contact with these people can do."

A young man from Swarthmore who worked at a resort hotel: "I was made to feel at home. Through my summer job . . . I have learned much about the people of Southern Hesse—their customs and tastes. I have come to share the great pride they take in the beauty that surrounds them."

A girl from the University of Illinois who worked in a supermarket: "I had to break into a new group and every time you break into a new group you learn to understand people. . . . I gained an insight into the culture of the Belgian people. I saw how they lived, heard what they thought of our country, even noticed what they ate for lunch and the detail of how they cut their bread."

It must be emphasized that these are real jobs, not "made work" developed simply to foster international good will. The satisfaction and excitement that comes from taking on such a task and completing it well has been repeatedly attested to by students. But there is a serious drawback involved in blithely signing up for such a position, for sometimes the jobs turn out to be far different from what the average American student, accustomed to working part-time during the summer to earn pocket money, expects. It is not merely that the hours are long and the work hard, although ASIS warns applicants of this by telling them: "The European working day is probably longer and harder than you are accustomed to. You will have to adapt yourself to an entirely new environment. If you do not think you will be able to adapt, or if you are unprepared to work hard, you should not apply for a job." ISIS goes so far as to warn prospective applicants that they may be fired by their foreign employers if they do not do an honest day's work and that under such circumstances the organization will not help them find a new position. "We don't expect our members to be overjoyed about having a hard job. But we do expect them to be prepared for it and do the best they can."

The problem is that American students may not appreciate exactly just how menial a job as an unskilled laborer in Europe can be. And still more important, some of the jobs provide little or no chance for the student to practice the language or get to know local people. Some European employers hire students merely because they represent the cheapest possible labor and exploit them callously and cynically. One young man from Tennessee reports being hired as a restaurant helper. The boss put him to work peeling potatoes and washing endless stacks of dishes from dawn to late evening. He was entirely alone in a windowless room while working and after hours so tired that all he could do was fall into bed. A girl from Denison University in Ohio accepted a post as an assistant in a German *Kinderheim* because she wanted to work with foreign children. She found that she was busy from 7 A.M. to 10 P.M. doing housework. "I've washed floors before, but not the way the Germans wash floors," she reported ruefully after completing her contract. "I didn't mind that it was hard," she quickly added. "But some of the people were *unpleasant*. They didn't even consider the fact that I wanted to learn German and see a little of the country."

Such cases are not typical, for most people in any country will take an interest in a willing and curious visitor and will not exploit him simply to save a few marks or francs or shillings. But an American student who signs up to work abroad ought to be sure that he understands exactly what is expected of him; that his own objectives will be achieved within the framework established by the position; and that, once a contract is signed, his employer will carry out his part of the bargain in full.

Educational Tours

There remains the question of organized group touring. The number of organizations that run tours is almost infinite, the variety of their offerings tremendous. One may take an art tour, a music tour, even a tennis tour, and travel by boat, plane, bus, bicycle, even on foot. What concerns us here primarily is the so-called educational tour, organized specifically for students. While the idea of improving one's education through travel is very old, *organized* student tours are almost entirely a product of the present century. The earliest-known study tour was one organized by the Pedagogical Institute of the University of Jena in 1892, and American colleges began to grant credit for travel programs in the 1920's. Most of these tours were for teachers and prospective teachers and stressed comparative education. In the years immediately after World War II, more than one hundred colleges in the United States had such programs.

Today education tours have increased to such a degree in both numbers and variety that generalization and even summary are impossible. Careful investigation before deciding on a tour program is mandatory if disappointment is to be avoided. The advertisements in various editions of the *New York Times* offer a program of "castles, conversation, countryside, capers, cafés, cities, credits [and] coeds" sponsored by Happenings International; an invitation to "Paint and Travel in Spain" with a Michigan professor; "40 Marvelous" student and teacher tours run by the National Student Association; a "study" program at Oxford that includes "dances, all sports, films, TV" sponsored by the International Travel Council for Education and Students; programs in Spain, Italy, Austria, and France sponsored by the Educational Travel Association; and many, many others.

Some educational tours combine travel with a course at a summer school abroad; others feature short periods of residence with private families in various countries. Here is the itinerary of a "typical" tour organized by the United States National Student Association.

1st day: Sail from New York or Montreal.
2nd to 8th: At sea.

VISITING HOLLAND

9th: Arrive in Rotterdam. Continue by motor coach to Amsterdam.
10th to 12th: Amsterdam. Excursion to Leiden, Delft, and The Hague. *Party with Dutch students.*
13th: Leave Amsterdam in morning for Hamburg.

VISITING GERMANY

14th Day: Hamburg. Orientation program on life in Germany. *Evening at student club.*

15th: Transfer to airport by motor coach for flight to Berlin.

16th to 18th: General city sightseeing in West Berlin and visit to East Berlin. *Evening party with West Berlin students.*

19th: Fly to Cologne in the morning. Visit the famous cathedral and continue by motor coach to Blankenburg.

20th: Leave Blankenburg by Rhine Steamer for Heidelberg. *Evening party with German students at a typical student inn.*

21st: Continue to Rothenberg.

22nd: Leave Rothenberg in the morning for Munich.

23rd and 24th: Munich. *Evening entertainment at the Hofbräuhaus.*

VISITING AUSTRIA

25th Day: Leave Munich for Innsbruck. *Party with Austrian students in evening.*

26th: Innsbruck. Morning excursion to the Hafelekar for a view of the Austrian Alps. Afternoon departure for Salzburg,

27th: Salzburg. *Attend evening performance of the Salzburg Marionettes.*

28th: Leave Salzburg for Vienna.

29th and 30th: Vienna. *Evening at a "Heurigen" Inn at Grinzing.*

31st: Leave Vienna for Klagenfurt.

32nd: Klagenfurt. Morning sightseeing, then continue to Venice.

VISITING ITALY

33rd and 34th Day: Venice. Excursion to the Lido Beach. *Evening gondola ride on the Grand Canal.*

35th: Leave Venice in the morning for Rimini by way of Ravenna. Lunch in Ravenna with a visit to the tomb of Dante and the great mosaic works.

36th: Rimini. Full day of swimming, sunbathing and relaxation.

37th: Leave Rimini for Rome.

38th to 41st: Rome. Excursion to Tivoli. *Attend an evening performance of an opera at the Baths of Caracalla.*

42nd: Leave Rome for Florence.

43rd to 45th: Florence. Meeting with Italian students. *Evening concert in the courtyard of the Pitti Palace.*

46th: Leave for Milan in the morning.

VISITING SWITZERLAND

47th Day: Leave Milan and continue by motor coach for St. Moritz and Sils Maria.

48th and 49th: St. Moritz or Sils Maria. *Fondue party with Swiss students.*

50th: Leave by motor coach for Lucerne.

51st: Lucerne. Swimming and boating.

VISITING FRANCE

52nd Day: Leave in the morning for Dijon via Basle and Belfort.

53rd: Morning sightseeing in Dijon, then continue to Paris.

54th to 57th: Paris. Excursion to Chartres and Versailles. *Attend evening performance of the Folies Bergères or the Opéra.*

VISITING ENGLAND

58th Day: Leave in the morning by rail and steamer or air for London.

59th to 62nd: London. Excursion to Oxford and Stratford-on-Avon. *Attend a performance at the Shakespeare Memorial Theater in Stratford.*

63rd: Tour ends after breakfast in London.

64th to 70th: A week (or less) free time.

71st: Sail from Southampton.

72nd to 80th: At sea. Arrive New York or Montreal.

It is extremely difficult to compare the prices of various tours because so much depends on distances traveled, accommodations provided en route, and the number and quality of such "extras" as theater tickets which are included in the total package. Is a sixty-day tour of ten countries for $1,200 a better buy than a fifty-day tour of fourteen countries for $2,000? Only a careful study of the details of both tours will yield an answer to this question.

Generally, however, tours organized by foreign student groups are the cheapest (and in our opinion, the best), for while the facilities offered are likely to be simple, the opportunities to meet and get to know Europeans are greater by far than those available on American-sponsored tours.

At one time, Stephen Freeman, vice-president of Middlebury College, prepared an admirable summary of the pros and cons of student tours for the Institute of International Education. Professor Freeman's essay offers sound advice for anyone considering an educational tour, and since the *Bulletin* in which the article appeared is out of print, we have, with the permission of the author and the Institute, reproduced most of it here:

Choosing a Summer Study-Travel Program

Anyone who is fortunate enough to have next summer free, and also to have adequate financial resources, is likely to be thinking of joining some kind of a travel tour. Many persons, especially students, teachers and other professional people, will wish to consider adding some serious educational aspects to the tourism. Summer study-travel programs abroad have become amazingly popular in recent years. . . . There are thousands of travel agencies eager to plan group or individual travel including educational or study features.

Objectives of travel vary widely. Some people wish to spend most of their time traveling, seeing new sights, covering as much ground as possible; others wish to visit intensively in one country, concentrating on one certain aspect, and no one can deny that these activities are educational in a real sense. Still other people, however, wish to subordinate the touristic features of their summer to a well-defined program of study at an educational institution. Most teachers and many undergraduate students are interested in securing academic credit or other official recognition for the time and money expended. The purpose of this article is to explain the various criteria by which the multitude of study-travel tours can be evaluated, and to assist the prospective student-traveler in choosing the one best suited to his objectives.

The first factor of a travel program which should be examined is the type and quality of sponsorship and leadership. One should look carefully at the names of individuals and organizations accepting responsibility and determine whether the sponsor is a college or university, an individual professor at an educational institution, a travel agency or a private individual. A travel agency generally will be more interested in, and place more emphasis upon transportation, hotels and sightseeing. It will tend to organize tours which move rapidly from place to place and to stress the broadening aspects of travel. It generally will leave the student on his own if and when he wishes to stay in one place and take courses. Some travel agencies advertise that their tours are prepared by "an educational advisory committee," but neglect to say who composes the committee.

On the other hand, when a college offers a summer program, and officially takes responsibility for it, even though the traveling arrangements are made by an agency, as they often are, emphasis usually will be placed on the courses of study offered, and the college will endeavor to insure a high quality of instruction. Tours sponsored by an individual professor at a college should be examined with care to discover to what extent the professor has the sanction and support of his institution. Sometimes he has it; but this is not necessarily the case.

Least responsible of all are private individuals who organize study-tours. Unless they have been in the travel business for many years, they may lack necessary contacts and experience to make satisfactory arangements. They may even be financially unreliable. Some reliable travel companies offer a free trip to the person who enrolls a group. This in itself is not objectionable if an experienced leader is put in charge; but if the organizer then also becomes the leader of the group, the plan should be viewed with suspicion. Special caution should be used before becoming involved with tours which use high-sounding names implying connections with a foreign university, but which have only a post-office box number. All such programs can be checked with the Institute of International Education.

A second criterion for evaluating study-tours is their admission policies. It appears self-evident that any bona-fide study plan would have some entrance requirements or limitations. If study is to be done at a foreign university, inquiry should be made into the applicant's competence in the foreign language to be used at the university. Study programs cannot be well organized for an indiscriminate mixture of college freshmen, seniors, teachers, graduate students and even general public. A tour which accepts anyone willing to pay the price of admission admits that it is not really a *study* tour, and that if any real study is to be done, it will be the responsibility of the individual to select the proper group or level or subject matter at some available institution. Some tours make extravagant claims about shipboard orientation. We read statements

382 • THE NEW GUIDE TO STUDY ABROAD

that "daily lectures during the ocean crossing will provide an adequate introduction to the history, literature and culture of all the countries to be visited." Or we read that "three weeks of intensive instruction in the foreign language will enable the participants to follow university lectures on the history, art, music and literature of the country." Particularly if the prospective student-traveler wishes some official recognition of a study program, he should expect to be asked about his college standing, previous courses taken in the subject and his knowledge of the pertinent foreign language. If no such questions are asked, he should be highly suspicious of the program.

This brings us to a third criterion—accreditation. As a general rule, a study-tour officially sponsored by a recognized college or university will give, after scheduled final examinations, its own formal transcript indicating the courses followed and the number of hours of approved credit. Such a transcript usually is accepted for transfer of credit by other colleges, but the participant should inquire about credit acceptance from his own college or university in advance of his departure. Any other type of certificate promised by a tour agency is open to question. Foreign universities freely give "certificates of presence" which mean nothing. Unless the period of study is properly timed, final examinations will not be available, and without them no reputable institution will grant credit. Private study-tour agencies can only recommend a certain amount of credit, and most colleges do not allow credit on that basis. Some tours make vague claims that "no registrar will have any difficulty in evaluating these courses," or that "our study courses are approved by the highest educational authorities." It would be more honest if they made no statement at all, but let the individual student arrange for placement examinations at his own college after his return home.

The most important criterion of all is, of course, the description of the program to be followed. The prospective traveler should investigate carefully whether the tour does what he wishes to do: what proportion is study and what proportion travel, where and under what sort of instruction the study is done, and how rapid or leisurely the pace of travel is.

One of the most common plans is the combination of about four weeks of study in a regular program of courses at a foreign university, with about three weeks of travel. This can be a good arrangement if properly supervised. Those interested in such a program should make sure that the sponsoring organization actually enrolls participants in the proper level of courses, that final examinations and a certificate are to be given and that suitable living accommodations are arranged. It should be remembered that private families in Europe do not readily open their homes to boarders, and that living arrangements even in hotels are scarce and expensive anywhere in Europe in the summer. No one should embark on a summer study-tour without reliable assurance that room and board have been arranged during the period of study.

There are scores of different kinds of study courses being offered in connection with travel tours. Prospective students should inquire carefully into the details. If a course is taught regularly at a foreign university or institute, it should be easy to discover what subject matter is covered and by whom, whether the student will be placed at the proper level for his greatest profit, whether the courses are taught in English or in a foreign language—in the latter case, whether his knowledge of the language is adequate, whether final examinations and a certificate showing the results are guaranteed and whether academic credit can be expected.

On the other hand, if a study course is specially arranged by the sponsoring agent or the travel company for members of a tour, greater caution is necessary. Instruction may well be organized, systematic and given by competent professors drawn from university circles abroad; or it may be haphazard, sandwiched in between excursions, taught by substandard teachers or by tour personnel who may be getting a free trip for their services. Pertinent questions to ask are: how long does the group stay at the educational center; where and by whom are the courses taught; what is the daily schedule of instruction; how much study outside of classes is expected (some tours glowingly promise none); can everyone expect to pass the exams if he "tries hard"; in other words, what is the quality of the study program?

A summer tour which describes its program as "instruction while traveling" cannot really be called a study program. The usually advertised features of these tours are: orientation lectures aboard ship (if seasickness does not intervene); series of lectures given by the tour leader en route; explanations of points visited, often by a local person such as a museum guide; interviews with "distinguished persons"; instruction in a smattering of foreign language phrases for several countries; vague promises about lectures in the foreign language on subjects like Alpine geography or the organization of the French community. Usually no examinations are given in these programs, and any statements about academic credits are vague, implying that no college could fail to recognize the value of such travel. The fact is that such tours may be and often are really educational in the broadest sense, but they are not likely to be bona-fide study programs; and those who are led to expect academic credit for them are likely to be disappointed.

It should be clear that there are many excellent summer travel tours which make no claim to be academic study programs and which describe their objectives plainly and honestly. . . . This article simply is a plea to the prospective student-traveler . . . to read the "fine print" in the mass of attractive brochures which he will receive, and be sure that the tour he selects corresponds clearly and reliably to his objectives and needs.

Stephen Freeman's warnings are made more pertinent by the reduced air fares now available to groups. This "discount rate" can be a stimulus to shoddy "study tours." When you choose— choose with care!

Tours Operated by Student Unions

One special class of educational tours consists of those sponsored by student groups. They are generally good bargains, but, of course, you will have to arrange your own transportation across the Atlantic. The following organizations operate such tours or provide information about them:

AUSTRIA: Buro für Studentenwanderungen, Schreivogelgasse 3, Vienna 1, Austria.

BELGIUM: Federation of Belgian Students, 60 Rue de l'Association, Brussels, Belgium.

DENMARK: Danish International Student Committee, Pederstræde 19, Copenhagen K, Denmark.

ENGLAND: National Union of Students, 3 Endsleigh Street, London, W.C.1, England.

FINLAND: National Union of Students in Finland, Kampinkatu 4–6, Helsinki, Finland.

FRANCE: Office du Tourisme Universitaire (OTU), 972 Fifth Avenue, New York, N.Y. 10021.

Cité-Club Universitaire, 33 Boulevard de Courcelles, Paris 8, France.

GERMANY: German Student Travel Service, Kaiserstrasse 71, Bonn, Germany.

Akademische Auslandstelle, Schlüterstrasse 7, Hamburg 13, Germany.

GREECE: National Union of Greek Students, 15 Hippocratus Street, Athens, Greece.

IRELAND: Students' Representative Council (ISTA), Newman House, 86 St. Stephan's Green, Dublin, Ireland.

ISRAEL: National Union of Israeli Students, 7 Petach Tikvah Road, Tel Aviv, Israel.

ITALY: Corda Frates, Via Frattina 41, Rome, Italy.

National Union of Italian Students (CRUIE), Via Palestro 11, Rome, Italy.

NETHERLANDS: Netherlands Office for Foreign Student Relations, 29 Broadway, New York, N.Y. 10016, or, Rapenburg 6, Leyden, Netherlands.

NORWAY: National Union of Norwegian Students, Uranienborgveien 11, Oslo, Norway.

SCOTLAND: Scottish Union of Students, 30 Lothian Street, Edinburgh, Scotland.

SPAIN: Oficina de Viajes Universitarios del Sindicato Español Universitario (SEU), Central Glorieta de Quevedo 8–20, Madrid, Spain.

SWEDEN: Swedish National Union of Students, Korsbarsvagen 1, Stockholm V, Sweden.

SWITZERLAND: Swiss National Union of Students, Eidg. Techn. Hochschule 47A, Zürich, Switzerland.

TURKEY: National Students Federation of Turkey (TMTF), Babiali Caddesi 40, Cagaloglu, Istanbul, Turkey.

YUGOSLAVIA: National Union of Yugoslav Students, Trg Marksa-Engelsa 1-a, Belgrade, Yugoslavia.

The annual *Official Student Guide to Europe,* published by the United States Student Association, contains descriptions and prices of many of the tours run by the organization. This volume also lists the names and addresses of student travel bureaus in thirty-nine European cities through which American students may buy reduced-rate plane, train, and bus tickets.

Appendix

List of Organizations and Agencies Promoting Foreign Study

Europe

AUSTRIA

Austrian Committee for International Student Exchange
Türkenstrasse 4/III
1090 Vienna

Provides information on study opportunities in Austria and introductions to professional societies. Arranges trainee exchanges, study tours, travel programs, and home hospitality and helps in making housing arrangements. Publishes *Study in Austria*, which is distributed in the United States by the Austrian Information Service.

Austrian Foreign Student's Service
Dr. Karl Lueger-Ring 7
Vienna

Provides information on study opportunities, living conditions, scholarships, and student organizations in Austria. Conducts German-language courses. Publishes *Study in Austria, A Guide to Austrian Universities and Academies for Foreign Students with an Appendix on Austrian Secondary and Vocational Schools* and the following listings: "Information for Foreign Students at Austrian Universities," "Scholarships for Foreign students at Austrian Universities," "German Language Courses for Foreign Students at Austrian Universities."

Austrian Information Service
31 East 69th Street
New York, N.Y. 10021

Publishes, in co-operation with the Austrian Institute, two listings: "American Educational Programs in Austria" and "Summer Schools in Austria."

Austrian Institute
11 East 52nd Street
New York, N.Y. 10022

Provides information on education in Austria; distributes listing: "Summer Schools in Austria."

Austrian State Tourist Department
444 Madison Avenue
New York, N.Y. 10022

Provides information on travel and furnishes list of student organizations in Austria.

Austro-American Institute of Education
Operngasse 4
1010 Vienna

Provides information on study, teaching, and travel to students, teachers, university and study groups in Austria; arranges cultural programs for groups; plans trips; arranges professional contacts.

Austro-American Society
Stallburggasse 2
Vienna

Arranges study tours and social contacts for American students. Conducts German-language courses.

BELGIUM

American Belgian Association
4, Rue St. Jean
Brussels

Provides information and arranges tours and visits for American students. Helps with housing arrangements.

Belgian Information Service
50 Rockefeller Plaza
New York, N.Y. 10020

Provides information on academic and related matters in Belgium. Publishes A *Guide to Higher Education in Belgium* (1967).

International Cultural Affairs Service
Ministry of National Education and Culture
158, Avenue de Cortenbergh
Brussels 4

Provides information on education in Belgium.

Tourisme des Etudiants et de la Jeunesse
226 Rue Royale
Brussels 1

Provides information on travel in Belgium.

DENMARK

Danish Information Office
280 Park Avenue
New York, N.Y. 10017

Provides information on study in Denmark. Maintains reference library of catalogues and other publications. Distributes *The University of Copenhagen—A Brief Survey of Its Organization and Activities* and *Educational Facilities for Students and Visitors in Denmark*.

Danish Institute for Information about Denmark and Cultural Co-
operation with Other Countries
Kultorvet 2
1175 Copenhagen K

Publishes material on education in Denmark. Organizes summer schools and study tours; offers courses, lectures, and seminars. Helps in making living arrangements. Maintains a reference library of catalogues and other publications.

Danish Students, Information Bureau
Studiestraede 6
1159 Copenhagen K

Provides information and assistance with housing for foreign students.

Denmark America Foundation
Nytorv 9
Copenhagen K

Provides information on study in Denmark and introductions to professional societies. Helps in making living arrangements.

Denmark International Student Committee
Skindergade 36
1159 Copenhagen K

Provides information regarding study and employment in Denmark. Helps in making housing arrangements; runs hostels in Denmark for students and teachers from abroad. Offers courses, lectures, and seminars. Publishes material related to the above, including *Undergraduate Studies in Copenhagen* and *Student Guide to Copenhagen*.

Royal Danish Embassy
3200 Whitehaven Street, N.W.
Washington, D.C. 20008

Provides information on employment in Denmark; distributes material related to study in Denmark; maintains reference library of catalogues and other publications; provides introductions to professional societies.

FINLAND
Embassy of Finland
1900 Twenty-Fourth Street, N.W.
Washington, D.C. 20008

Provides information on Finland.

Finnish American Society
Mechelininkatu
Helsinki

Provides information and advice to foreign students and organizes local excursions.

Finnish Commission for International Fellowships
Ministry of Education
Helsinki

Provides information on study opportunities in Finland and publishes *Study in Finland.*

National Union of Students of Finland
Mannerheimintie 5C VII
Helsinki

Provides information and advice to foreign students. The Student Service at Kampinkatu 4–6, Helsinki, arranges home hospitality, helps in making housing arrangements, organizes student tours.

FRANCE

American Center for Students and Artists
261 Boulevard Raspail
Paris 14

Centre National Oeuvres Universitaires et Scolaires
39 Avenue de l'Observatoire
Paris 5

Operates regional centers in each *Académie.* These centers provide a variety of services, including help with housing arrangements. A complete list of these centers is contained in the French Cultural Services brochure *Advanced Studies in France for College Students.*

France–Etats Unis
6 Boulevard de Grenelle
Paris 15

Provides information and help with housing for American students.

French Cultural Services
Cultural Services of the French Embassy
972 Fifth Avenue
New York, N.Y. 10021

Provides information and advice to American students and publishes a wide variety of printed material relating to educational and other matters.

Office of University Tourism
137 Boulevard St. Michel
Paris 5
and
972 Fifth Avenue
New York, N.Y. 10021

Provides information and advice regarding travel in France; arranges low-cost student travel and tours.

Service d'Orientation Pédagogique des Etudiants Etrangers
Centre Albert Chatelet
6–8 Rue Jean Calvin
Paris 5

Provides information on study and related academic matters in France. Publishes *Année d'Etudes à Paris.*

GERMANY

Association of German Universities
Dammtorstrasse 20
2 Hamburg 36

Provides information for teachers on opportunities for study and travel in Germany.

Educational Exchange Service
Nassestrasse 8
52 Bonn

Provides information to teachers on opportunities for educational visits and so on.

German Academic Exchange Service (DAAD)
Kennedyallee 50
532 Bad Godesberg

Provides information and advice for foreign students and publishes a variety of material relating to study in Germany, including *Foreign Student in Germany*. In the United States these books are distributed by the German Consulate and the Embassy.

German Consulate General
460 Park Avenue
New York, N.Y. 10022

Provides information on Germany and distributes the various DAAD publications.

German National Union of Students
Georgstrasse 25–27
53 Bonn

Provides information on study in Germany and on various student activities. Publishes *Deutscher Hochschul Führer*.

German Student Travel Service
Kaiserstrasse 71
Bonn

Provides information on travel in Germany and organizes study tours for groups of ten or more.

National Carl Schurz Association, Inc.
339 Walnut Street
Philadelphia, Penna. 19106

Provides information to Americans (particularly teachers) on educational assignments in Germany.

GREECE

Consulate General of Greece
69 East 79th Street
New York, N.Y. 10021

Provides information on Greece.

Greek Alumna of American Universities
c/o Mr. C. Anastasopoulos
14 Riqhillis
Athens

Provides information, advice, and help with housing for American students.

State Scholarship Foundation
14 Lysicmate Street
Athens

Provides information for foreign students.

IRELAND

Department of External Affairs
80 St. Stephan's Green
Dublin

Provides information and advice for foreign students.

Embassy of Ireland
2234 Massachusetts Avenue, N.W.
Washington, D.C. 20008

Provides information on Ireland and distributes IIE's *Study in Ireland*.

National University of Ireland Club
Box 171
Grand Central Station
New York, N.Y. 10017

Gives advice to foreign students who wish to study in Ireland.

Students' Representative Council U.C.D.
Newman House
86 St. Stephan's Green
Dublin

Provides information and helps with housing for foreign students.
Also arranges local excursions and tours.

Union of Students in Ireland
43 Dame Street
Dublin 2

Provides information on travel in Ireland.

ITALY

Centro Internazionale di Coordinazione Culturale
La Storta
Via Cassia
Rome

Provides information on study in Italy, arranges home hospitality,
helps make living arrangements, and arranges student tours.

Italian Center for University Relations with Foreigners
Via Palestro 11
Rome

Provides information and advice for foreign university students.

Italian Cultural Institute
686 Park Avenue
New York, N.Y. 10021

Provides information and advice to American students and distributes a variety of informational material.

Italian Society for International Organization
Via San Marco 3
Rome

Provides information for foreign students and organizes lectures
and meetings dealing with international organizations.

THE NETHERLANDS

Foreign Student Service
Oranje Nassaulaan 5
Amsterdam

Provides information and advice regarding study in the Netherlands and helps with housing arrangements for foreign students. Organizes study tours, excursions, lectures, conferences, holiday programs. Publishes *Vademecum—A Concise Guide for Foreign Students in the Netherlands.*

Netherlands-America Institute
Museumplein 4
Amsterdam

Provides information and advice for American citizens. Helps make living arrangements.

Netherlands Information Service
711 Third Avenue
New York, N.Y. 10020

Provides information on the Netherlands and distributes *Study in Holland—A Guide for Prospective Students.*

Netherlands Office for Foreign Student Relations (NBBS)
Rapenburg 6
Leyden
Branch office: Pier 40, North River
New York, N.Y. 10014

Operates special student sailings which include shipboard orientation. Maintains student hostels in Europe and arranges summer tours. Publishes *A Student Travel Guide to the Netherlands.*

Netherlands Universities Foundation for
    International Cooperation (NUFFIC)
Molenstraat 27
The Hague

Arranges cultural functions for foreign students during the

academic year. Publishes *Higher Education and Research in the Netherlands,* "Scholarships and Fellowships for Foreign Students Tenable in the Netherlands," and "Basic Data on International Courses Offered in the Netherlands."

NORWAY

Embassy of Norway
Information Service
3401 Massachusetts Avenue
Washington, D.C. 20007

Provides general information on education in Norway.

Norsk Studentunion
Kristian Augustsgate 21
Oslo

Provides information on study opportunities in Norway.

Norway-America Association
Kirkegatan 15
Oslo

Provides information on study opportunities in Norway.

Norway Information Service
290 Madison Avenue
New York, N.Y. 10017

Provides information on Norway. Distributes *Facts about the University of Oslo* and a brochure on the Oslo Summer School.

Norwegian Student Travel Office
Universitetssentret, Blindern
Oslo 3

Provides information on travel in Norway.

Office of Cultural Relations
Royal Ministry of Foreign Affairs
Roald Amundsengate 6
Oslo

Provides information and advice for foreigners. Publishes *An Outline of Norwegian Education* and *The Organization and Administration of the Educational System of Norway.*

Office of Foreign Students
University of Oslo
Karl Johansgate 47
Oslo

Provides information on study in Norway. Publishes *Facts about the University of Oslo.*

PORTUGAL

American Portuguese Cultural Society
29 Broadway
New York, N.Y. 10006

Provides information on education in Portugal.

Association of Students of the Instituto Superior Tecnico
Avenida Rovisco Pais
Lisbon

Welcomes foreign students; provides information about language courses, scholarships, educational institutions, tours, and so forth.

Casa Portugal (or Portuguese Government Tourist Information Bureau)
570 Fifth Avenue
New York, N.Y. 10036

Provides lists of agencies in Portugal that help foreign students, and other information.

Portuguese Embassy
2125 Kalorama Road, N.W.
Washington, D.C. 20008

Provides information on Portugal.

SPAIN

Departmento de Asistencia Universitaria
Sección Estados Unidos
Instituto de Cultura Hispánica
Ciudad Universitaria
Madrid 3

Provides information on study opportunities and scholarships in Spain and related matters; helps make living and housing arrangements and organizes student tours.

Office of Cultural Relations
Spanish Embassy
1629 Columbia Road, N.W., Apt. 625
Washington, D.C. 20009

Provides information on study and education in Spain and distributes a variety of material related to the above.

Spanish University Syndicate
Office of University Tours
Glorieta de Quevedo 8
Madrid 10

Provides information to foreign students about Spanish universities, work camps, and summer schools. Issues a "carnet de cortesia" entitling foreign students to the same rights as Spanish students in libraries, student restaurants, hostels, and so on.

Students and Painters Residence
Plaza del Conde de Cheste 8
P.O. Box 42
Segovia

Provides information for students of Spanish art and literature.

Travel Office of the National Union of Students
Fernando el Católico 80
Post Box 8048
Madrid 15

Provides information on travel in Spain.

SWEDEN

Central Organization of Student Unions
Studentbacken 21
Stockholm N

Provides information and advice to foreign students. Publishes *Foreign Student in Sweden.*

Royal Consulate General of Sweden
61 East 64th Street
New York, N.Y. 10021

Provides information on Sweden.

Sweden-America Foundation
Grevturegatan 14
Stockholm

Provides information and advice to American students. Publishes *Travel, Study and Research in Sweden.*

Swedish Central Committee for International Exchange between
   Schools
Storkykobrinken 11
Stockholm, C

Provides information and advice for secondary-school students wishing to study in Sweden.

The Swedish Institute for Cultural Relations with Foreign
   Countries
Küngsgatan 42
Stockholm 3

Provides information on study in Sweden and arranges summer courses. Publishes a number of pamphlets, including *Studying in Sweden: Hints and Suggestions for Foreign Students.*

Swedish National Union of Students
Aluddsvägen 7
Stockholm K

Provides information and advice for foreign students.

SWITZERLAND

Central Office of the Swiss Universities
Beckenhofstrasse 31
8035 Zürich

Provides information for foreign students. Publishes *The Swiss Universities: A Short Guide.*

Embassy of Switzerland
2900 Cathedral Avenue, N.W.
Washington, D.C. 20008

Provides information on Switzerland.

Swiss American Student Exchange
Swiss Federal Institute of Technology
Leonhardstrasse 6
Zürich 6

Provides information on study in Switzerland.

Swiss Friends of the U.S.A.
P.O. Box 174
8034 Zürich

Provides information on study in Switzerland and arranges home hospitality.

Swiss National Union of Students
Leonhardstrasse 19
8001 Zürich

Provides information on study in Switzerland.

Swiss Student Travel Office
Leonhardstrasse 19
8001 Zürich

Provides information on travel in Switzerland and offers language courses.

TURKEY

Turkish-American Association
42 Mithat Pasa Caddesi
Ankara

Provides information and advice for American students; conducts Turkish-language courses and organizes cultural programs and study tours.

Turkish Educational Attaché
Turkish Embassy
Empire State Building
Room 7307
New York, N.Y. 10001

Provides information and advice regarding study in Turkey.

UNITED KINGDOM

British Information Service
845 Third Avenue
New York, N.Y. 10022

Provides information on Great Britain. Publishes and distributes a wide variety of informational material, including *Higher Education in the United Kingdom.*

British Travel Association
680 Fifth Avenue
New York, N.Y. 10019

Provides information on travel in the United Kingdom and on summer study opportunities. Distributes *A Guide for Students*

Visiting Britain, which contains information on summer opportunities, travel, and living arrangements in Britain.

British Universities Student Travel Association
157 Victoria Street
London, S.W. 1

Provides information on study in the United Kingdom and ad-makes travel arrangements; arranges study/travel and group tours.

Central Bureau for Educational Visits and Exchange
91 Victoria Street
London, S.W. 1

Official British government information agency for foreign students.

National Union of Students
3 Endsleigh Street
London, W.C. 1

Provides information and advice to students and organizes student tours through the N.U.S. travel department.

World University Service
(United Kingdom Council)
59 Gloucester Place
London, W. 2

Provides information on study in the United Kingdom and advises students regarding other organizations providing services. Organizes an international study course providing an introduction to contemporary life in Britain.

YUGOSLAVIA

Embassy of the Socialist Federal Republic of Yugoslavia
2410 California Street, N.W.
Washington, D.C. 20008

Provides information on study in Yugoslavia.

League of Yugoslav Universities
Palmoticeva No. 12
Belgrade

Provides information on study in Yugoslavia.

Travel Department
Yugoslav Union of Students
Mose Pijade 12/1
Belgrade

Provides information on travel in Yugoslavia.

Yugoslavia Publishing House
Borisa Kidrica 70
Belgrade

Publishes *Foreign Students in Yugoslavia.*

North America

CANADA

Association of Universities and Colleges of Canada
151 Slater Street
Ottawa, Ontario

Provides information on study in Canada. Publishes "Admission Requirements of Canadian Universities" (annual reprint from Commonwealth Universities Yearbook), *Handbook of the Association of Universities and Colleges of Canada,* "Notes for the Guidance of Students Considering University Study in Canada," *Canadian Universities and Colleges,* "Awards for Graduate Study and Research."

Canadian Education Association
151 Bloor Street West
Toronto 5, Ontario

Provides information on education in Canada.

Canadian Embassy
1746 Massachusetts Avenue, N.W.
Washington, D.C. 20036

Provides information and advice to foreign students, including student visas, colleges and universities in Canada, educational material on Canada, and job opportunities. Also maintains reference library.

Canadian Government Travel Bureau
680 Fifth Avenue
New York, N.Y. 10019

Provides information on travel in Canada and publishes *Summer Courses in Canada*.

Canadian Service for Overseas Students and Trainees
338 Somerset Street West
Ottawa 4, Ontario

Helps in making living arrangements; organizes trips and arranges home hospitality.

Canadian Union of Students
45 Rideau Street
Ottawa, Ontario

Provides information on study in Canada and organizes study trips.

Canadian Universities Foundation
75 Albert Street
Ottawa 4, Ontario

Provides information on study opportunities, graduate scholarships, education exchanges, and teaching in Canada. Publishes *University Study in Canada: A Guide for Students from Other Countries Who Are Planning to Study at Canadian Universities and Colleges*.

Friendly Relations with Overseas Students
22 Wilcocks Street
Toronto 5, Ontario

Provides information and assistance with housing for foreign students.

National Federation of Canadian University Students
Room 221, 375 Rideau Street
Ottawa, Ontario

Provides information and advice for foreign students.

Latin America

ARGENTINA

Asociación Universitaria Argentino-Norteamericana
Santa Fe 1145
Buenos Aires

Provides information on study in Argentina and introductions to professional societies. Arranges home hospitality and study tours. Helps in making living arrangements. Offers orientation for American students.

Consejo Nacional de Investigaciones Científicas y Técnicas
Rivadavia 1917–R.25
Buenos Aires, C.F.

Provides information on study in Argentina. Publishes *Guía de Carreras Universitarias y de Enseñanza Superior en Argentina.*

Embassy of the Argentine Republic
Press and Cultural Affairs Section
1600 New Hampshire Avenue, N.W.
Washington, D.C.

Provides information on Argentina.

Instituto Cultural Argentino-Norteamericano
Maipú 686
Buenos Aires

Provides information to Americans on study in Argentina.

Instituto de Intercambio Cultural Argentino-Norteamericano
Avenida Vélez Sarsfield 187
Córdoba

Provides information on study opportunities in Argentina and introductions to professional societies. Arranges home hospitality and helps with living arrangements.

Servicio de Información Educativa
Centro Nacional de Documentación e Información Educativa
Parera 55
Buenos Aires

Provides information on education in Argentina, primarily for teachers and administrators.

Bolivia

Centro Boliviano-Americano
Avenida 6 de Agosto 2100
La Paz

Provides information on study opportunities in Bolivia.

Brazil

Brazilian-American Cultural Center
Avenida N.S. de Copacabana, 690
Rio de Janeiro

Provides information and aid to American students, including advice about language study, scholarships, and housing.

Brazilian American Cultural Institute
4201 Connecticut Avenue, N.W.
Washington, D.C. 20008

Provides information on Brazil.

Cultural Department
Brazilian Embassy
3007 Whitehaven Street, N.W.
Washington, D.C. 20008

Provides information on Brazil.

CHILE

Instituto Chileno-Norteamericano de Cultura
Moneda 1467
Santiago

Provides information on study in Chile and helps with living arrangements. Offers Spanish-language instruction.

Intercambio Cultural Estudiantil Americano
Ahumada 131, Oficina 917
Santiago

Gives information on study opportunities in Chile and helps make living arrangements.

Office of General Information
University of Chile
Santiago

Provides information on all universities in Chile.

COLOMBIA

Instituto Colombiano de Especialización Técnica en el Exterior
(ICETEX)
Apartado Aereo No. 5735
Bogotá

Provides information and orientation for foreign students and co-ordinates foreign student exchange.

MEXICO

Embassy of Mexico
2829 16th Street, N.W.
Washington, D.C. 20009

Provides general information on Mexico and on research and educational facilities, particularly at the university level, summer schools, and the like.

Institute of Mexican–North American Cultural Relations
Hamburgo 115
Mexico 6, D.F.

Provides information on study in Mexico and organizes cultural programs. Also conducts Spanish-language courses.

Mexico City Christian Association of Students
Justo Sierra 28
Interior 201–2
Mexico 1, D.F.

Provides information and advice for foreign students, with special reference to the Mexican educational system.

National Confederation of Students
Avenida Juarez 56–203
Mexico, D.F.

Provides information on study and travel in Mexico and helps with housing arrangements for foreign students in student hostels.

Orientación Universitaria Internacional
Liverpool 48, 3er Piso
Mexico 6, D.F.

Provides information on study in Mexico, arranges home hospitality, and helps make living arrangements.

NICARAGUA

Centro Cultural Nicaraguense-Americano
Managuan-American Cultural Center
Avenida del Centenario 403
Managua

Provides information and advice to American students. Helps
make living arrangements. Conducts Spanish-language classes.

PERU

Asociación de Ex-Becarios y Estudiantes
Peruanos en los Estados Unidos
Máximo Abril 599
Lima

Provides information on study in Peru. Arranges home hospitality
and holiday trips and helps make living arrangements.

Embassy of Peru
Washington, D.C.

Provides general information on study and travel in Peru.

Peruvian–North American Cultural Institute
Jirón Cuzco 446, Apartado 304
Lima

Provides information and advice for foreign students.

Studies Abroad
Edifico Ingelio, Oficina 101
La Colmena, 3ra. Cuadra
Apartado 10223
Lima

Advises American students and teachers on study possibilities in
Peru, particularly Lima.

VENEZUELA

Centro Venezolano-Americano
Apartado 5715 del Este
Caracas

Provides information on study in Venezuela and helps make living arrangements.

Embassy of Venezuela
Institute of Information and Culture
2437 California Street, N.W.
Washington, D.C.

Provides information to Americans regarding Venezuela.

Near and Far East

INDIA

Bharat Darshan (Know India)
"Prerna"–K–29
Jangpura Extension Link Road
New Delhi 14

Arranges visits with Indian families for foreign students and provides information and advice. Payment of a registration fee and advance notice of one month are necessary.

Embassy of India
2107 Massachusetts Avenue, N.W.
Washington, D.C. 20008

Provides information on India.

Indo-American Association
Y.M.C.A. Royopettah
Madras 14

Provides information on study in India and arranges for visiting students to meet teachers and students from India.

International Cultural Exchange Organization
Post Box 559
New Delhi 1

Sponsors study tours, seminars, and cultural exchange programs.

Ministry of Education
Information Section
Room 26, 1 Block
Central Secretariat
New Delhi

Provides information and advice to foreign students.

Ministry of Education
Publications Section
31 Theatre Communications Building
Connaught Circus
New Delhi

Publishes *Living in India, Directory of Institutions of Higher Education in India,* and other items of interest to foreign students.

National Council of University Students of India
F–13 South Extension, Part 1
New Delhi 3

Provides information on travel in India.

Universities Information Bureau
Bombay University Club House
"B" Road, Churchgate
Bombay 1

Provides information and advice to foreign students.

ISRAEL

America-Israel Cultural Foundation
4 East 54th Street
New York, N.Y. 10022

Provides information on schools in the arts, particularly the performing arts.

Association of United States University Alumni in Israel
c/o Joseph Epstein
18 Dubnov Street
Tel Aviv

Provides information and advice to American students.

Embassy of Israel
1621 22nd Street, N.W.
Washington, D.C.

Provides information on Israel.

Information Department
Jewish Agency for Israel-American Section, Inc.
515 Park Avenue
New York, N.Y. 10022

Provides information on various types of short- and long-term study and work programs in Israel, including kibbutz living, language study, and tours. Publishes *A Guide to Israel Programs.*

Israeli Center of the World Union of Jewish Students
Students Center
University Campus
Jerusalem

Provides information on study in Israel and arranges student trips.

Israel Students Travel Association
2 Pinsker Street
P.O.B. 4451
Tel Aviv

Provides information on travel in Israel and organizes study tours.

National Union of Israeli Students
Students Center
Hebrew University of Jerusalem
Jerusalem

Provides information and advice for foreign students.

JAPAN

Association of Private Universities in Japan
c/o Shigaku-Kaikan, 4 Kudan
4-chome, Chiyoda-ku
Tokyo
Provides information on opportunities for teacher training.

Embassy of Japan
2520 Massachusetts Avenue N.W.
Washington, D.C. 20008
Provides information on Japan.

Exchange Student Association
Room 304
Joshi Kaikan
12 Shiba Park
Minatoku
Tokyo
Provides information and assistance for American students.

International Education Center
21, Yotsuya 1-chome
Shinjuku-ku, Tokyo
Provides information on study and teaching in Japan, arranges home hospitality and study tours, and helps make housing arrangements.

International House of Japan
2 Toriizaki-machi, Azabu
Minato-ku, Tokyo
Provides information on study in Japan, helps make living arrangements, conducts lectures.

International Students Institute
No. 985, Kashiwagi 4-chome
Shinjuku-ku, Tokyo
Provides information and advice for foreign students and housing at its International Students House.

Japanese National Commission for UNESCO
2–2, Kasumigaseki 3-chome
Chiyoda-ku, Tokyo

Publishes *A Guide to Study in Japan.*

Student Exchange Section
Research Bureau
Ministry of Education
4, Kasumigaseki 3-chome
Chiyoda-ku, Tokyo

Provides information on education in Japan.

LEBANON

Alumni Association of the American University of Beirut
Beirut

Provides information and operates a social center available to American students.

Embassy of Lebanon
2560 28th Street, N.W.
Washington, D.C. 20008

National Union of Lebanese University Students
c/o Lebanese University
Beirut

Provides information on study in Lebanon and help with housing for foreign students. Also organizes tours.

PHILIPPINES

Embassy of the Philippines
1617 Massachusetts Avenue, N.W.
Washington, D.C. 20036

Provides information on the Philippines.

The Philippine Fulbright Scholars Association
P.F.S.A. Center
Thomas Jefferson Library Building
Sta. Mesa, Manila

Provides information on study in the Philippines; arranges cultural programs and holiday trips.

The Philippine International Friendship Organization
Department of Foreign Affairs
Taft Avenue
Manila

Provides information and advice to students and helps make housing arrangements. Maintains a reception service and arranges a week-long orientation program for foreign students.

UNESCO National Commission of the Philippines
1580 Taft Avenue
Manila

Provides information and advice for foreign students. Helps make living arrangements. Offers orientation program on cultural and social conditions in the Philippines. Publishes *Scholarship Opportunities in Philippine Educational Institutions.*

TAIWAN

Chinese Information Service
100 West 32nd Street
New York, N.Y. 10001

Provides information on Taiwan.

Office of the Cultural Counselor
Embassy of the Republic of China
2311 Massachusetts Avenue, N.W.
Washington, D.C. 20008

Provides information on study in Taiwan. Handles applications for admission to the three universities which accept foreign students as well as the Chinese Language Training Center.

Taiwan Committee of the China Institute in America
c/o International House
Hsin Yi Road
Section 3
Taipei

Provides information on study in Taiwan and introductions to professional societies. Arranges home hospitality and student tours. Helps in making living arrangements.

UNITED ARAB REPUBLIC

Student Counseling and Orientation Center
American Friends of the Middle East
2 Midan Kasr El Dobara; Apt. 40
Garden City, Cairo

Provides information on study opportunities and scholarships in the U.A.R.

United Arab Republic Education Bureau
2200 Kalorama Road, N.W.
Washington, D.C. 20008

Provides general information on education in the U.A.R.

Australia and New Zealand

AUSTRALIA

Australian Consulate General
636 Fifth Avenue
New York, N.Y. 10020

Provides information on education in Australia. Also maintains a reference library and loan copies of university catalogues.

National Union of Australian University Students
405 Bourke Street
Melbourne CL

Provides information to students on study and living in Australia.

NEW ZEALAND

Embassy of New Zealand
19 Observatory Circle, N.W.
Washington, D.C. 20008

Provides information on New Zealand. Maintains a reference library of university catalogues.

New Zealand University Students Association
P.O. Box 6397 Te Aro
Wellington

Provides information on study and travel in New Zealand. Helps with housing arrangements for foreign students and organizes holiday trips. Publishes *The Overseas Student's Handbook.*

Organizations and Agencies Covering More than One Country

American Friends of the Middle East
1605 New Hampshire Avenue, N.W.
Washington, D.C. 20009

Provides information on study in the Middle East and assists American scholars and educators in making professional contacts. Publishes *Institutions of Higher learning in the Middle East* and *Study and Research in the Middle East and North Africa—Scholarship Opportunities for American Students.*

American-Scandinavian Foundation
127 East 73rd Street
New York, N.Y. 10021

Provides information on study, scholarships, and employment in Scandinavia.

American Youth Hostels, Inc.
20 West 17th Street
New York, N.Y. 10011

Arranges travel and study programs abroad and housing and home hospitality for students who participate in their program. Publishes *International Youth Hostels Handbook,* which describes the facilities of all youth hostels abroad.

Council on International Educational Exchange
(formerly Council on Student Travel)
777 United Nations Plaza
New York, N.Y. 10017

Arranges transatlantic travel on student ships. Provides information on summer and academic-year study opportunities abroad. Publishes *Students Abroad: Summer Study, Travel and Work Programs; Students Abroad: High School Students Programs; Students Abroad: Semester and Academic Year Programs.*

Institute of International Education
809 United Nations Plaza
New York, N.Y. 10017

Clearinghouse for information on study opportunities abroad. Publishes *Handbook for International Study: For U.S. Nationals; Undergraduate Study Abroad; Summer Study Abroad;* and also a wide variety of free informational material.

International Schools Services
392 Fifth Avenue
New York, N.Y. 10018

Provides information on American schools abroad. Publishes *Overseas Schools Serving American Students.*

National Catholic Education Association
1785 Massachusetts Avenue, N.W.
Washington, D.C. 20032

Provides information on study and teaching abroad particularly relating to Catholic education.

National Education Association
1201 Sixteenth Street, N.W.
Washington, D.C. 20036

Provides information on employment and study opportunities abroad for teachers. Division of Educational Travel organizes tours.

Pan American Union
Nineteenth Street and Constitution Avenue
Washington, D.C. 20006

Provides information and counseling to persons visiting Latin America.

United States Department of State
Public Information and Reports
Bureau of Educational and Cultural Affairs
Department of State
Washington, D.C. 20520

United States National Student Association
Educational Travel Division
265 Madison Avenue
New York, N.Y. 10016

Provides information on student travel and related matters and makes travel arrangements for students. Issues International Student Identity Card. Publishes *Work, Study, Travel Abroad; The Student Traveler;* and *Official Student Guide to Europe.*

United States Office of Education
Bureau of International Education
Department of Health, Education, and Welfare
Washington, D.C. 20201

World University Service
20 West 40th Street
New York, N.Y. 10018

Provides information and advice to students through its members in various countries.

Index

About the Authors

John A. Garraty is Professor of History, Columbia University. Walter Adams is Professor of Economics at Michigan State University and a member of the U.S. Advisory Commission on International and Cultural Affairs. Cyril J. H. Taylor is president of the American Institute for Foreign Study.